Standing at the Grave

Minneapolis

First Edition May 2023

10 9 8 7 6 5 4 3 2 1
ISBN: 978-1-960250-85-8

Cover and book design by Gary Lindberg
Cover photo of headstone by Stefan Heyn

Standing at the Grave

Gary Heyn

Minneapolis

This book is dedicated to my great grandma, Lydia Heyn, whose front porch stories about the “olden days” started me on the journey to this book.

Table of Contents

Introduction **1**

Part I: Gembitz Hauland **5**
September 29, 1793 – Gembitz Hauland 5
March 19, 1819 – Polajewo Hauland 8

Part II: The Home Place **13**
July 16, 1840 – Gembitz Hauland 13
December 13, 1842 – Gembitz Hauland 18
January 14, 1854 - Gembitz Hauland 22
November 19, 1865 – Gembitz Hauland 31

Part III: Emigration Begins **35**
July 19, 1867 – The North Sea 35
December 25, 1867 – Gembitz Hauland 44
January 24, 1868 – Gembitz Hauland 48
August 6, 1871 – Gembitz Hauland 53
September 30, 1876 – Viola Township Minnesota 65
December 25, 1882 – Grafton, Dakota Territory 75
July 7, 1883 – Gembitz Hauland 82

Part IV: 1883 Rochester Tornado **89**
August 21, 1883 – Viola, Minnesota 89
August 22, 1883 – Olmsted County Minnesota 97

Part V: Emigration Ends **105**
July 9, 1885 – Owatonna Minnesota 105

Part VI: Murder in the Hub of Hell **119**
July 26, 1887 – Minneapolis, Minnesota 119
January 4, 1888 – Minneapolis, Minnesota 129
February 8, 1888 – Minneapolis, Minnesota 134

Part VII: Anna's Final Homes **153**
October 17, 1889 – Bottineau, North Dakota 153
December 26, 1891 – Devils Lake, North Dakota 160
July 11, 1893 – Gembitz Hauland 167
March 21, 1894 – Bremen, Minnesota 171

Part VIII: First North Dakota 181
October 2, 1899 – Grafton, North Dakota 181

Part IX: The Evangelical Church of Peace 191
October 6, 1904 – Viola Township, Minnesota 191
November 6, 1906 – Rochester, Minnesota 195
May 12, 1907 – Rochester, Minnesota 207

Part X: Final Legacies 221
February 19, 1916 – Minneapolis, Minnesota 221
June 27, 1920 – Elgin, Minnesota 231
February 6, 1931 – Grafton, North Dakota 243
October 15, 1941 – Glenburn, North Dakota 255

Part XI: Epilogue 263
October 30, 2019 – Gebiczyn Poland 263

About the Author 273

4th great grandson kneeling at the grave. Spring 2022. Personal photo

Introduction

Spring 1819 added two girls to male-dominated Europe. Two days before the equinox marked the official start of the season, Anna Christina Schmidt, whose contributions to the world were destined to remain anonymous, began her life of subsistence farming. Two months later, Alexandrina Victoria, who would have the age she lived in named for her, was born into wealth and privilege.

Anna's birthplace fell into disrepair and disappeared into the Polish forests. Victoria's is still the first home of future monarchs, and every year hordes of tourists pay to see the room where she was born.

Anna's life is not well documented. She is one of hundreds of forgotten mothers whose children sailed across the vast ocean for better opportunities. In contrast, the curious can learn about Victoria's life in books, letters, photographs, motion pictures, and popular historical fiction television shows.

Forty-six of Anna's fifty-one grandchildren have spread her DNA across America, barely leaving a footnote in a history book. Today her descendants quietly blend into the constantly changing and active world, not even knowing when by chance, they pass each other on the streets. Victoria's forty-two grandchildren spread her DNA to almost every throne and palace in Old World Europe. After two centuries, blazing headlines that describe her descendants' lives still capture international attention.

While Victoria's children and grandchildren sat securely on their thrones and directed the wars their petty jealousies and competition triggered, Anna's American grandsons and great-grandsons returned to Europe with the mission to kill her German grandsons and great-grandsons.

In 1840 both women married German men. Victoria's marriage to Prince Albert is legendary. Anna's marriages to two men named after the Prussian king exist now only in scattered records. Shortly after their marriages, each was visited by a midwife, who delivered a baby girl. The midwives returned eight more times for one and seven for the other. At the end of their long lives, each had six surviving children to mourn their passing.

Before either celebrated a silver wedding anniversary, they planned funerals for their husbands. They faced widowhood with grieving young children. Victoria's sorrow turned inward, and she nearly abandoned her children and royal duties. Anna did not have the luxury of extended grief. Her children and farm depended on her to survive.

Victoria took her last breath less than one hundred miles from where she took her first. Her earthly remains are preserved in a black Belgian marble sarcophagus next to her husband. The bodies of the couple are protected from the rain and wind by a gray mausoleum that is decorated inside with bright gold and blue murals that Victoria ordered to honor her husband. In the gardens surrounding the building lay many of her descendants.

Anna took her last breath halfway across the world from where she took her first. Her body lies far from those of her husbands, slowly disappearing into a depression in the grass marked by a tall, moss-covered, gray stone whose inscriptions the rain, snow, and wind gradually wear away. None of her family is near her in the country churchyard. Instead, she and the other forgotten German immigrants are protected from the surrounding cornfields by tall pine trees that encircle a closed church.

The lives of these women are not lesser or greater than the other, but Victoria's legacy is well documented while Anna's is lost. This book is an attempt to commemorate her life and that of her children, as well as the hundreds of immigrant families who left the familiarity of their homeland to build what they hoped to be a better life in a new country.

Anna often found herself straddling a divide. Whether the conflict between Prussian and Polish ancestry among the residents of her birthplace, the teachings of the church where she was baptized, and the reforms instigated by her Prussian king or the decision to die where she was born or in the new world with her children, Anna was always pulled in opposing directions.

This book also straddles a divide between fiction and nonfiction. The chapters that follow are accurate in terms of people, places and time unless a footnote explains otherwise. The dialogue and interactions that endeavor to restore life to cold facts are fiction.

Many history books, especially family histories, are a compilation of confusing names, dates and places. They record the *who*, *what*, *when* and *where* of people's lives. They lack a description of *how* or *why*. Those books become as cold and removed as the gravestones that mark a life only with the birth and death years separated by a dash. Readers become lost in the dates and names and lose interest before they can appreciate the dash that was the person's life. With no letters or diaries surviving, the depth and richness of that dash fade as each succeeding generation goes to the grave.

For many, cold facts are sufficient. For others, emotion is required in order to appreciate the dash. By weaving the facts together with the feelings provided in a novel, one can imagine the joy, grief, hope and fear of the lives portrayed. With a little imagination, a life that has been covered with dirt for more than a century can be partially revived.

Records might also allow us to imagine where we inherited our dysfunctions. An individual's dysfunctions tend to be buried with them. I chose the side of nonfiction here, only writing about the negative aspects of a character's life only when they could be documented. In this book, these people are presented in the overly positive light that is neatly chiseled on their tombstones, and for the most part, the negative will stay buried beneath that marker.

Finally, a brief comment on spelling. There are three possible spellings for the Heyn name in both Germany and the United States. Early Germans spelled the name with the special German alphabet character ÿ. By the mid-nineteenth century, the umlaut was dropped, and the name was spelled interchangeably Hein and Heyn. In this book, I spell the name Heÿn for the parents in Europe. For the children in America, I give the spelling they used at the time of their deaths.

A cliché states that to truly understand a person, you must walk a mile in their shoes. I hope you enjoy taking a stroll with Anna and her children.

Church of St. John of Dukla in Gebiczyn Poland 2019. Built in 1903 as an Evangelical Lutheran Church in Gembitz Hauland Posen. Given to the Catholic Church in 1945. Fall 2019. Personal photo

Part I
Gembitz Hauland

September 29, 1793 — Gembitz Hauland

The afternoon sun shines warmly on the citizens of Gembitz Hauland sitting in the community courtyard. The courtyard is not a typical German beer garden: a combination school and prayer house is to the south, with the teacher's house to the north and his barn to the east. Long tables and benches are arranged parallel to the prayer house, encouraging fellowship and rousing conversation. The men's accordions and tubas stand against the teacher's house, ready for an afternoon concert.

The men have just finished drinking their first barrel of the landlord's beer they are required to buy only from Martin Wanke's *Krug* and eating the overloaded tables of meat, potatoes, sauerkraut, bread, pies and cakes that were prepared by their wives, mothers and sisters. The children are playing games and mischievously sneaking tastes of beer. The horses' heads are outside the windows of the barn as they observe the activities. Dogs under the tables quickly eat the food that falls from above.

As the men start the second barrel, they share their usual complaints about weather, crops and wives. Politics is always an exciting topic at these gatherings. This week the second partition of Poland contributes to the festivities of the occasion. The weak Polish nobles will no longer rule these proud German farmers. Once again, they are citizens of Prussia, a right their forefathers had given up in search of land, treasure and freedom.

The older members of the group begin grumbling about the broken promises that were made to their families almost sixty years ago. They are members of the first thirteen families who crossed the Netze River at the invitation of the estate owner, Nikolaus von Mielecki, to replace his serfs, who had moved to eastern Poland for opportunity. Several of the wives shake their heads as the men start the same story they tell every time they drink too much.

The oldest of the group pounds his walking stick on the hard ground. "He offered us seven free years with no manual labor or plowing if we turned his private estate of sand, swamp and thick forests into productive farms. We were each to receive one *hufe* (thirty morgens) of acreage. We were also given one half a *hufe* to be used for our school, prayer house and cemetery. We would pay only a small rent."

With those inducements, the farmers had cleared and improved the land. Rather than living in a traditional German village and traveling to their farms, they chose to live scattered among the trees and fields in what was called a *Hauland*. These independent families preferred to see a pretty cow when they looked out a window in the morning rather than an ugly, unshaven neighbor.

With the next round of beer, the scabs of old grievances begin to be picked off. "Only nine years after the signing of the original charter, the new owner of the estate, Martin von Radomski, broke our contract." Each man spit brown tobacco juice on the ground at the mention of Radomski's name. "He harassed us into accepting his terms by driving away our livestock and destroying our work. His new charter doubled our rent, forced us to work for him twelve days a year, plus we had to make payments to the lazy Polish bastard from our livestock and grain." The angry old man again pounds the walking stick he had spent the summer carving on the hard ground, and it broke in two.

Not only are the old men angry now, but also the younger, barely surviving farmers. One of the farmers calls out, "We should sue for our original charter!" The drunken vote easily passes. After the vote, a loud and rousing "Prosit!" is joined by the whinnies of the horses.

With each new toast to King Friedrich Wilhelm II, the anger of the group increases. The grievances, real and imagined, against the Poles boil over. For hundreds of years, the Polish nobility had offered land, freedom and opportunity to generations of their families, enticing them to settle the cities and land owned by their families. The weak Polish government knew it could not be a European economic power without the skills of the German farmers and tradesmen. Once the hard work was established and the fruition of effort was evident, the next generation of Poles would greedily forget the promises that had been made.

The Catholic landowners promised religious freedom to the Lutherans. Another angry man exclaims, "How many times was Pastor Benicke forced, in the dark of night, to flee with his family to escape a mob of Poles?" Their pastor had been lucky. Other towns had their churches burnt, their ministers killed, and their schools closed. The rage of the group increases when a younger man says, "I was forced to be married and baptize my children in a Catholic church." Another man yells out, "No more! The Poles now live in a country run by a Lutheran government. They are going to learn how it feels to have a foreign culture forced on them."

Weakness of honor is always repaid. The Polish people tried to reform their government, but it was too little too late. The nobles feared that the revolutionary spirit of France would grow in Poland, and they made an alliance with the Russians to save the country from the revolutionaries. Their efforts backfired, and now the country is being divided between the Prussians and Russians.

A calmer voice says, "Maybe if the Poles had treated us better, we would have defended them," then, shaking his head, "but they didn't." One of the drunker farmers broke the moment of reflection by shouting, "Brains only pass to Poles from generation to generation randomly!" The intoxicated men cheer and laugh. They pick up their instruments and start playing an upbeat German melody off-key. The commotion wakes up the horses in the barn and the dogs under the table, rousing them to accompany the musicians with whinnies and howls. A couple of the wives at the adjacent table have Polish parents. One whispers to another, "Brains skipping a generation is not an affliction suffered just by the Poles."

With the emptying of the second barrel of beer, the sun and enthusiasm of the afternoon both wane. The women gather their tired children, empty dishes and drunken husbands. Slowly, everyone wanders back to their farms, animals and daily lives. The heady events of the past several days will not make the land more fertile, the cows produce more milk or the preparations for winter easier. That will happen only by continuing to work.

Slowly, the families walk back to reality.

March 19, 1819 – Polajewo Hauland

Farmer-settler Michael Schmidt walks through his flock of clucking chickens and squawking geese after throwing swill to his gray and black spotted hogs. In the narrow passageway between his house and barn, he can see his half-dozen cows and oxen grazing in the meadow he shares with his neighbors along the Flinta River that separates his farm in Polajewo Hauland from those of his in-laws in Wischen Hauland. He smiles with satisfaction at the improvements he has made to the farm where he was born thirty-five years ago.

He leans on the short fence that connects his house to the barn and watches the heifer calf born this morning nudge her mother's udder for more milk. Most cows grazing in the pastures and woods in the farming community are a solid orange color that is almost black. This little heifer is bright orange with random white spots across its belly and a distinctive white hourglass face marking. Michael's first cow, which he received as part of his wife's dowry, had the exact same markings. But the markings of that first cow were not what made it special but rather the large amounts of milk and cream she produced. If her granddaughter frolicking in the tall grass can produce the same quantity and quality of milk, Michael's reputation as a dairy breeder will be secure.

Today the population will increase not only in the pasture. Behind him, in the timber and plaster house with a high-pitched thatched roof, his wife is giving birth. When Christina's pain began, he sent his scared five-year-old son across the field to get the neighbor's wife. The breathless short woman greeted Michael by placing her hands on her ample hips, narrowing her eyes and ordering him out of the house. In a sharp tongue familiar to all the husbands in the community, she said, "You did your work in the house nine months ago. Now it is time for the women to finish the job."

A refreshing light spring breeze blows across the expectant father as he leans against his fence. In the distance, the branches of the budding trees wave gently. To the west, smoke from a chimney in Gembitz Hauland moves gently across the sky.

The peace of the moment is broken by his wife's latest scream of pain. Michael recalls the moment a quarter century ago when he first noticed her on the day the German settlers across the region celebrated their freedom from Polish rule. That afternoon the ten-year-old boy had no idea that the ugly Reign of Terror had begun in faraway France. Later, when the Protestant Germans heard about the beheadings and social upheaval in the far-off Catholic country, they simply ignored the news; they thought it would never concern them. Yet, by the time Michael was a man, the chaos in France was present at the door of their church.

The people of France turned to a little Corsican corporal, Napoleon Bonaparte, to restore order and honor to their country. French armies were amassed, and numerous wars were fought against their neighbors. When Napoleon decided to invade the vast country of Russia, the little corporal stopped along the way to create an alliance with the Polish nobles. Together they created the Duchy of Warsaw of territories taken from both Prussia and Russia. In only thirteen years, the bright future they celebrated as subjects of King Friedrich Wilhelm II was lost as King Friedrich Wilhelm III fled with his family to East Prussia. The proud Lutheran settlers were again the subjects of the Catholic Polish nobles on whose neglected estates they farmed.

Michael is grateful that indignity was short. After the cruel Russian winters defeated the French armies, Czar Alexander I wanted to absorb the entire Duchy of Warsaw into his kingdom. Fortunately, Austria and England, fearing that Russia would become too powerful, forced a compromise. The Duchy of Posen, where Michael's farm is located, was given back to the Prussian kingdom. Looking at the smoke floating across the sky in the distance, the farmer thanks God that it once again drifts across fresh, clean German air.

The farmer's thoughts shift from old conflicts in grand palaces to the painful shrieks coming from his simple house. He smirks at the irony that he is not welcome in either building right now.

Usually, he is in control. Decisions about what to plant or when to harvest, should an animal be bred or butchered, or how his family and farm are to be protected are his alone. But when his wife is giving birth, he feels as useless as his old dog sleeping under the tree behind him. Tomorrow he will be back in charge.

There is another loud scream in the house. Michael's heart stops for a minute. Then he hears the squeaky cries of a new baby. The father says a small prayer of thanks and hopes for another safe delivery for both his wife and child.

The beautiful songs of the birds in the trees are shattered by a thunderous crash as the door of the house is flung against the wall. The pensive father, sleeping dog and grazing cows snap their heads in unison in the direction of the alarming noise. A silhouette of a woman fills the width of the doorway but only two-thirds of its height. Michael hears the dark figure order him to come into the house. The woman, who received her childbirth education by giving birth to nearly a dozen children, steps back into the house.

The noise in the smoky one-room home with a low ceiling, large fireplace and hard dirt floor where the family and an occasional wandering farm animal reside is deafening. In the corner of the room, a healthy baby girl protests her removal from the safe womb of her mother with screams that vibrate off the thick log walls. The parents are both happy to hear the noise: a baby with strong lungs has a fighting chance for a long, productive life.

When the baby finishes her first meal, the midwife takes her, and the exhausted mother falls asleep. The midwife places the baby in the rough-cut cradle Michael made from scrap logs for his first child. Relieved, he throws another log in the fireplace and sits in his chair. Tired from the long day, he puffs on his pipe and stretches his short leg to touch the corner of the cradle. Slowly he moves his foot to rock the baby's bed and hopes the motion will calm his new screaming daughter.

Two weeks later, the Schmidt family climbs into a wobbly oxcart to travel four miles for the baby's baptism. They cross the Flinta River, swollen by spring rains, and then follow a well-worn path past the homes and through the flat farm fields of their siblings and cousins. For almost two hundred years, generations of their families, through oppression and hope, have taken this route to baptism in the small timber-frame church in the center of the village of Gramsdorf.

This old church, with its simple altar, hard benches and leaky thatched roof, is not nearly as grand as a Catholic church, but it is theirs. Maintaining a church is not easy for farmers who are always one crop failure away from starvation. With the death two years ago of Pastor Christoph Benicke the baby will be the first member of the Schmidt family in seventy years not to be baptized by a member of the Benicke family. This morning, Pastor Grutzmacher traveled to the village to officiate the sacrament.

Several babies have been born since the last time a pastor came here to conduct the sacrament. Pastor Grutzmacher, a father of young children, knows he has only a short time to complete his mission before chaos overwhelms this cold dark room. Parents and godparents step forward. One by one, at the clay bowl of water on the altar, he asks the parents for the baby's name and sprinkles holy water on its forehead. When it is the Schmidt family's turn, the pastor pours cold water on the girl's head as he gives the baby her mother's name. Church mice flee, and other babies quickly join the chorus as the shocked girl once again exercises her strong lungs.

Later that afternoon, the parents sit on a backless bench outside their house, enjoying the end-of-day warmth of the sun on their faces. Mina, their four-year-old daughter, bravely chases the honking main course for this year's Christmas dinner through the garden. The family's newest member of God's kingdom suckles on her mother's breast. The tired farmer rests the back of his head on the rough wall of his house. Taking a deep breath of the clear spring air, he wonders what the future will be for Anna Christina Schmidt.

The former farm number 40 Gembitz Hauland Posen.
Today Gebiczyn 66. Fall 2022. Personal photo

Part II
The Home Place

July 16, 1840 – Gembitz Hauland

No longer hidden by thunder clouds, a nearly full moon illuminates a small Gembitz Hauland farm. Outside the farmhouse, unsure if it is day or night, wild and domestic animals are active. In the house, Anna is nearly lulled to sleep by their sounds, but just before she drifts off, the window-rattling snores of her husband snap her back to consciousness. To silence the irritating man, with whom, after today, she owns this farm, she pokes her elbow into his side.

Irritation would not be the word she would use to describe her feeling nearly a year ago when the man with a prominent large nose walked into her church and life. A few distinctive lines were beginning to form on his face, and his hair was starting to recede to a peak. He stood straight, and his chest and arms looked strong. Most important, he had a twinkle of mischief in his eyes. Anna was smitten and determined to be introduced.

The century-old church in Gramsdorf was showing its age. Anna decided to use her knowledge of the building to her advantage. When the service was completed, she rushed out of her seat and approached the stranger. Positioned next to her prey, she purposefully stepped on a floorboard that she knew to be weak. She appeared to begin to tumble, and the unsuspecting man reached out to stop the fall. He held her in his arms longer than needed. Anna blushed, and the man gave her a sweet, charming smile. At that moment, a chemical reaction ignited that had not quieted up to this moment.

Since the spring evening when she screamed her first breath, Anna has always been independent. That Sunday, she shocked her potential suitor by asking, "Do you want to share some cake in the village square?" Under the large oak tree across from the church, he introduced himself as Friedrich Wilhelm Heÿn.

After that Sunday, the two had many conversations under that oak. Friedrich was nine years older than Anna. He did not inherit land from his father and was working day jobs until he saved enough to buy his own farm. To Anna, Friedrich's story sounded the same as all of her other potential suitors—what was different was when she first saw him sign his name. Most of the men in the village had little education, and if they were able to sign their name, their signature was very shaky, with no natural flow. But Friedrich signed with the flourish of an artist. Anna thought this man had an education and would be a success. They had a short courtship, and within months he asked her to marry him under that tree.

However, the obstacles the authorities place in front of young lovers wanting to marry are high and expensive to vault over. The first two barriers had been cleared: Friedrich was older than twenty-five years and had completed his required military service. The next impediments were not as easy for a young couple without resources to resolve. Both the government and the church required fees before granting approval to marry. Friedrich was a hard worker, but money was not easy to save. The couple had to make a decision. Do they wait to marry? Or should they, like other young people who could not satisfy the marriage requirements, live as husband and wife, hoping their first baby does not arrive until they can afford to get married?

The decision was made for them this spring when Daniel Hoeft made an offer they could not refuse. He had traded his farm in Wischen Hauland for one owned by his brother-in-law Martin Krueger in Gembitz Hauland. Not wanting to farm it himself, he told Friedrich that if he agreed to plant the wheat, cabbage, and potatoes and tend the animals, he would have the first opportunity to purchase the farm. Over thirty *morgens* of flat and fertile property was a rare opportunity. That March afternoon, they enjoyed a piece of warm bread in the house that would soon be their first home together. Then the two men shook hands across the table to agree to the deal.

Finding the courage to ask Anna to marry him was easy, but Friedrich needed all of his nerve to ask Anna's father if he might marry his daughter. Michael Schmidt was a practical man who was not so old that he could not remember the difficulties that young people faced. He was also a proud man who fiercely protected his family's reputation. That afternoon, even after Anna's mother begged her husband to be polite, he was stubborn and combative.

He took the man who wanted to be his son-in-law for a walk in his pasture. Just as he had done twenty-one years before, he leaned on his fence rails and admired his new heifer frolicking in the spring grass. Memories of that day and the dreams he had for his little baby with the strong lungs made him more determined. The father asked, "You say you want to buy the old Krueger farm, but first, do you have enough money to pay the marriage fees? Too many men never have that money, and they live with the girl and have multiple children out of wedlock. That will not happen with my daughter. Do you understand?"

Hearing the tone of the man's voice, Friedrich knew that an unconfident incorrect answer could result in a physical confrontation. He needed to convince his prospective father-in-law that he had a plan to support his daughter and the expected grandchildren. With a clear firm voice, he responded, "I have saved enough money for the marriage fees. If we have a good harvest this year, I am sure we will also be able to buy the farm."

It was the right response to diffuse the situation. The protective father responded, "Good."

Certain he had sufficiently scared the young man, Michael returned his attention to his pasture. After a long silence, he asked, "Which of these cows will you want for your dowry?"

The next day, with the permission of his prospective father-in-law, Friedrich went to Czarnikau to pay the marriage fees. Then the couple asked

Pastor Friedrich August Grebel, who had led the church in Gramsdorf since shortly after Anna's baptism, for permission to marry. For three consecutive Sundays, the pastor asked the congregation if anyone knew of any reason why the couple could not marry. After the third reading, Pastor Grebel recited the delayed marriage vows to the couple. The rain outside, which started as a slow drip from the many holes in the roof, began falling as a steady stream on the couple, their family, friends and the pastor as they promised to spend the rest of their lives together.

The rain and the ceremony ended at the same time. With a large rainbow in front of them, the guests navigated the muddy trail to the Schmidt farm for a wedding celebration. Food was abundant. Beer flowed freely. Music and laughter could be heard for miles. Glass after glass of beer was raised to toast the happiness and future of the young couple.

After most of the guests left, the remaining men loaded Anna's few possessions into the back of an oxcart, and the couple set off to start their new life. Along the way, they stopped at the cemetery on the dirt road that separated Anna's girlhood in Polajewo Hauland from her life as a woman in Gembitz Hauland, and they lay flowers on her grandparents' graves. Then the couple traveled to the Vordere Reihe.

Arm in arm, the excited couple walked the final five hundred feet through the tall pine trees that led to the stone hut in the clearing. They were about to begin their new life! Friedrich quickly unloaded the cart and unhitched the oxen, then returned to the house and slammed the door shut.

Inside her new home, tears were streaming down Anna's face. Her entire sex education had been watching her father's animals breed. Her normal confidence was weak now, and Friedrich, seeing her distress, pulled her close and gave her a tender kiss. Slowly Anna forgot her fears as they sank into the bed Friedrich had built for them.

Later, as she lay in his arms, she wondered why her mother had told her that she would not enjoy the evening. When the first rays of sun began to shine in the window, the couple enthusiastically repeated their enjoyment.

Later that morning, Anna sat on a simple wooden bench, her face warmed by the spring sun as she cut seed potatoes to be planted that afternoon. She stared at the trail that she had walked yesterday as an anxious virgin. She smiled as she quartered a potato with four eyes, thinking she was now a farmer's wife.

As she sliced the potatoes, Anna saw her father leading her dowry by a rope on the lane to the Mittel Reihe. He was coming to give his new son-in-law his finest two-year-old heifer. The cow with the bright orange body, white markings on her belly and a distinctive white hourglass on her face, was so large from carrying her first calf that she scraped the bushes along the way to her new home. Her udder was round, high and full between her hind legs in anticipation of the coming birth.

Friedrich came out of the barn to receive his payment from his new father-in-law. He was pleased by the agreement he had made that afternoon in the pasture. Daniel Hoeft had left them a milk cow but not one as fine as this one.

Friedrich smiled as he watched his new wife hug the animal as tight as she had earlier hugged him. He teased her, "I think we should name her Pils after the new beer brewed in Czarnikau."

Anna turned to her husband and huffed. "No cow of mine is going to be named for a beer. She will have a good Christian name like Maria, the mother of Jesus."

The father chuckled, telling his new son-in-law, "This is the first of many arguments you will lose."

As spring progressed into summer, the couple's hard work was visible. The vines of the potatoes they planted that first day were tall, dark green and sprouting pink flowers. In the rows next to potatoes, heads were forming on Anna's cabbage. The coats of the cows in the meadow were no longer dull and matted with manure; eating the rich grass had made the coats so shiny that the sun reflected off them. Friedrich's first crop of wheat was turning yellow, and the weight of kernels was so heavy that the stalks nearly drooped to the ground.

Friedrich used his carpentry and masonry skills first to improve the homes of their animals. He promised Anna that when he was done in the barn, he would turn his attention to the house. When Anna protested the order of his repairs, he responded, "We make our money in the barn, not in the house."

Last week, confident about their future, Friedrich met Daniel Hoeft at the beerhall in Althutte. After a large gulp of beer for courage, he said, "I will pay you 650 *thaler* for the farm. I need a mortgage, and if you agree I will pay you the whole sum after next year's harvest."

Hoeft was a shrewd negotiator, and Friedrich could not read from his face what the answer would be. Sitting on the backless bench, his back hurt as each man continued drinking beer. When the mugs were empty, Hoeft extended his hand. He made his counteroffer, "If you buy me another beer, I will agree."

Today, Friedrich and Daniel met again at the office of the notary to finalize the agreement. All day Anna was nervous as she dashed between the chores in the house, to the barn, to the garden and back again. The black clouds of the approaching storm were building when Friedrich finally returned. His face was stern as he approached the house, and Anna's stomach tightened into a hard knot. Then that mischievous smile she loved so much crossed his face. In a voice loud enough for the Wankes, Martens, Hoffmanns and maybe even the Westphals to hear, he announced, "We own this farm!"

The summer storm washed away her initial excitement. Unable to sleep, Anna's mind wanders between the fear of failure and the euphoria of satisfying her dreams. She rolls over and throws her arm over the chest of her loud husband. She whispers into his ear, "Soon, we will create many children in this bed. We are going to have a great life here." Those pleasant thoughts push the fears from her mind. She is finally able to fall asleep.

December 13, 1842 – Gembitz Hauland

The sky is gray and the wind raw as Anna waddles from the barn to the house. Steam rises in the cold air from a full pail of warm milk. The combination of her unsteady movements and the strong wind whipping against the pail causes some of the creamy contents to splash against her dress. Usually, the young farmwife would be upset by spilling milk, but this morning she has other worries.

A half-hour ago, when she walked to the barn, it was a typical day. As she did every morning, she gave her cow fresh hay, then slowly lowered herself onto a three-legged stool. To balance herself, she leaned forward, placing her head gently on the loose skin of the cow that connects its leg to its stomach. She then gently touched the cow's udder and slowly began pulling on her young cow's teats, and fresh warm milk started to hit her wooden pail.

Suddenly the rhythm of the morning changed. Two of the cow's four quarters were empty when Anna felt a sharp pain. She panted hard for a second, waiting for the pain to pass before quickly finishing her work. Then she pulled herself up by grabbing the cow's bony shoulder, picked up the pail of fresh milk and left the barn.

Now Anna feels her second contraction. Her dress is suddenly wet and clings to her legs. Looking down, she is relieved that she has not spilled more milk. Her first child is ready to join the world.

At the edge of the forest, past the chickens, geese and pigs, Friedrich is chopping wood. She needs his help. Straining her voice against the strong north winds, she gets no response. Then the wind lulls, and she shouts again in a stronger, commanding voice. This time the man's head turns. Seeing his wife leaning against the yellow stone wall of his house, a wave of fear overcomes him. Swiftly he hurdles over his rail fence like an ancient Greek Olympian.

After reaching his wife, he guides her to their bed. The couple needs help, but he is afraid to leave her. Anna meekly assures him, "I will be fine while you are gone."

He asks, "Are you sure?"

Then Anna has another painful contraction. She yells, "Go to the neighbors and get help now!"

When he steps out the door, sleet is falling hard. Susanna Wanke has delivered many of the babies in the neighborhood, and the quickest route to her home is to run southeast across their shared meadow. When he crosses the Ryga River, his face stings as if being hit by thousands of birdshot pellets. When he arrives at the Wanke farm, Susanna's daughter-in-law Minnie is nursing four-month-old Julius. Without disturbing the baby, she orders her husband to go with his mother and the nervous father back to the Heÿn farm. Remembering how important it was for her mother to be with her the first time she gave birth, Minnie also sends her older son Ludwig to the farm of Anna's parents.

While Friedrich is gone, Anna, in an effort to forget the paralyzing cramps, thinks about her life since they bought the farm. After their first harvest, the sausages were curing in the smokehouse, the crocks of sauerkraut were fermenting in the root cellar, and the females in the barns were becoming heavy with the next generation. Through the summer and fall, Friedrich divided any *thalers* he earned into two small pouches Anna had sewn. The first was to purchase seed and supplies for the next year, and the second was to pay their mortgage to the Hoefts. At the end of their second harvest, the pouch for the mortgage was nearly full, and after Christmas, Friedrich paid Hoeft the last of the 650 *thalers* they owed.

The air was fresh with the sounds and smells of early spring when Friedrich made the nine-mile journey to Czarnikau to record the transfer of the property to them. When he returned from the registry office that afternoon nine months ago, the couple celebrated their achievement with slow passionate love.

The fresh scent of lilacs filled the spring air when Anna began to feel sick in the mornings. On a beautiful May evening, every branch and twig on the apple tree next to the newly planted cabbage field had a deep pink blossom. The young farmers sat on the bench outside the house and watched Maria's calf nuzzle its mother for more milk when Anna whispered to Friedrich that he was going to be a father. That evening the entire world looked and felt fertile.

As the summer continued, Anna grew bigger and felt more uncomfortable. Friedrich occasionally called her the princess, but unlike a real princess, she got out of bed every day to bake bread, milk cows and gather eggs. She worked with him side by side, planting the crops, hoeing the weeds and harvesting the produce when it was ready. A month ago, she held the knife that killed the pigs whose meat was stuffed into their own intestines and was now curing in the smokehouse. Survival in this inhospitable world required work. Pregnancy was just another discomfort to overcome.

Now, lying alone in bed, anxiety crowds out her happy memories. Women and babies often die at this time. A small tear runs down her face as she thinks she is too young to die.

Just when despair begins to overwhelm her, the door is thrown open.

Anna laughs when she sees her out-of-breath husband, covered with ice, clumsily bound into the room. Last summer, her mother reminisced how excited and useless her father had been every time she gave birth. Anna looks at her frozen, scared husband and thinks that her mother is right. She is grateful that someone who knows something about childbirth is behind him at the door.

This has been a busy year for Susanna Wanke. Anna's child is the third baby she will deliver in the neighborhood in four months. The sixty-year-old farmwife, who always has a gentle smile, is the mother, grandmother, aunt or midwife to most of the families clustered together among the forests, ponds and pastures of Gembitz Hauland. After examining Anna, she assures the couple everything will be fine. Then she turns to the two men and sternly gives them two instructions, "Heat some water in the fireplace and then get out of my way."

As they leave the house, the two men grab a jug of homemade beer for companionship and another jug of homemade brandy for courage. They take refuge a short distance away in the corner of the barn where Friedrich repairs his tools. On the other side of the barn, the cows, horses and pigs stare at the two intruders. Under the animals' watchful eyes, the men first take a nip of the strong golden brandy and then wash it down with a large swig of beer.

The homemade liquor calms Friedrich's nerves until he hears Anna yell again. He jumps up, but his neighbor places his hand on the nervous father's shoulder. Christoph offers the beer to Friedrich as he says, "You have to be patient."

They hear voices outside the barn. Anna's parents have arrived. Her mother goes into the house to help with the delivery, and her father goes to the barn to help empty the jugs of liquor. Michael takes over Christoph Wanke's role of attempting to calm the new father. Seeing that Friedrich is now in expert hands, Christoph returns to his farm.

When he sees the fear of his son-in-law, the experienced man smiles, remembering the birth of his first son thirty years ago. That day he also needed the support of neighbors, a father-in-law, and strong homemade alcohol to survive the terrifying event happening in his house. By the time Anna was born, he was confident enough that he waited for the birth alone. The expectant grandfather is not as brave now when he hears the frightening screams of his daughter, but he does not betray himself to his son-in-law.

The screams from the house come quicker and louder. The shots of liquor washed down by beer are taken at the same interval as the cries from the house. By the time the screams from the house are almost constant, the jug is nearly empty. The last two slugs are saved, waiting for the final cry.

When sounds from the new baby are finally heard, the new father and grandfather toast their good fortune. Then on unsteady feet, they stagger through the barn door. When they swing open the door to the house, they hold themselves up with the door frame.

Anna's mother is startled by the noise. She turns to see her husband and son-in-law against the door frame with sleepy drunken looks on their faces. The woman shakes her head in disgust and tells Friedrich, "You have a girl."

The words quickly sober him. No longer needing the door frame for support, he stands straight. His eyes lose their drunken cloudiness as he walks to the bed. Anna's face is white, and her body wet with sweat. On her stomach is a small pink baby covered with the mucus of birth and screaming at the top of her lungs. When she sees her husband, Anna reaches out her hand, and a large smile spreads across her face. Grabbing her hand, the new father admires and examines his daughter. Friedrich breathes a quiet sigh of relief when he can see that the baby has ten toes, ten fingers, black hair, and a familiar large nose. Relieved, the father leans down and gives his wife a gentle alcohol-flavored kiss. Across the barnyard, they hear Maria bellow a greeting to the newest resident of the farm. The new parents look at each other and smile.

The new grandmother asks what the baby's name will be. Anna looks at her husband, who nods in agreement, and then weakly says, "Johanne Pauline Friedricke Heÿn."

January 14, 1854 - Gembitz Hauland

Anna is awakened by the sounds of dogs howling at the large full moon that fills the frigid night sky. She is in pain and exhausted after delivering her sixth baby. The light of the moon through the windows creates six dark shadows around her bed. She adjusts her eyes to see Friedrich and their five children staring at her new son.

Eleven-year-old Pauline takes her new brother from Anna's arms. Friedrich examines his fingers and toes while holding the envious two-year-old Ottilie. Standing in front of their father are the couple's other three sons. Gustav, the practical nine-year-old, asks when this brother will be able to help with chores. Albert, the stubborn six-year-old, pouts after being told to stop playing. August, the even-tempered four-year-old, proudly shows his mother the fresh bruise he received trying to keep up with his older brothers. Their new brother, who will be named Julius, is not interested in making a good first impression on his siblings. His high-pitched cries echo off the plaster walls, and his brothers think that he is imitating the howling dogs. Little Ottilie becomes scared and provides harmony to the newborn's cries.

In the middle of the chaos, Anna looks at her husband and gives him a contented smile at their good fortune. Six healthy babies are envied by many parents in their community. Still, Anna worries for her new son. From Christmas to Easter, disease is prevalent in the community. In addition to tending to the animals and preparing the farm for spring, one of Friedrich's winter tasks is digging graves in the frozen ground. At the funerals, there is always someone coughing or itching violently for whom the next grave will be dug.

The discomfort of pregnancy and the pain of childbirth are becoming harder for Anna. She is not sure how many more babies her body can bear. At only thirty-four, she could be fertile for another ten years. The only way to stop her cycle of childbirth every other year would be to deny her husband, and looking at the man standing before her, she recognizes that it is no more possible now than it had been on their wedding night.

Life during their marriage has not been easy, but it has been successful. With each additional mouth to feed, the risk that a bad harvest or an epidemic might destroy the family increases. So far, they have been able to avoid disaster. Friedrich has been a resourceful husband.

When they married, he had masonry skills. Now he builds brick houses and barns across the region. He transformed the stone hut where they spent their wedding night into a three-room brick house. Standing perpendicular to the house is a new large brick barn home to the offspring of their first cow, Maria. After completing the building, Friedrich wandered the roads from Althutte to Radwonke, adding the best cows he could find to their herd. On the day Pauline was born, Anna was able to milk their one cow by herself. Now she needs the help of all of her children to milk their herd.

Shortly after Gustav was born, Anna was scrubbing her children's clothes in a large tub of gray water. In the distance, she heard a team of horses pull a squeaking wagon up the farm lane. She was surprised to see Friedrich holding the reins attached to two large chestnut-colored horses with black legs and matching manes. Bringing the team to a stop, he announced, "I am not going to need oxen to pull the plow anymore."

The practical Anna asked, "Do you think the farm can produce enough food for these large animals?"

Friedrich responded, "I am going to rent more parcels of land. Plus, they will help me haul the bricks I have been making." Anna rolled her eyes at her husband's overly enthusiastic plans.

The farmwife had her own overly enthusiastic dreams for those magnificent animals. After the births of Pauline and Gustav, the couple made the grueling four-mile trip to the dilapidated church in Gramsdorf for their baptisms in a wagon pulled by two oxen. For her next baby's baptism, Anna imagined arriving in a wagon pulled by these impressive horses. She knew that vanity was a sin, but sometimes sin overcame her.

It is not how you arrive outside the church, but the words spoken inside that created conflict in the community, however. Nearly twenty-five years ago, King Friedrich Wilhelm III forced the combination of the Lutheran and Reformed Protestant churches into the Evangelical Church as the official church of Prussia. Some Lutherans chafed under the edict and continued to worship with the old prayer books. Across the community, as in all of Prussia, some of the Old Lutheran believers have been seeking religious freedom in America.

Not only Old Lutherans but also the second and third sons of Gembitz Hauland's first families are beginning to leave. The subject of emigration is discussed after the new liturgy is heard in the church, when a poor harvest forces another family to go hungry, when a young man without sufficient financial resources is refused permission to marry or when most of a family is lost in a matter of a few days to a mysterious disease. These conversations occur in the beerhalls, the clandestine church services or when young lovers cuddle after sex. They also happen late at night in the Heÿn house.

Shortly after August was born, a travel agent from Posen organized a meeting at the prayer house. "In America, there is abundant, almost free land that has never been farmed," he told the struggling farmers. "Never again will you live one crop failure away from starvation. Your prayers will not be dictated by the king. In America, you vote for your leaders."

The farmers were skeptical. Their grandfathers had received the same promises to entice them to move here. When those promises were broken, their uncles followed the same siren song to the Volga River in Russia. Once again, they found themselves asking, "Why should we trust you to get us to the promised land?" The agent working for land speculators assured the men, "For only a small fee, I will arrange your passage all the way to the new state of Wisconsin."

At the end of the meeting, several young men without prospects signed up for the trip. Letters received later told of a harrowing passage across the ocean. The free fertile land was really forests between steep rocky cliffs and needed to be cleared. They described unimaginably brutal cold winters and scorching hot summers. Politics was not so easy either. Different views about slavery had driven their new country to the edge of war several times. To Friedrich, this did not sound like a great improvement from where they lived now.

At his second wedding, their neighbor Gottlieb Radel confided to Friedrich that he was going to Wisconsin in 1854. He asked, "Does your family want to come with us?"

Friedrich and Anna were faced with the biggest decision of their marriage. They could stay and expand their farm or leave everything and everyone they knew for an uncertain bet on a more prosperous future.

An emigrant must make their decision nearly a year before the ship leaves the harbor. First, the passage is booked. Then all of the emigrant's property is divided into two piles. One small pile will be taken to the new country. The other larger pile is sold with the hope that the money raised from the sale is enough to settle debts and pay for the tickets. Finally, emigration documents from the government granting permission to leave must be received. There is risk at every step, and if there are any failures, the family is ruined. Thinking about the process overwhelms Friedrich.

Unlike those of her husband, Anna's concerns were less practical and more emotional. She feared for her children. Last spring, when they had to make their decision, she began getting sick in the morning. Eleven years ago, she had to ask the neighbors what it meant. This time she knew. If they decided to join the Radels, she would be traveling with five children between the ages of three and twelve, plus their new baby. Dark thoughts overcame her. She was sure if she took her children on the seven-week trip in the hull of a cramped sailing ship, they would not all survive.

The stress of the pregnancy and the thoughts of leaving the only home she ever knew made Anna unusually emotional. She realistically acknowledged that at any time, disease could take one or more of her children. If that happened on dry land, at least she would have a grave on which to plant flowers and grieve. If her babies died on the open sea, their little bodies would be lost forever to the vast ocean. One day Friedrich came from the barn to see Anna sitting on her bench, grieving their unborn baby's burial at sea. He dismissed this unusual weakness of his normally strong wife to the stress of her latest pregnancy.

Anna walked her farm and felt sentimental about every object, animal and plant. When the branches on the apple tree in front of the house hung low from the weight of its pink flowers, she cried. She thought how it only bloomed that full in the springs when she was pregnant. If the family moved, that tree would never again welcome her future children.

She turned her back to the tree to see the cows grazing in the meadow behind the barn. Three cows looked up at her, each with the distinctive white hourglass face markings of her father's herd. If they sold the farm, those cows would be scattered. Anna's connection to her youth would be lost forever.

Looking past the cows in the pasture, Anna could see the midwife, her head down and her gait swift, going to deliver another baby. Anna was overcome with fear. If that woman's gentle hands were not with her when she delivered her future babies, would she and the baby survive?

That night Anna looked at her farm lit by the moon. She took one big deep breath and made her final decision. She is not going to America.

Friedrich had not yet come to the same decision. While he knew his opportunities were limited if the family stayed, he had serious financial concerns if they left. With the addition of the expected baby, he would have to pay for passage for six children and two adults. If he sold the farm and all the personal property, he was not sure he could pay for the passage, settle his debts, plus have enough to begin a new life. The other men who planned to go assured him they would all work together in America, but he was too proud to rely on others to help feed his family.

Both parents were sure that some or all of their children would one day have to cross the ocean. The opportunities in this small community for this many children were extremely limited. The parents had long discussions about whether they should make that decision for them now or let them decide in the future.

The decision weighed heavily on the couple. On the evening that Anna announced she was staying, they argued so loudly it frightened the children. In the middle of the heated exchange, she stated, "If you decide to go to America, you are going alone. I am staying here with the children."

A wounded Friedrich stormed out of the house. He angrily rode his horse to the beerhall to escape the indignity of being dictated to by an independent wife. Humiliated, he sat at a long, well-worn table with other men of the village who were also escaping from their strong-willed wives. Friedrich took a sip of beer and told the men he had just lost another fight. The warm beer going down his throat helped to wash down the shame he felt.

Later that evening, the horse returned Friedrich safely home. The next morning, even with a hurting head, Friedrich woke with the sun. He sulked out to the barn to feed the cows and horses, slop the hogs and chop wood for the family's new stove. Slowly he came to the conclusion that his wife was right. They should not move. When he returned to the house, drenched with sweat, he apologized and announced his decision in agreement with Anna.

Peace returned to the family, and the normal rhythm of life went on. By Christmas, little Ottilie turned into a terrible two-year-old with a fury that would test the patience of any parent. Anna endured the girl's inquisitiveness and stubbornness with experienced, unflappable patience. After preparing the Christmas dinner, she enjoyed watching her family devour the roast goose while her next baby sat on her bladder and mercilessly kicked her stomach. Even though she was very uncomfortable, she said a small prayer of thanks that the family would eat their Christmas goose in this house next year, not in a faraway unknown place.

During the cold winter, Julius was more difficult than his siblings had been. First, he refused to take his mother's breast, and then he could not get enough of her milk. Every evening when the tired family crawled into their beds, he would cry uncontrollably. No amount of food or diaper changes calmed him. By spring, the distressing nightly disturbances lessened, but the entire family was exhausted.

On a warm, late spring day, Friedrich hitched his wagon and drove to the Radel farm. Across the yard, all of the family's possessions were on display. Slowly an auctioneer moved from item to item, selling to the highest bidder the combination farmer–tailor's life work, from a simple hammer to the man's finest horse. That day Friedrich purchased a sow heavy with piglets, woodworking tools, and a new table and chairs large enough to comfortably seat his expanding family.

When he returned home, the boys helped him carry the new table and chairs into the house. When she visited the Radel home, Anna had always admired this furniture. Unlike her table, which was roughly built by Friedrich to serve a utilitarian function, this one had been made by a master woodworker. She could not believe that this beautiful table was now hers, and she smiled, thinking about the future family dinners they would have around this table.

On the first Sunday of July, the Heÿn family wagon was loaded full again. This time the cargo was children and food. Slowly the family made the familiar trip on dusty dirt roads to the prayer house in Gembitz Hauland for another goodbye. During Lent, Pastor Grebel made a special trip from Gramsdorf to pray for a safe trip for Karl Hoffmann and Michael Wanke. He still did not know if his prayers had been answered, and now he was back on this hot Sunday to pray for the Radels and Sawalls.

Once the prayers were completed, the heads of the two families walked behind the pastor to the tower of three bells that had been given to the community by the king. Each man grabbed a rope and began ringing a bell. Members of the close community gathered around the tower, bowing their heads and shedding a few tears. The peel of the bells sounded the same as they did when a wooden casket was slowly carried to the cemetery down the road. Today's grief felt greater. After a funeral, only one person is missing. Today they were saying goodbye forever to fifteen friends, nearly two percent of their village.

When the men finished ringing the bells, everyone turned to the farewell party in the prayer house yard. The men set up tables and rolled out barrels of beer. The women filled the well-used tables with food they had been cooking all week. The elderly pulled their favorite chairs under the large trees in the shade from the hot summer sun. From their vantage point, they supervised their children and grandchildren, mostly not approving of what they were doing. The children were running wild as they always did. The Radel and Sawall children excitedly told the others of the adventure on which they were about to embark.

After the food was served and the beer barrel was tapped, the men and women split into opposing camps. The men moved their chairs around the beer, complaining about the quality of both their crops and the politicians in equal measure. Across the yard, under a big maple tree, the women fed their babies and shared the latest foibles of their children and husbands.

Louise Westphal rejoins the women after scolding the preteen children, who are growing up too fast and too insolent for her satisfaction. With an exaggerated annoyance, she says, "I will be glad when there are a couple less of these mouthy brats around." She does not mean it. After each family leaves the community, these parties become a little quieter and less familiar. So far, the departures have been just a trickle. Yet a small stream that joins other streams creates a small river, which can become a raging river before it empties into the ocean. Louisa fears this fate for her community. She wonders if, in thirty years, there will be enough eligible young people for her children to marry.

Sitting away from the group is Gertie Radel, sullenly nursing her baby, Gustav. The other women are concerned for the twenty-two-year-old, Gottlieb's second wife. When his first wife died, he was left with young children. He quickly convinced this girl, half his age, to marry him. The carefree twenty-year-old suddenly found herself the unappreciated stepmother of grieving children, the oldest only eight years younger than she. Then just when she was sure she was pregnant, her new husband announced that he had booked them passage to America.

She struggled to care for the baby through the long winter. Now she had the responsibility to keep the baby and the rest of the children alive for the next six weeks in a cramped, disease-infested ship. The fear of the voyage and the thought of leaving her family overwhelmed her.

The women discussed their concerns about Gertie with Anna Sawall, who was traveling with the Radels. The fifty-year-old mother of seven dismisses them. "Of course, I will look out for her, but I won't have the time to play mother to her. I have my own children to take care of."

The sun is beginning to set as the barrel of beer is emptied. The women gather the remnants of the food and clear the tables. Before the wagons are fully loaded, Friedrich and Anna wish Gottlieb and Gertie good luck. Standing next to the couple are Martin Redel, his wife Minnie, and Friedrich and Christine Wegner. For a few minutes, the eight neighbors make small talk before their final goodbyes. Walking away, Christine, Minnie and Anna wonder if this will be the last time they will all be together.

That night as Friedrich and Anna lie in each other's arms, she snuggles into his shoulder and asks if he thinks they made the right decision. Friedrich takes a deep breath, thinks for a minute, then says yes. He says he would rather spend the next month fishing on the banks of the Ryga River with his boys than bouncing up and down on the ocean doing nothing. Anna sighs her relief.

Maybe someday she will want to leave her home for new opportunities. But on this warm summer evening, she cannot think of another place she would rather be than on her small farm, listening to the heavy breathing of her sleeping children, lying in the strong arms of her husband. Looking across the room lit by the half-moon, she thinks that maybe this house has enough room for a couple more children.

November 19, 1865 – Gembitz Hauland

Today is not only a day of worship and rest for the residents of Gembitz Hauland, but it is also Anna's wedding day. She stares out the window at the farmyard where she has spent her adult life. Tears stream down her face, shed for her future and then for her past.

The tears for the future are, of course, not silly concerns about the wedding night—she cried those tears a quarter century ago. For a forty-six-year-old mother of eight whose beauty of youth has been transformed into graying hair, wrinkled face and wider hips, the mysteries of the wedding night are not worth a tear. Today's wedding is much more practical. She has children to support and a farm to save. Her tears for the future are focused on if she has made the right decision for her family.

Her tears for the past continue those she has been shedding throughout the past year. Thursday marks the first anniversary of the day she suddenly became a widow.

Today's view from the window is eerily similar to that day. The sky was blue, the air crisp and the trees a colorful combination of green, red and yellow. Just like today, there was more work to do than people to do it. They needed supplies from town, and Friedrich climbed on his horse. As she had done so many times before, Anna watched him disappear through the pine trees on his way to the Vordere Reihe.

She stayed home to organize the children's chores. The older boys, under the watchful eye of their grandfather, cleaned barns, fed animals and cut wood for winter. The youngest, Adolph, tagged along with his brothers, thinking he was helping but spending more time getting in their way. The girls baked bread, washed clothes, fed chickens and prepared dinner. Anna stirred the crocks of pungent sauerkraut made from cabbage they had grown that year.

Anna was sitting on her bench by the door that afternoon when she heard the horse return—without Friedrich in the saddle. Fear immediately welled in her chest. She sent the boys to find their father. She hoped for the best but knew she had to prepare for the worse. Her fears were confirmed when her sons found their father's body alongside the road.

They did not know what had happened. Had the horse bolted after seeing an animal? Did Friedrich become sick? As she walked away from his fresh grave, Anna knew for sure that she was now a widow solely responsible for the survival of her family and their farm.

Anna's memories drift further back in time. She remembers her and Friedrich moving to this farm as young lovers, with stars in their eyes and more hopes and dreams than money in their pockets. The farm was and still is small, about thirty *morgens.* Through Friedrich's hard work, the single stone hut has been expanded to three brick buildings that house humans, animals, and food for both. Their land is not as productive as the fertile flat plains in the surrounding villages, but it has provided well for the family. Anna smiles as she remembers how in their youthful enthusiasm, they thought they had a royal estate—Friedrich even called her princess.

Looking out the window, Anna sees the spot where the apple tree once stood that had a peculiar habit of producing fruit every other year. The tree frustrated Friedrich, but Anna always appreciated it: eight times, she and the tree had been on the same reproductive schedule. Anna cries as she thinks that Friedrich had removed the tree and also left her here with their five boys and three girls, ages seven to twenty-three, plus her eighty-two-year-old father, who lived in a one-room pensioner's hut next to the garden.

With her father's life estate to the farm, Anna had a short window of time to adjust to widowhood. That window closed when he died three months ago. A widow with no sons yet at the age of majority needs a man to run the farm. Walking away from the cemetery after she buried her father, she knew she had to remarry as soon as possible.

Not wanting another widow with children on their support roles, the men of the community found a rare bachelor only three years younger than Anna. Friedrich Wilhelm Beutler would be young enough to run the farm but too old to expect more children. Anna knows it is the right decision, but it is hard to start over.

Her situation is not unique. The early death of a spouse, leaving young children to feed and raise, is a fate many of her neighbors have experienced.

For her, the saddest sight is a lost father holding a newborn whose mother just left the world while bringing the baby into it. But fathers have support in these tragedies. The women of the community jump to action with food, daycare, and support for the family. A girl will be found to manage the household. Quite often, that young girl becomes the new wife and mother of the family. It feels unfair to Anna now that death does not stop the flow of life for the men.

This morning the children are in a flurry of activity as they prepare for the trip to the old prayer house that is now their church. Pauline, the oldest, feeds and dresses the younger children. The only child to have reached the age of majority when her father died is a perpetual godmother. She is also spending too much time alone with the Westphal boy from the neighboring farm. He has his military service to fulfill and money to save before they can marry. Anna worries about them. Every year Pastor Wenig baptizes four or five babies of single mothers who had been impatient to celebrate their wedding night. Anna regrets that Friedrich will never have the same stern talk with August Westphal that her father had with him.

Gustav, Albert and August are old enough to do farmwork but not old enough to own the farm. They also must fulfill their military service. War clouds are always brewing in Prussia, but right now, this is a bigger worry for all mothers. The relations between Catholic Austria and Lutheran Prussia are getting tense. Anna frets that she may not only have lost a husband but could also lose a son to war.

The four younger children, Ottilie, Julius, Maria and Adolph, are doing well at the Lutheran school built by the citizens of the community across the road from the church. But losing their father and grandfather within one year and anticipating a new stepfather moving into their house has been stressful for them and for their mother. They are having trouble learning and accepting how unfair the world can be.

The ringing of the distant church bells returns Anna to the present. It is time for Pastor Wenig to recite marriage vows to her for the second time. She and the children prep and primp their clothes one last time, then go outside. They climb into the wagon, pulled by Friedrich's horses, for the trip to the church. The horse that witnessed the end of Anna's previous life is pulling her to the beginning of her new one. She will save the farm.

The S. S. Reichstag on its maiden voyage July 19, 1867. Source: Ernst Hieke, Veroffentlichungen der Wirtschaftsgeschichtlichen Forschungsstelle e.v., Hamburg, Band 30

Part III
Emigration Begins

July 19, 1867 – The North Sea

The moon is bright and nearly full. The reflection of its top half on the water creates the illusion that it is rising out of the vast sea. Transfixed by the mirage are five naïve ship passengers leaning on the railing of the *Reichstag* on its maiden voyage to America. Each of the young travelers is quiet, thinking that their future will be as great as the infinite number of stars twinkling in the sky. They are lost in their dreams of the rich property they will own, the beautiful spouses they will meet, and the perfect children they will have. The sparkles of starlight on the polished railing of the ship, not yet scuffed by overuse, give them the same excitement they felt as children watching candles flicker on the Christmas tree.

A summer thunderstorm has turned the early evening sky black at their former homes. Three hardened mothers sit by their windows, waiting for the deluge. Their thoughts, as dark as the sky, are of the children who left them forever ten days ago. Each sullen woman thinks about the chair at the dinner table that will always be empty, the weddings they won't attend, and the grandchildren they will never meet. An occasional flash of lightning illuminates the tired, sagging roofs of their barns, reminding them how tired and broken they also feel.

On the ship, twenty-year-old Albert stands between his friends Fred Schultz and Julius Wanke and fills his lungs with a deep breath of cool sea air. The water provides him welcome relief from the stifling heat of the cramped city of Hamburg. For a young man who had never visited a city larger than a few thousand people, the crowds and the hustle of Hamburg were exciting but also overwhelming. He likes open spaces and is excited to finally be on his way to America.

At twenty-seven, Fred is the oldest of the group. He is traveling with his niece, Louise Wegner, who, at thirteen, is the youngest. They will live with Fred's sister, also named Louisa but whom they call Beate, on a large farm near Potsdam, Minnesota. Ten years have passed since he has seen his sister after she joined the steady stream of families emigrating from Gembitz Hauland to Honey Creek, Wisconsin. In Wisconsin, she married Friedrich Hoffmann, who had left four years earlier, at the same time as his brother Karl and the Radels and Sawalls. Now he is a successful farmer in Minnesota and paid the duo's passage in exchange for badly needed labor.

To Albert's right is twenty-four-year-old Julius. He and his sister plan to live with the family of their older sister Wilhelmine. Like Fred's sister, Wilhelmine and their brother Ludwig joined the transplanted Gembitz Hauland community in Honey Creek nearly ten years ago. She also married a boy from down the road at home. Since the end of the war, members of the Hoffmann, Radel and Wanke families have left Honey Creek to settle on farms in southeastern Minnesota. Rather than live near the Hoffmanns, however, Wilhelmine and the Radels moved farther west to a town with the American Indian name Owatonna.

Julius's sister Mina carefully slips herself between him and Albert. She is one day older than Albert and never misses an opportunity to use this accident of birth against him. This evening on the open sea, she lets the boy, who has been like another brother to her, know that the balance of power will not shift in the new world.

Many in their community think of them as twins. At the end of their last church service in Gembitz Hauland, Albert and Mina were standing in a circle of friends and siblings, bragging about their upcoming adventure. From the corner of his eye, Albert saw the nearly eighty-year-old midwife who, in one busy day, had delivered them both, hobbling in their direction. The aged woman wildly swung her cane to part the circle of self-absorbed teenagers. Time had shrunk her body, fogged her sight and dulled her hearing, but her mind was clear as she stood in the center of the circle. She told the two about how she crossed pastures, dodged angry bulls, scolded their drunken fathers and encouraged their mothers, who were now standing outside the circle, to push one more time. Albert and Mina blushed as their friends began snickering. Then in midsentence, the formidable little grandma's joyful smile changed to a bitter, angry scowl. Poking the two red-faced twenty-year-olds with her cane, she declared, "If I had known that you would abandon your homes and families, I would not have moved so fast that night." The woman spun around and walked away from the ingrate children.

The spray of the corrosive seawater dampens not only the new deck of the ship but also the travelers. While the two girls cautiously step back from the railing, the men pensively continue to admire the dark water and bright moon before them. Salt spray stings their eyes and leaves a tang on their tongues when they lick their lips. Each man thinks about the new strange journey they have begun. To three young men with no responsibilities, this is an adventure that stirs their young hearts.

Without testosterone inhibiting their common sense, Mina and Louise are more realistic about what lies ahead. Like the men, they look forward to the future but still feel tugged from behind from the life they are leaving. Louise, who last year was still playing dolls with Minnie Marten, is having an especially hard time. The lightly rolling sea moves the ship up and down and does the same to her stomach. The homesickness that started ten days ago as they slowly traveled dirt roads to the train station in Budsin is now consuming her like a deathly fever. Since this morning, when the ropes tying the *Reichstag* to her homeland were released, she was overcome with uncontrollable tears several times.

When she first learned of her aunt's offer, she thought, like a typical teenager, of a rosy future of freedom from her demanding mother. Without the supervision of her father, she also dreamed of the exotic new boys she would be able to meet. Now, finally out on the open sea this evening, the queasiness of her stomach vanquishes the thoughts of handsome boys better than her father ever could. While her uncle interpreted the endless stars as a symbol of the unlimited possibilities before them, she saw a sad, cold, barrier-free world that made her long for the warm comfort of her mother's endless commands and rules.

When the first gusher of tears started to fall, her uncle attempted to console her, but the clumsy man failed as a replacement mother. He tried reassuring his niece, "Don't worry, your aunt has the same temperament and personality as your mother." With no memory of her aunt, Louise was not calmed by his words.

When Fred's awkward compassion did not soothe his niece, he turned to bad-tempered guilt. He told the crying girl, "You should be grateful that your Aunt Beate sent the money for the trip. Being a domestic servant for your aunt and uncle in a strange place is a better opportunity than any that your sisters you left behind will have." The mature portion of her thirteen-year-old brain knew her uncle was right, but the little girl portion was still stronger. She was in pain. When Mina witnessed the exchange, she decided to take the poor girl under her wing.

Mina also looks forward to her future, but not with the same wild-eyed optimism as her brother. She is eager to see her sister again and meet her four nephews and nieces for the first time. Yet she is also uneasy. Her sister's life in America has not been trouble-free, and Mina expects she will have similar woes. Unlike Louise, she is not a teenager escaping comforting parental control but rather a young woman who will be missing the benefit of her mother's advice.

Albert is not dreaming about family reunions with lost family members. He is the first in his family to leave and will be facing America alone. When they arrive, he will have to separate from his companions. He does not have enough money to finish the trip and must instead find work in New York before he can complete his journey. He promises the others that he will join them in Minnesota next spring.

Mina teases him that he will go to Wisconsin, where one of their confirmation classmates has been living for the past two years. With a devilish grin, Mina reminds Albert how mad his mother had been when he and Auguste snuck into the woods behind the church on the Sunday before she left. "You can't wait to repeat that experience in Wisconsin," Mina teased. Albert takes the teasing from his almost sister with noncommittal irritation when they are alone and bright red embarrassment when she behaves like this in front of others. This evening, however, Auguste is far from Albert's thoughts. Owning his own farm is his first priority.

At home, a fatherless second son's only prospect for owning a farm would be to marry a widow. Marrying an older woman with a house full of children did not strike the same passion in the young man's loins as his first kiss with Auguste behind the church. That Sunday, as she rode out of his life, he decided that if he wanted both her and a farm, he would have to follow her to the new world.

Albert would have left with her that June afternoon, but it was the first summer after his father had died. His brother Gustav was preparing to join the army ahead of the brewing conflict between Austria and Prussia. His mother suffered so much loss, and he would not add to her burdens. He also acknowledged to himself that he did not have enough money for the trip. After that night, the always frugal Albert saved every *Thaler* he earned for this trip to America.

Three months ago, when he turned twenty, he was required to register for conscription into the Landwehr, the country's civil army. Like other young men who had reached conscription age, receiving the necessary authorization to emigrate before completing his military service could be a problem. The unscrupulous travel agent, hungry for his fee, told him, "Don't worry. I will add four years to your age on the documents." Albert pointed out that he was traveling with Julius, who obviously looked older than he did. The agent responded, "Again, no problem. I'll just add four years to his age also."

Recording their ages as twenty-eight and twenty-four rather than twenty-four and twenty did not guarantee their success in boarding the ship. As the train chugged from their home to the port, each man worried their deception would be discovered. The travel agent had assured them that the chances were low that they would be found out and denied passage. Still, their fears increased the closer the hour they were scheduled to set sail approached.

When the ship's manifest was being created, Albert's fear of being denied boarding overcame his natural cautious common sense. Waiting in line for the tired clerk, he suddenly made an impulsive decision. He placed his hand on Julius's shoulder, whispering to his friend to block the soldier's view of him. With the prying eyes blocked, he removed a precious *Thaler* from the pouch he had tied around his waist. When they reached the clerk, Fred and Julius each took positions to block the view of Albert from the others around them. With his hand concealing the coin, Albert slipped it across the table as he leaned over to whisper in the clerk's ear, "Please check the box that says I am a female." There was no further conversation as the deceptive transaction was completed.

Once safely on board, the three relieved men sat on their new bunks in the steerage section of the ship. From his sack, Fred pulled out a bottle of brandy he was saving to celebrate Julius's birthday during the voyage. They proudly toasted their ruse. Mina outwardly registered her disapproval at the impetuous men but inwardly smiled about the great new story she now had that would embarrass Albert in the future. Louise forgot about her homesickness for a few minutes and laughed in approval of the deception.

The wind blowing across the sea becomes cold. The five hopeful young people decide to descend to their bunks in the steerage for their first night on the open water. Not supported any longer by the ship's railing, they wobble a bit and link their arms together. At that moment, even the melancholy Louise is enthusiastic about the adventures that lie ahead. It is a wonderful time to be young and free. Youthful optimism looks forward only to the bright blue opportunities—they are too young and inexperienced to worry about any dark clouds that may come.

On the plains of Posen, the summer thunderstorm begins to rage. Three mothers stare into the dark and stormy sky and reflect on their past.

Louise's mother Christine has little time for reflection. Six other children need her attention. The mother bounces her one-year-old son Wilhelm on her hip while giving three-year-old Ottilie hard bread to distract her from her latest dangerous escapade. Behind her, the two oldest daughters prepare dinner while ten-year-old Pauline and six-year-old August fight with each other to relieve their boredom. Meanwhile, her husband Friedrich has run from the barn, slamming the door to the house and making a puddle on her clean floor. Christine takes a deep breath and wonders why with all of this activity, the house seems so quiet and empty.

When her sister wrote that she needed domestic help and offered to pay for the passage of her namesake to America, Christine faced one of the most difficult decisions of her life. She has lost children to death, but Louise would be the first child she would lose while alive. As her family grew, it was harder and harder to feed all the children. Her two older daughters, Ernestine and Henriette, both nearly twenty years old, would soon find husbands, but there was always another baby coming. There was little discussion with her husband that their third daughter should leave for America. When her brother Fred said that he would also go, Christine agreed. The girl took the news that she was going to live with an aunt she did not know with equal amounts of enthusiasm and rejection. She had reached that stressful age when mother and daughter disagreed about everything. Christine felt relief that she would not have to argue any longer with her challenging daughter, but tonight, as the thunder shakes her home, she regrets those thoughts. One of her children, whom she will probably never see again, is wandering the earth alone. Her feeling of emptiness worsens.

As the boom of thunder shakes Minnie Redel's house, she also thinks about her two children. The gloom of the storm affects her the least of the three mothers, as her soul has already been toughened by loss. She married Christoph Wanke in her early twenties, and they had a good life together. His family was one of the founders of the community, which provided her stability. She and her husband added a child to the family every two or three years for the next twenty years. They felt blessed that five of their children had survived infancy.

Minnie's good luck ran out at the time of Mina's birth. Christoph died, and Minnie's secure future suddenly crumpled. She was a thirty-six-year-old widow with six children to feed. She quickly made the practical decision many women before her had also been forced to make. She married a neighbor boy, Martin Redel, who was barely old enough to meet the legal qualifications to be called a man. Shortly after the wedding, she was pregnant again, and with her young husband, she added three Redel children to her Wanke clan. After the wedding, the gossip at the church was intense, but most women privately knew they would have done the same as Minnie.

Bringing a stepfather to the family who had been her older children's playmate created tension. One day Ludwig, her oldest son, announced without warning that he was leaving to join his cousins and friends in Honey Creek. That afternoon Minnie noticed that her twenty-year-old namesake was sitting at the end of the table and looked distressed. Minnie confronted her daughter, and the girl admitted that she planned to join her brother on the voyage.

Ludwig and the younger Minnie arrived in America as the political tumult in the country was reaching its breaking point. Within three years of their arrival, the country split in two over slavery and civil war broke out. When Minnie learned that Ludwig, who had avoided military conscription in his native country, had joined the army in his adopted country, she was overcome with fear. Her son wrote that he was stationed in the river city of Memphis and was fighting down the Mississippi River to free the movement of supplies. Minnie asked the teacher at the school to show her on a map where Memphis was, and her anxiety increased when she saw how far her son was from the family in Wisconsin. That was the only letter she received from him.

In the late spring of 1863, a letter arrived from her daughter. Minnie, who cannot read, asked her fourteen-year-old daughter Bertha to read it to her. The letter began with the exciting news of the birth of Minnie's latest grandson, August Ludwig Kriesel. Then suddenly, the girl stopped reading. She stared at her mother with a shocked, pained look. When she regained her composure, she read, "We named him in memory of his uncle, who has died in the war." She continued, "He did not die on the battlefield but rather from disease, which is rampant in the army." The letter concluded, "He is now lying in a mass grave on the grounds of a recaptured fort near Memphis."

As the words were read to her, the familiar weight of grief grew in Minnie's chest and then expanded throughout her body. Her legs became immobile, and she could not rise from her chair. For several minutes Bertha watched her mother sit motionless, staring straight ahead. Then suddenly, the grief poured out with her cries. *"My baby!"*

Pastor Wenig conducted a short memorial service for the young man. In the front pew, Minnie's grief turned to anger. She looked at a picture of Jesus on the wall and asked the image, "Why did you protect my son from war here but not in America?"

Tonight as the hole in the roof drips rain on her head, Minnie prays that the last son she had with Christoph will be protected.

The third mother, Anna Beutler, sits quietly by her window, darning the latest hole in a child's sock. As she watches the fury of the storm, she fears that similar winds may plunge Albert to the bottom of the open sea. Thirteen years ago, Anna's first husband, Friedrich, had predicted that at least one of their children would leave for America. That night, wrapped in her husband's arms, Anna agreed, but she assumed she would face that day with the child's father by her side. Instead, a different man supported her as she watched her excited son throw his small trunk into the back of a wagon. Her other seven children crowded around her as he disappeared between the trees. The sight of the nearly grown man waving goodbye, with his legs dangling over the back of the wagon, broke her heart as Anna remembered him as a howling newborn.

She turns her back to the window and watches the activity in the dark room. All appears normal. Food is being prepared. Games are being played. Chores are being completed. But Anna can feel the difference in the room: not only is there one less body but the attitudes of the other children also have changed. From the look in their eyes and from their questions, she knows that they envy their brother's adventure. This will not be the last time she sits at this window and worries about a traveling child. She misses the children's father now more than she has since she remarried.

Two days after setting sail, the five travelers stand on the deck of the *Reichstag* and are led in prayer by the captain. These Sunday prayers on the open seas with the white sails snapping in the wind and the seagulls squawking is a sharp contrast to the solemn services at home. The sun shining on their necks and the sea breeze blowing the girls' skirts feel liberating, but by the time they reach New York after five more of these services, they will not have the same sense of liberation; rather, those services will feel sad without the community and familiarity of their old church. When the ship sails into the New York harbor on the last day of August, each of the young travelers will vow to rebuild that community they are now missing when they settle in their new homes.

While their children pray on the deck of the ship, the three mothers sit in their usual places at their church. Pastor Wenig is droning on. The gloom of Friday night has been replaced by bright sunshine. Each woman fans the thick air to cool herself and her remaining children. They stare straight ahead to the place in front of the altar where the wooden caskets containing the remains of their husbands, sons, and daughters have rested. Each woman quietly decides that it is far better to lose a member of the family to a faraway country than to the cemetery down the road, and each woman accepts that her children must, just as she once did, leave home to establish their own lives.

The three women are magnetically drawn together when the bells ring at the end of the long service. They share their personal grief without a word spoken. When the ringing ends, they raise their heads and look ahead with an icy resolve. These resilient women will not let the events of the past two weeks defeat them.

They climb into their family wagons. Their husbands maneuver the teams into a single-file parade heading south on the narrow dirt road from the church. The mothers individually conclude that the best way to stop grieving the past is to celebrate the future with an abundant Sunday dinner.

December 25, 1867 – Gembitz Hauland

Wilhelm Beutler woke this morning excited to celebrate Christmas with his family. He had married Anna, a widow with eight children, two years before, so this is his family by marriage, which he inherited after a long life as a bachelor. He is almost forty-six years old and is thrilled to finally have his own family to celebrate the holiday.

He faced a typical winter day when he stepped out the door of his warm house this morning to do the chores. The sky was a depressing gray with a damp cold that reached deep into the ground and then sucked back up through his body. He walked across a thin layer of snow, and a raw wind blew into his face from the flat pasture to the west.

This time of year is hard on the mind but even harder on the body. Influenza, pneumonia or typhus starts quietly in one corner of the community and then spreads through the woods like wildfire in the dry heat of summer. Typhus epidemics are particularly devastating. Last year, one broke out during the holiday season and killed three residents in the eight days before and after Christmas, then a consumption epidemic a few weeks later during Lent killed four more.

People are not the only ones who have a difficult time in this weather. The horses and cows that just a couple of months ago were shiny and fat during the summer on the rich pastures now have long, dull hair matted with manure. Bare spots are visible on some animals' hides from rubbing on the walls of the barn as they try to scratch off bugs that take a winter residence on them.

And not just the animals are scratching. It is too cold to take baths and wash clothes regularly. Every day the children scratch and tug at their hair or clothes, trying to get rid of the lice they pass on to each other. Even though winter has just begun, Wilhelm longs for the first day of spring when it will be warm enough for everyone to leave their buildings and go to the freshwater spring down the road. Until then, the family will cough and itch.

Last night everyone took a turn in front of the fire for a rare bath—Christmas is too important to be dirty. After the baths, the tree that Wilhelm and the boys cut in the woods was brought into the house and decorated with simple handmade ornaments while the family drank warm Gühlwein and ate a simple lunch of smoked meats and Christmas cakes. After the tree was decorated, the family exchanged gifts. There is not enough money for fancy presents, but new clothes, handmade toys and fruits purchased in town are shared with each other. Wilhelm thought that his best gift was the warm house, the good food and the joy of his family. At the end of the evening, he sat by the fire, smoking his pipe with a sly happy smile.

This is the third Christmas Wilhelm has been the head of this family. The first Christmas, one month after he married Anna, all eight children sat around the large table that stretched across the main living area of the house, apprehensive about the new man who now occupied their father's previously empty chair. Just like every Christmas since Friedrich bought this table at a neighbor's auction, the table's surface was overloaded with meat plates, apple and sausage stuffing, red cabbage, potato dumplings, and a Christmas Stollen. The guest of honor at that dinner was a large goose who had not approved of Wilhelm's joining the family—whenever he fed the horses, it chased him. Wilhelm got even with that fiend on that first Christmas Eve, and tension around the table that day was broken by a spirited discussion of the bird's demise.

Last Christmas was especially joyful. They ate a goose whose more docile temperament still had not saved it. Gustav, the oldest stepson, had returned home from the Prussian army. He spent the summer fighting a war against the Catholic Austrian Empire, and every warm night while he was gone, Wilhelm comforted his new wife that her son would return home safely from the war. Unfortunately, his military service is not yet over. The Prussian government is gearing up for the next war, and Gustav, who has shown great skill as a stone mason, is not thrilled to return to the army. He is very patriotic, however, and is prepared to do his part for the country.

At today's dinner, there will be another empty chair. This is the first Christmas since stepson Albert left for America. They received a Christmas letter from him, saying he was now in New York and eager to join his friends in Minnesota in the new year. Staring at Albert's empty chair, Anna sighs sadly. She knows that unlike her first husband's empty chair filled by Wilhelm, Albert's chair will be empty this Christmas and every Christmas thereafter.

After Anna places this year's goose in the oven, the family leaves for church. They climb into the old wagon, and the horses start down the familiar road for the one-mile trip without any guidance. As the family bounces over the frozen and snow-covered road, they meet neighbors also on their way to worship, and everyone is greeted with a hearty Christmas wish.

At the crossroads by the cemetery, the family meets the Westphals, coming from the north. Pauline quickly jumps down and crawls into their wagon for the last half-mile of the journey. Behind the Westphals comes the wagon from Martin and Justine Wanke's farm. The mixture of children in their wagon reminds them that life is never guaranteed. On one side of the wagon sit the three grown children from Daniel Marten's first marriage, and on the other side are the teenage daughters from Justine's marriage to him. In between are the young children from her marriage to Martin. Fourteen-year-old Minnie Marten, who bloomed into a woman last summer, stares with teenage angst at Wilhelm's stepson August. The eighteen-year-old ignores her.

When they arrive at the church, they meet the families who live on the Mittel Reihe. Martin Redel tells the men, "The Domkes will not be here today. The Christmas curse of typhus has struck the family. The children are slowly recovering, but Wilhelm has slipped into a coma." The men discuss who will have time to dig his grave this week. A couple of the inquisitive children, as they scratch lice from their hair, ask how people get typhus. Not knowing the answer, the adults ignore the question as they, too, scratch parasites loose from their heads.

The families from the west meet the families from the east, south, and north in front of the church. The children compare the gifts they received last night, the teenagers exchange shy greetings, the women describe their difficulties making dinner, and the men discuss the weather. Minnie Redel, Christine Wegner and Anna console each other on their first Christmas without their children, who had traveled together to America last summer. The three worried mothers share a quick prayer of thanks that they arrived safely in America.

The large group of worshippers fits into the timber-framed building with no room to spare. Crowding into hard wooden pews, they sit as close as possible to experience the Christmas spirit. The bells ring loud and joyously, and the sounds of joy affect not only the people inside the building but also the horses tied up outside. They whinny as if they are sending season's greetings to one another.

Pastor Jacobowski soon begins a long sermon. Bored children squirm in their seats. Today, in addition to normal fidgeting, they also scratch their heads and arms. Before long, the adults are also scratching. As he concludes his sermon, the pastor looks down from his wooden pulpit at the peculiar sight of his congregants itching and squirming. He smiles, thinking that today's sermon must have been particularly effective—the devil is clearly trying to escape from his flock.

When the service is over, the events of two hours ago replay in reverse. Christmas greetings are exchanged at the door; families divide into four groups as they return home. At each farm and crossroads, another family leaves the group with hearty well wishes. Once the Beutler/Heÿn family is home, Wilhelm and the boys unhitch the horses and lead them to the barn while Anna and the girls finish preparations for the meal. Fresh hay and grain are given to each animal so that they, too, can celebrate.

The women place the last of the dishes on the table. The rich, sour smells of the sauerkraut and red cabbage that fill the room are balanced by the aromas of fresh bread and baked goose. The goose is placed in front of Wilhelm's chair. As the head of the table, he will carve.

Before he begins to cut up the unfortunate bird, Wilhelm leads the family in prayer. It is easy for him to give thanks this year. He is now accepted as the head of the family after two years. This year the crops were good. The family is healthy and safe. A special prayer asks that the missing Albert will not be alone this Christmas. The prayer of thanks ends with a loud *Amen* followed quickly by everyone scratching their heads.

After the meal is completed and the furniture is returned to its usual places, Wilhelm sits in his chair by the fireplace, as he did last night on Christmas Eve. He smokes a bowl of the sweet tobacco he received as a gift from the children. As the smoke drifts up around him, a smile of contentment crosses his face. His life is good. Removing several lice from his head, he thinks that 1868 will be another great year.

January 24, 1868 – Gembitz Hauland

On this cold, clear Friday morning, Anna is once again sitting by her window crying. And once again, the tears are alternately shed for the uncertainty of her future and then for the truth of her past. Behind her, lying in bed where she spent her first wedding night and where she gave birth to eight children, is the lifeless body of her second husband, Wilhelm.

Her pain becomes sharper when she thinks that the house was full of laughter only thirty days ago as they celebrated Christmas. Evil spirits are always active in the community during the twelve days between December 25 and January 6. Each year Anna scrubs and cleans every inch of the house to protect it from the Rauhnachte spirits. When the children complained about this work this year, she reminded them of the typhus epidemic in their community last year. On the third day of the season, the death of their neighbor Wilhelm Domke from the latest outbreak of the disease reinforced her admonishments to clean everything. Now, sitting by the window, she bows her head, ashamed that she failed. Her penalty is that she is again solely responsible for her family.

On the morning after the Epiphany, the last day of Rauhnachte, Wilhelm started his day as he always did. He stoked the fire in the fireplace and roused the family to feed and care for themselves and the animals. After breakfast, the weather was particularly bitter as he chopped wood. The sky was a glum gray with no sign of the sun, which had disappeared weeks before. A strong, cold wind howled across the pasture, blowing snow into Wilhelm's face. His clothes and body became soaked from a combination of sweat and snow. The cold wind violently slashed through him, turning his damp body to ice.

Feeling cold and damp was not usual at this time of year. As so many times before, Anna laid out dry, clean clothes. Wilhelm, as he also had done so many times before, dutifully changed into them and sat by the fire. When the fire could not warm him, Anna became worried. Wilhelm dismissed her concerns, saying, "I will be fine tomorrow, but if it makes you happy, I'll rest today."

The next morning, he still had a fever and chills. Knowing that those were the first symptoms of typhus, Anna became even more worried. Wilhelm again bravely assured his wife, "I just have the *grippe*." That did not reassure Anna. Six years ago, Michael Westphal died of pneumonia on New Year's Eve after telling his wife Louisa he just had the *grippe*.

Six days after the end of Rauhnachte was Wilhelm's forty-sixth birthday, usually another day of celebration. Neighbors would have stopped at the farm after church to enjoy the day of rest by drinking beer and eating cake. That Sunday, Wilhelm was not feeling better, and the neighbors, fearing that disease had entered the Beutler house, stayed away. The fears of the neighbors were confirmed when a red rash developed on Wilhelm's chest and back. The worry Anna had carried for almost a week now changed to fear, and Wilhelm quit trying to be brave. They both knew what this new symptom meant. Dozens of people in the village had contracted typhus and survived, but they were mostly children. For an adult, typhus is often deadly.

The next morning Anna stood among her chickens. Her concerns for her husband's health suddenly turned to anger. An old chicken that no longer produced eggs came to her, seeking undeserved food. Anna leaned down and grabbed the freeloading bird by its neck and twisted its head until it was dead.

After removing the feathers and digestive system of the unlucky bird, she put it in a pot with water and vegetables from her root cellar to make soup for her sick husband. While the chicken stewed in the pot, Anna mixed flour and water to make dough. She rolled it thin and cut it into thin strips to make noodles for the soup. Wilhelm could not eat meat, vegetables or noodles. He weakly attempted to drink the broth. Watching her formerly strong husband quickly weaken, Anna wondered if he had just celebrated his last birthday.

The next day Wilhelm was weaker, and Anna was stronger. Clearing away the breakfast dishes, she told Gustav to hitch the wagon. He looked at his mother skeptically, and she answered with a sharp retort. "I need to go to Czarnikau to confirm that the deed is properly registered as community property, just as it was with your father. I am not going to lose my farm to in-laws I don't know."

While Gustav hitched the wagon, his mother prayed her husband would be better when she returned, but after saying goodbye to Wilhelm, she was certain this prayer would not be answered. Her second husband would undoubtedly soon join her first. She had to secure her future.

As the week continued, the disease's progress was unrelenting. The rash spread from his chest and back to his legs and arms. He had headaches and neck pain. The fevers worsened. Some days he completely soaked the bed with sweat several times.

Strain and fear could now be seen not only in Anna but also in the children. Wilhelm, who became a father of eight at forty-three, told Anna he was worried about them. The five eldest were old enough for independent lives, but for the three youngest children, it was different. Only three years had passed since they had lost their father, and now they may lose him, too. Wilhelm, the tough, stoic farmer, began to cry. He had waited so long to have a family, and he was not ready to leave.

Anna remembers when she became a widow for the first time—the day their horse returned without her husband. Today that same horse will leave on the same path pulling a wagon carrying away the body of her second husband. Life is just too hard here. She begins to understand why some of her children want to leave for America.

Thoughts of Friedrich remind her of Wilhelm's delirium earlier that week. A week after his birthday, Wilhelm told her, "Friedrich wants to know what you will do now. He said he had trusted me to take care of his wife, children, and farm and asked why I wasn't more careful."

Anna felt stricken when Wilhelm told her about Friedrich's visit. He asked her, "Why don't you believe me?" He kept insisting that it had happened, and she soothed him by saying she had seen Friedrich also.

During the next couple of days, Wilhelm had other visitors. On Tuesday, he was talking to Albert, who had flown home from America on the back of the goose they ate their first Christmas together. The next day their neighbor Christoph Spletter came to complain that the fence between their properties was not maintained. Wilhelm ordered his stepson August to fix it. August stammered, "Christoph Spletter died during the typhus epidemic last Christmas. There is nothing wrong with that fence." Wilhelm became agitated and angry when his insolent son contradicted him. He thrashed in the bed and attempted to swing at the boy.

Yesterday Wilhelm quit thrashing and talking about his visitors. He fell into a deep sleep. Once an hour, Anna would hold her ear to his mouth to hear if he was still breathing. Knowing that the end was near, the always practical Anna asked Gustav and August to go to the barn to build a casket. Their backs were turned when Wilhelm's eyes suddenly opened wide, and a look of anger crossed his face.

After the boys left the house, Maria asked, "What is going to happen to us?" Anna exploded at the eleven-year-old girl. "I buried one husband and saved this family and farm. I'll do it again, but not until your stepfather takes his last breath." Then they both broke into tears. Hearing the combination of anger and tears, Wilhelm again opened his eyes for a minute.

Today for the first time in weeks, the morning sun could be seen rising on the horizon. A rare beam of winter light shone on Wilhelm's face. When his father and mother arrived at the house to say goodbye, he opened one eye as if he recognized their presence. One hour later, he left the world to the same sounds he heard when he entered it—the wails of his mother.

As soon as their stepfather passed, Gustav and August left to dig a grave in the frozen ground next to their father. They return with Pastor Jacobowski to conduct a private funeral for the family. Because of the epidemic, there can be no service at the church. Instead, after offering his condolences to Anna and to Wilhelm's parents, the pastor moves to the foot of the bed where Wilhelm lies. He opens the book of Lutheran prayers, and the ten mourners in the house form a circle around the deathbed. At Christmas, the pastor had been sure that his words had driven the devil out of his congregants. Today, looking at the withered body before him, he is not so confident.

After the last Amen, the pastor, Gustav, August and fourteen-year-old Julius each lift a corner of the blanket that wraps around Wilhelm. They slowly carry the body from the house and place him in the coffin the brothers built. Each brother grabs a hammer and nail and pounds the lid shut. Then the casket is lifted into the wagon. Gustav helps his mother into her seat. The other six siblings find a place to sit on the casket. Then Gustav climbs up and snaps the reins, commanding the horses to take them to the cemetery.

When they arrive, Gustav maneuvers the wagon as close to the grave as possible. All the males, including nine-year-old Adolph, lift the coffin off the wagon and struggle to carry it across the uneven ground where the graves of long-gone neighbors are sinking. They set it on two logs placed across the hole, turning it so Wilhelm will be able to see the bright lights of resurrection day. The four strongest hold the ends of ropes that suddenly support all the weight of Wilhelm and his casket after the logs are pulled away. They struggle to lower the coffin into the ground.

When the coffin reaches its final resting place, Pastor Jacobowski recites the famous words: "Ashes to ashes, dust to dust." Anna stands between the graves of her two husbands. She reaches down and grabs a handful of frozen dirt that has been piled on top of Friedrich's grave. She throws it on Wilhelm's coffin. One by one, each of her children does the same. Then she nods to her sons to begin shoveling the dirt off their father's grave onto the grave of their stepfather.

Once the grave is covered, another prayer is recited, and more tears are shed. Anna pulls her shawl tighter around her shoulders to block the cold January wind. Then she turns her back to the past and slowly begins her journey home to face the future.

August 6, 1871 – Gembitz Hauland

This Sunday morning is not a typical wedding day. There will be no exchange of dowries. No large wedding feasts will be eaten. The disappointed young men of the parish will not steal the bride from the groom. There is no time. The bridal couple has a boat to catch.

At the end of his sermon, Pastor Jacobowski asks twenty-two-year-old August Heÿn and eighteen-year-old Minnie Marten to step forward. August exchanges a nervous smile with Minnie. The pastor looks over the shoulders of the couple at their parents, sitting in their usual pews, and asks, "Do you approve of this marriage?" Three voices respond, "I approve."

Pastor Jacobowski gives the final blessing, and the church bells toll. A tear runs down Minnie's cheek as she stands in the doorway of the church. She takes a mental picture of the people loading the tables with the food they brought to celebrate. These are the only people she has ever known. This is the last Sunday they will worship and celebrate together.

During the past seven years, thirteen-year-old Adolph lost two fathers to death and two siblings to America. The loss of another brother is too much for his hormone-ravaged body. He conspires with a group of friends to steal some beer and cigars, then they sneak into the woods to enjoy their plunder. As he becomes sick, he sulks to his friends that life is unfair.

The couple's wedding night is not private. They spend their first church-sanctioned night together in the bed where August was born. When his mother offered them the bed, he protested the lack of privacy. Anna snorted at her embarrassed son, "Your father and I did not need privacy to create eight children in that bed."

Before the snickering teenage siblings run past the bed in the morning to begin their chores, the marriage is consummated. With the silence of the early morning broken, the newlyweds reluctantly start their first day as a couple.

August dresses in his manure-stained barn clothes for the last time. He gives Minnie a short kiss before walking outside to feed the horses. The two roan horses run to him, and he gently strokes the face of his favorite. The animal's large black eyes appear sad. Man and beast both know this will be their last morning together.

Heartbroken, August turns away. One of his mother's cows with a unique hourglass face marking is tied to the fence. Maria sits on a wobbly, three-legged stool, balancing herself by pressing her head into the cow's flank. August can hear the rhythm of the milk hitting the pail between his sister's feet. How many mornings, he wonders, has he watched this scene?

He enters the barn. This was where, every two years, his father took his frightened children while their mother gave birth to a new sibling. His hand caresses his father's tools.

Stepping back outside, he surveys the farm. The stone and brick buildings with their steep roofs and sagging doors are tired. Just as with an old, worn-out pair of shoes, August knows it is time to move on. Still, as with the shoes, it is hard to leave behind something that is so comfortable.

The original stone portion of the house is a combination of a kitchen, living room and bedroom. At the table, Minnie reviews the recipe for August's favorite Easter cake with her new mother-in-law. When they finish, Anna feels guilty. She has purposely left out an ingredient. She justifies her spiteful act as an innocent protest against losing another member of her family.

Anna stares at her table. Five years ago, the table was crowded with ten chairs. Tomorrow she will need only six. Near tears, Anna quickly leaves the house and takes her usual position on the old wooden bench by the door. From behind the barn, the old wagon squeaks and squawks. The irritating sound becomes louder as the horses and wagon approach. The two horses stare at Anna, and their loud whinnies break her sad solitude.

Adolph senses that his mother's grief is greater than his own. He sits next to her as they watch Gustav and Julius load a wooden trunk onto the wagon. August and Minnie step out of the house, now wearing their wedding clothes again.

One by one, the siblings step forward to say goodbye to their brother and sister-in-law. Anna takes a deep breath and resolves not to cry. Mother and son stand two feet apart, not speaking. She is determined that her son's last memory of her will be of a strong, independent woman, and he is determined that her last memory of him will be of a strong, independent man, not a weak boy.

August helps his wife into the wagon. Gustav climbs onto the driver's seat. He grabs and snaps the reins to begin the couple's journey. With one arm on her hip, Anna stands with Pauline and Maria on her left and Julius and Adolph on her right. Her eyes are now damp. As her old wagon disappears through the trees, she waves goodbye to another member of the family.

The first leg of the journey is only a half-mile to Minnie's family's home. As they near the house, Minnie's mother, Justine, is already crying. Two years ago, she lost two small children to typhus within three days. Today, two-thirds of the proof of her short first marriage will leave for America. She can accept standing at her child's grave on a cold February afternoon—all mothers know that death lingers in the mortar that holds the houses of the community together. But on this warm morning, she is not as accepting.

Minnie's sixteen-year-old sister, Amalie, is traveling with the couple. Stepping out of the house, she wipes tears from her clear blue eyes. With all eyes now on her, she regally throws her head back, her breasts out and flicks her black hair over her shoulder. She is ready to go.

Minnie and Amalie first say goodbye to their older Marten siblings from their father's first marriage. Then they bend down to hug their younger Wanke siblings from their mother's second marriage. Their sister Ernestine steps forward. The three daughters of Daniel and Justine Marten embrace for the last time.

August helps his wife and sister-in-law on the wagon. He then takes the empty seat next to Gustav. Before the reins are snapped, Minnie's stepfather Martin gives August a letter addressed to his brother and sister. "When you get to Minnesota, please give this to Michael and Anna," he requests. Justina, nestling her wailing nine-month-old daughter in her arms, cries as the wagon disappears into the woods.

The two brothers are quiet. When they reach the fertile plains between Glasshutte and Budsin, Gustav attempts to break the silent tension. "Now that the war is over, Bertha and I will also be married before the end of the year!" The women behind him have the reaction he expects, but his brother seems even more sullen. He regrets that he will not be his brother's best man at his wedding.

They arrive at the brick train station built in the middle of wheat, potato and beet fields a mile outside Budsin. The agent, whose back is perpetually sore from loading immigrant trunks, comes out of the station to greet them. When he helps the brothers take the trunk off the wagon, he notices it is lighter than most. This couple is not taking much of their old life to their new one.

In the distance, the train whistle is heard as it leaves the Jankendorf station. In a few minutes, they will have only a moment to board. August says goodbye to the brother who taught him to fish, hunt and swear.

From the train, August watches his big brother disappear in the fog of smoke. The weight of adulthood crushes him. His title in government records is no longer *farmer's son.* The shrieking train whistle declares that he is now husband, emigrant, and, he hopes, *farmer.*

Adulthood dampens August's excitement on the journey to Bremen. Three times he is responsible for navigating a connection. After their first connection in Schneidemhl he tells Minnie, "A week ago, my hardest travel decision was whether to visit the beerhall in Gembitz or Althutte on Saturday night." Minnie gives her new husband the first eye-roll of their marriage.

In the larger cities of Berlin and Hamburg, Minnie and Amalie rely on August to read the train schedules, check that their trunk is loaded, protect their money, and plan their next connection. August finds maturity exhausting. His worry increases when they reach Bremen. Human ants from across Europe are scurrying to board ships that will take them to a new life. When he disturbed an ant hill as a child, there were always several separated ants that became food for the circling sparrows. In this chaotic city, he is afraid they will become ants like that, isolated and in danger.

August purchased the tickets to America from an agent working for the B&O railroad and the North German Lloyd Company. Four years earlier, the two companies signed an agreement that if the railroad built an immigration office in Baltimore, the German shipping company would bring a shipload of German immigrants to the city once each month. For sixty marks each, the travel agent promised August ocean passage and a rail ticket to Troy, New York.

In Bremen, the trio spends two sleepless nights in a cramped boardinghouse. The second week of their marriage begins with a forty-mile cruise down the Weser River to meet the SS *Baltimore* in Bremerhaven. In the harbor, they see an iron steamship of a size they never could have imagined. To August, the length of the vessel appears as long as the distance from his house to the Ryga River. Minnie looks into the sky at the two masts of the ship and wonders where trees grow that tall. Amalie, who has been struggling with homesickness, cries when she sees the iron vessel. "There is no way any boat that big and heavy can float on water," she sobs. A woman behind her agrees and bursts into tears; she runs away in fear with her husband chasing close behind.

More than 570 passengers climb the gangway onto the ship, anticipating what life will be like where the B&O tracks end. First, thirty-five well-dressed people board the ship. After they are in their first-class cabins, the trio follows the mass of travelers to the steerage deck. There they find a cramped, dark space with beds stacked to the ceiling. During their ten-day marriage, the honeymooners, accompanied by a sixteen-year-old chaperone, have had little privacy. August sighs, thinking that it will be a long, frustrating journey.

For eighteen days, except for a short stop in England, they have no connection to land. Saturday night's air is hot and humid when the SS *Baltimore* drops its anchor at the mouth of the Baltimore harbor. August and Minnie spend the evening wrapped in each other's arms as they stare at the city from the ship's deck under the nearly full moon.

On their four-week anniversary, at eight o'clock in the morning, the ship and the couple are tied to America. They are disappointed that they must wait until Monday to stand for the first time on the soil of their new country.

The sights and sounds of the docks at Locust Point overstimulate the trio's senses. August whispers to Minnie, "This must have been what it was like at the Tower of Babel." The railroad agents, most of whom are also German immigrants, help the scared travelers through the immigration office. Once outside, they divide the travelers into groups based on their final destination.

August, Minnie and Amalie stand alone, the only ones with tickets to New York. A railroad agent who seems barely older than Minnie greets them in German. He asks where they are from and says he immigrated from near Frankfurt two years ago. "I will take you to the train station. Then I will ride with you to New York to make sure you board the correct train to Troy. Do not worry."

As he promised, the young man delivers the trio to Troy. August wonders if he can finally relax, but his sister Ottilie, who immigrated shortly after Albert did, is not at the station. Instead, Heinrich Bethmann, the son of a former baker in Czarnikau, stands on the cold platform.

Curious, August asks his old acquaintance, "Where is Ottilie? Why are you meeting us?"

Heinrich answers, "I am your brother-in-law now." August welcomes him to the family with a slap on the back. While loading the trunk (which feels to August like it gets heavier with every transfer), the unexpected brother-in-law explains that the town of Troy is now suffering from an outbreak of typhus. "Your sister is showing the early symptoms."

August's stomach feels as if it has been caught in a vise. His mind flashes back to his stepfather's death from the disease three years ago. He remembers the horror of the man's final hours with Ottilie by his bed, placing cold, wet rags on his burning forehead. Now the disease she fled has found her in America.

Ottilie fights the disease until scarlet fever also strikes. Six weeks after leaving home to join the two siblings closest to him in age, August watches his nineteen-year-old sister take her last breath.

The next day he stands at her grave in New Mount Ida cemetery. The sun's rays have the warmth of summer, a contrast with the chill of winter in the light wind. Usually, a Monday afternoon with a clear blue sky, leaves on the trees turning from green to yellow, and a flat piece of ground covered with a thick carpet of green grass would stir farmer August's spirit to match the day. Instead, as his brother-in-law throws a clod of dirt on his sister's coffin, August feels as if he is standing in the middle of a raging deadly blizzard. How, he wonders, will he write the letter to tell his mother of the burial of one of her children, which she could not even attend?

With only a mound of dirt now connecting the new immigrants to Troy, they decide to continue to Minnesota. The air is crisp, and the trees show more of their fall canopy of color as the train pulls away from Troy. They wave goodbye to the man, who for a few short weeks, had sprouted the now withered Bethmann branch of the family tree.

August guards his precious trunk three more times as they change trains before the final train screeches to a stop in Rochester, Minnesota. After more than two months of traveling, they stand at last on the Winona and St. Paul train platform, almost at their final destination.

For the last time, August paces up and down the train depot platform, worrying about where they go next. He is relieved when he hears many people speaking his language. A boy not more than ten years old approaches the group, asking, "Do you need help?" August shows him the letter the women's stepfather had given him. "This is where we want to go," August says. The boy responds, "Potsdam is fifteen to twenty miles away. There are farmers from there selling wheat at Van Dusen's grain elevator right now. I will find someone to take you."

Minnie and Amalie sit on the battered trunk while August continues his pacing. After the clock on the depot wall announces the quarter hour for the second time, he is certain the boy has abandoned them. He is ready to find a driver on his own. Then he hears the boy shouting, "Mister, I found a driver!"

The man behind the boy bears a striking resemblance to the half-boy, half-man August remembers leaving home four years before. The boy has found Albert. They greet each other with comfortable brotherly banter. Albert feigns anger when his younger brother teases him about his American goatee. Then he returns the favor. "Minnie, did you ask him to marry you? He has never been able to complete a full sentence around a girl." Then Albert turns serious. "I thought you were going to spend the winter with Ottilie."

August takes a deep breath. "We were. The town was suffering from dual epidemics of scarlet fever and typhus. Our little sister had both and died."

Albert is stunned. He says nothing for a minute and then looks at the October sun. "It is getting late, and we have a long ride. Let's get this trunk loaded." The trunk and the women are quickly helped into the wagon covered with itchy wheat chaff. Before he climbs into the wagon, August digs into his pocket. He pulls out a coin. A large smile spreads across the boy's face. "Thank you for finding us a ride with my brother." The excited boy runs down the platform to find his next customer.

Immediately after the wagon crosses the tracks, Albert peppers his brother with questions he has been thinking of every night since he landed in New York Harbor. In rapid fire, leaving no opportunity for August to answer, Albert asks, "How has Mama adjusted to the death of our *Stiefvater*? Now that you have left, who is working the farm for her? Gustav never showed any interest. Has Gustav or Pauline made Mama a *Grossmutter* yet?"

Minnie and Amalie listen to the rapid questions of the usually quiet Albert and giggle. Embarrassed, he finally gives his brother a chance to answer. "Mama is as strong as ever. She is ruling, as she always has, the whole family and half the neighborhood from Papa's bench by the door. Pauline is becoming serious with August Westphal. He will take care of the farm with the help of Julius and Adolph. No, there are not any *Neffe* or *Nichte* yet. Minnie and I will give Mama her first *Enkel.*"

Minnie protests. Albert and Amalie smirk. August blushes. His face feels as warm as it did the first time his brothers noticed he was staring at a girl.

For the first five or six miles of the journey, the terrain is hilly and heavily wooded. To break the silence, Albert starts describing his life since the brothers had shared a farewell beer behind the barn. He tells his passengers, "The path I have traveled has been as crooked and dangerous as this road. We also traveled by train north to Albany after the *Reichstag* docked in New York. Unlike Fred, Louisa, Julius and Mina, who had tickets to Minnesota, I did not have enough money to finish the trip then. I stayed in Troy for a year, working day jobs in the factories and the surrounding farms until I saved enough money.

"Farming was booming when I arrived in Rochester. Many farmers were expanding and needed my labor. First, I worked for George Stoppel. George and his brother Fred are a great example of what we can accomplish here. They have a large farm west of Rochester. Their families lived in a cave their first winter. Within fifteen years, he has built a two-story stone house finer than the manor home of the Radomski family."

The brothers had never heard the name of the Polish family from whose estate their parents' farm was carved without having an angry reaction. Instinct forces both men to spit in disgust over the wagon wheel at the mention of their family's Polish nemesis.

Albert turns the wagon to the east. Suddenly prosperous farms dot the flat horizon. The older brother explains, "They call this area the Greenwood Prairie. Potsdam is in the center." August is excited to think that next spring, he will plant wheat on this endless prairie.

Albert continues his story. "After working at the Stoppel farm for a year, I decided it was time to move on. I thought about following the Wankes west to homestead free land in southwestern Minnesota. Instead, I decided to join our old neighbors from Gembitz Hauland in Potsdam." He pauses for a minute, wondering if he wants to tell the next part of his story. Taking a deep breath, he decides his little brother needs to learn that life will not always be easy here.

"This summer, I was working for an Irishman. One day I told him that I was ready to move on. The man had a malicious disposition and two strong sons who had inherited their father's temperament. The man told me that if I left, he would have his sons beat me. There was no way I could defend myself against both of those athletic boys at once.

"A couple of days later, I was raking hay alongside the road when a man with arms as big as our legs came walking by. He introduced himself as Julius Rosolack. As we talked, we were surprised to discover that we came from the same place. His family had been one of the first in the community to leave for America. I confided my situation to him. Julius is a scrappy proud veteran of the Civil War with a volatile temper. He told me he was not going to let me be abused as if I were a serf of a Polish noble. He grabbed my arm and told me, 'We are going to confront that Irish bastard right now.'

"On the way to the house, it was as if the veteran was preparing his mind for his commanding officer to shout an order to charge the rebels. When we arrived, Julius looked first at one son and then the other before settling his angry stare on the cowering farmer. Blind rage had transformed into steely determination. The short man rose up on the tips of his toes to be able to look my boss directly in the eye. Very simple words were spoken with a strong accent as he told the quivering bully, 'Mein Freund will be leaving today.' He furrowed his large eyebrows. 'If you disagree, I will gladly come back with a half dozen of my fellow German Civil War veterans. We will demonstrate the training that won the war.'

"I packed my things, received my pay and walked with my new friend down the road to a better life. I quickly found work with a German farmer." Albert turned to his brother, advising him, "It is better to stick with your own people."

The sun is now low on their backs as they arrive at a small village of several houses and businesses close together at a crossroads. Unlike the villages at home, these buildings are made from wood rather than brick. There is no church anchoring the hamlet. Albert drives past the buildings toward a farm on the east edge of the town. He points to a small cemetery on his right and tells his passengers that they are planning to build a church here next year. Then he turns to the left into the farm.

The owner, John Meyer, has spent the day butchering. He recognizes Albert but not the three others in the wagon. His wife, Emelia, her apron stained with pigs' blood tight over her pregnant stomach, comes out of the house. Even though she has not seen them for six years, she immediately recognizes her brother's two stepdaughters. Standing back from the family reunion, August thinks that the children surrounding their mother's feet look like those who surrounded his mother-in-law two months ago. When the introductions are completed, Emelia offers her newfound family supper. Albert stays to enjoy the quickly prepared feast of pork roast, potatoes and gravy, then he tells his brother goodbye and returns to the farm where he has been working.

The next Sunday, they travel to a simple wood-framed church two miles across the prairie from the Meyer farm. It seems fitting to August that they worship at a crossroads named Bremen, after the city in Germany where they sailed from. After the service, Minnie and Amalie's step-uncle Michael Wanke hosts a welcoming party for them with other immigrants from Gembitz Hauland.

Before the guests arrive, August gives his host the letter that Minnie's stepfather had given him. As Michael reads, the homesickness that he was sure he had lost fifteen years ago overcomes him. He tells his nephew, "I will never return home. But one by one, my old home is coming to me."

The reunion is a strange combination of familiar and unfamiliar. Strangers who had been their parents' friends welcome them. Michael's neighbors Karl and Friedrich Hoffmann, who were born on the Mittel Reihe halfway between the Gembitz Hauland crossroads and the village of Gembitz, were among the first pioneers to settle here. They own large farms and are overjoyed to have new workers. The brothers slap August's back as they ask about their brothers, sisters and extended family back home. Then they add, "You could barely walk when we left. We have always regretted that we could not convince your parents to join us."

Friends and relatives who left for America after the war are also there. Those reunions are quick and easy. Minnie and her old friend Louise Wegner separate from the group, and within minutes they pick up where they had left off four years ago, sharing gossip and complaints about their sisters.

One of the sisters, Amalie, is using her fair skin and black hair at that moment to attract the attention of numerous boys from the neighborhood who had been born in Schleswig Holstein. Suddenly her homesickness is gone. These boys are much more interesting than the ones she left behind.

August and Minnie spend the rest of the fall and winter living and working on her uncle's farm. In the spring, they move to a farm on the edge of the prairie. Unlike the houses of the other Gembitz Hauland refugees, there is not an endless view from their door. They live next to a creek with steep limestone hills blocking their views and, too often, the sun. One afternoon when he is hunting on top of the hill, August looks across the field at Karl Hoffmann's farm. He asks himself, "Why didn't Mama and Papa join them when the good land was still available?"

August is the middle child of a large family. He values his independence from his parents and the friendships he has made outside the family. Yet with two older brothers, he also longs to be first in the family in some way.

As he predicted to Albert, it was not long before Minnie was pregnant. He was sure that bitterly cold night when it happened that he had achieved his goal of giving his mother her first grandchild.

Delicate white spring flowers bloom in the sun between the rocks, trees and remaining snow on a lazy Sunday afternoon when Albert visits his brother. He pulls two cigars from his jacket pocket. "We need to celebrate your first child and your first farm." When Minnie, still in the early months of her pregnancy, smells the cigar smoke, she orders both men out of the house. The brothers sit on two stumps outside, enjoying their cigars and the warm sun.

Albert now removes an envelope from the same pocket where he produced the cigars. "When I went to the store yesterday, there was a letter from Gustav." He hands the precious paper to August. While he devours the news from home, Albert teases him. "It seems our brother had a successful wedding night. You may give Mama her first American grandchild, but Gustav and Bertha are going to have her first German *Enkelkind*."

August turns to his older brother. "When are you going to start a family?"

Albert gives his usual unconvincing logical answer. "I have not saved enough yet to provide for a family."

August refutes his brother. "As if Minnie and I had any money last fall when we married."

Then Albert admits, "I have not met anyone who equals Auguste." August smiles, recalling their mother's anger that Sunday after church when Albert and Auguste disappeared into the woods.

"What happened to her?"

"I have been told she is living with her family in Wisconsin."

Exasperated, August asks, "Why are you here and not there? Are you waiting for her to find someone else?"

Albert changes the subject by commenting that it sounds like Julius will be the next Heyn brother to come to America. But he is thinking that, for once, his little brother may be right.

September 30, 1876 – Viola Township, Minnesota

An incoherent babble of English, Norwegian, Swedish and German fills the air in the entrance hall of the Olmsted County Courthouse. After leaving the individual speakers' mouths, the noise bounces off the high walls and worn wooden floors, mixing together into a tasteless stew that has not been given enough time for its distinctive flavors to blend. Today is the last day of the month, and the large room is filled to capacity with farmers looking forward to a successful future and land speculators eager to realize their profit from past investments. Every few minutes, the roar quiets when the heavy wooden door to the Recorder of Deeds office is opened. Everyone turns to see another optimistic entrepreneur leave the building while hoping their name is called next. Halfway up the stairs that lead to the second-floor courtroom, Albert Heyn and John Young patiently wait their turn.

Albert leans over the massive wooden railing of the stairs. His thoughts take him back nine years and one month ago to the day he was leaning over the massive wooden railing of the sailing ship *Reichstag,* staring at the city of New York. The events of the past five years flash through his mind.

Albert continued working near Potsdam until August's son Emil was born. Then after his new friend Julius Rosolack married his shipmate Louise Wegner the week before Christmas, he traveled two hundred miles east to Wisconsin. He quickly found work on farms near Auguste's father's farm in a region with towns named Berlin, Germania and Budsin.

August Priebe, the stern old stone mason with a second younger family, had not changed. He was still suspicious of this young man who became too familiar with his oldest daughter before he sent her to America three years before the rest of his family. Albert did not care what

Auguste's father thought of him as long as he was successful in becoming reacquainted with his first love.

The budding romance that had been only a weak flame seven years before was now reduced to just a few glowing embers—but that did not last long. After a couple of church picnics and an evening under the sky along the shores of the Fox River illuminated by the large orange ball of a full moon, the nearly cold ashes quickly reignited into a hot fire.

Three days after Christmas in 1873, the couple stood in the sanctuary of St. John's Lutheran Church nervously waiting to exchange their marriage vows. The fresh scent of pine from the Christmas tree in the corner filled the room. In front of them, Pastor Johann Hoyer took a deep breath and narrowed his eyes to reflect the seriousness of the vows he was about to recite. Behind the couple, Auguste's brother Wilhelm and her cousin August Ponto stood at attention as if they were guards preventing a prison break. Sandwiched between the gray-haired minister and their two guards, the couple exchanged their promises in a whisper that most of the observers in the small building could not hear. After being separated by oceans and circumstances, Albert and Auguste were finally able to proceed with the life they dreamed of as teenagers picnicking along the banks of Lake Niewiemko.

They spent their first winter in Wisconsin enjoying their long-delayed honeymoon. Six weeks after the wedding, Auguste confided to her aunt, at her brother Wilhelm's wedding, that she thought she was pregnant. By the time the snow was almost gone and rivers were moving fast, the couple knew that they would not be raising only wheat next spring.

The forests and wetlands around Princeton reminded Albert of the Haulands he had left behind. He told his new family there were better opportunities on the prairie surrounding Potsdam. As winter gave its last gasp, they all decided to move to Minnesota.

The Priebe family divided when they arrived in Minnesota. Auguste's three brothers followed her and Albert to Potsdam. Her father and his second family followed Auguste's stepmother's family to farms south of Rochester.

When Albert returned to Potsdam, the horizon around the hamlet had changed. With King Wheat preparing to yield another bumper crop, the area farmers banded together to build their own flour mill. Without moving water available to fuel the grinding wheels, the investors turned to wind power just as their families had for generations in their homelands. That spring, a large windmill competed with the new church's steeple to obstruct the view of the horizon.

Just like his father and grandfather before him, Albert was banished from the house on the night of his nine-month wedding anniversary. Outside, the nervous man paced in a circle from the house to the barn to the granary and back again. From the barn, John Meyer waved a jug of homemade beer at the nervous young man. Exhausted, Albert leaned on the horse's manger and took a large swallow of the bitter beer. The chestnut horse nuzzled Albert's neck, seeking attention. Lost in solitary thought, Albert ignored the horse; in his mind, he was a young boy again waiting with his father in a similar barn for his mother to give birth to his siblings.

After what seemed like an eternity, Emelia stepped out of the house to tell him he had a son. As he walked to the house he asked her, "Do you think my mother will ever meet her second American grandson?" Emelia, whose parents never met any of her children, responded, "Probably not."

Two months later, on the day Martin Luther had nailed his ninety-five theses to the door of All Saints' Church in Wittenberg, Albert and August were enjoying cigars as they waited for Minnie to give birth to their second child. The two brothers were only two years apart, and the competition between them had been legendary when they were growing up. In America, the rivalry continued.

That day, encouraged by a little homemade beer, they argued about how their name should be spelled in America. The German alphabet had thirty letters. They were told that in America, their children would be taught an alphabet of twenty-six letters. As their neighbors had done, they had to decide how to Americanize their names.

Albert said, "I think we should remove the umlaut from the y and continue to spell our name Heyn. That is what John Meyer is doing."

August argued equally forcefully, "That is too complicated for Americans. We should spell it Hein. Plus, that is how Gustav is doing it at home."

As their tempers started to flair, Auguste stepped out of the house to tell August he had a little girl. She scolded them, "Your name has always been spelled multiple ways at home. This subject is not worth breaking the family apart."

That spring Albert rented a farm several miles east of Potsdam. Shortly after baby Edward's six-month birthday, Albert drove his team to Potsdam to buy supplies to plant his first crop. It was a Friday afternoon, and the strong March winds had continued into the new month. Several times he had to grab his hat to keep from losing it.

When he reached the Meyer farm, he found John by the road, looking at four men twenty feet in the air standing on the windmill's small platform. They were trying to stop the out-of-control blades on the mill. As soon as Albert stopped to greet the godfather of his son, they heard a spine-chilling shriek that sounded like a rabbit or squirrel caught in the jaws of a fox or coyote. They saw three of the men frantically pulling on the fourth. The strong winds blew the man's final words—"Boys, save me, I'm caught!"—across the prairie.

John and Albert raced to the mill. From a distance, they could see blood beginning to paint the sides of the tower red. Passing Friedrich Hardt's store, they gasped when one of the men on the tower jumped or fell twenty feet to the roof below.

They arrived at the mill with the rest of the panicked community as the three surviving young men reached the ground. John Hoeft, his clothes covered with the blood and flesh of the twenty-year-old fearless and well-muscled blacksmith William McCarren, supported himself with the wall of the building as he explained what had just happened. "Shortly after dinner, he asked me, August Tradup, and Henry Peters to climb the tower with him to turn the blades into the wind to stop their wild spinning. It is only three feet wide up there where the gears attach the blades to the grinding stones below. William tried to shove a crowbar into the wildly gyrating mechanism, but as he leaned over with the iron rod, the wind caught the blades, and they swung around. It threw him off balance, and his foot got caught in the fast-spinning gears." Hoeft took a moment to gasp for air and then continued, "We grabbed his arms, but the gears just pulled him through a space only two inches wide." Hoeft cried, "We held on until only his upper chest, arms and head were not being crushed."

The farmers left the traumatized three men in the comfort of the women of the village and tried to stop the spinning blades by overpacking the grinding wheels. Ground flesh and bone fell on their heads as their frantic actions were unsuccessful. At last, the crowbar the young blacksmith had attempted to use to stop the wheel finally caught, and the gears became jammed.

When the grinding of the young man's flesh stopped, a shaken Albert sat on a log with his brother August, who had just arrived after hearing the screams from his farm two miles away. The two brothers, who had avoided the horrors of wars, sat stunned by the carnage they were witnessing. At the entrance to the mill a discussion started on how to free the blacksmith.

Many of the immigrants thought that they would have to call the coroner from Rochester before the remnants of the body could be removed. Unsure, they sought the advice of a prominent Yankee farmer, E. P. Whiting, who lived south of the village. When he arrived, he told the assembled men that they did not have to wait. With that advice, four volunteers agreed to climb the tower to complete the grim task. Albert and August had seen enough, and they returned to their farms.

On Sunday morning, John Hoeft was standing in the middle of a group of men in front of the church, therapeutically recalling his grim Friday. Calmly he told of volunteering to climb back up the tower to retrieve his friend. "On the platform, I saw only a head attached to half of a chest, two damaged arms, and a mangled partial leg. Four of us attempted to remove the body from the gears, but we were no more successful than I had been earlier when William was still alive." He took a deep breath. "The only way to free the body was to cut the remaining tendons and bones away from those crushed into the gears." Tears ran down the face of the usually stoic twenty-five-year-old as he continued, "I bent over with a knife and cut the chest of my friend free from his lower body just like I do when I butcher a hog." One of the other men who had been up on the tower added, "William's watch in his upper pocket kept perfect time through the whole ordeal."

Later that day, the undertaker from Rochester came to the village to prepare the body for transport to St. Paul for a funeral. He brought a proper casket for the scattered remains, some of which on Friday had been scooped into a flour sack. As Albert walked into the church, he wondered if he would have been able to exhibit that kind of courage—and, if he had, would he ever be able to sleep again.

Even after the tragedy, the farmers were still convinced that they had made a good investment in the mill. When the railroad line was built through their village, the mill would become more prosperous than any in Minneapolis. Even now, after the railroad announced it was bypassing Potsdam for a line that ran along the Whitewater River from Eyota to Plainview, Emil Seeman, the current miller, was still sure that he would soon be rich as Governor Pillsbury.

The overconfident exuberance of the village that was heard at the church, the half-dozen stores of the town, and the mill, was infectious. Albert told everyone that he would not be satisfied until he owned his own farm. He became even more diligent about saving. This spring, he told Auguste that if their crop was good, they would have enough money to purchase a farm in the fall.

As more immigrants arrived every year, the members of the church extended further from the village. One of the congregants, Albert Mueller, recently purchased a farm six miles to the south near the Yankee village of Viola. One Sunday, he gave Albert a flyer for a 160-acre farm that was for sale down the hill from his. Mueller warned him that the land was not as productive as the farm Albert was currently renting. Although a branch of the Whitewater River cut through the farm, resulting in many hills and swamps, Mueller assured Albert that there were many acres of very fertile soil. Mueller arranged a meeting for the next week with the current owner, John Young.

In his mid-forties, Young is not a farmer but rather spent the past twenty years as a wheat buyer, a grocer and a landlord throughout southeastern Minnesota. Wheat production in Olmsted County since the end of the Civil War has been the primary economic growth engine for the region. Through his various ventures, Young has done well.

His farm has been easy to rent to the steady flow of immigrants and settlers who moved into the county since the war. John Young is a savvy businessman who can see that there are dark clouds ahead. Continuous wheat planting on the same ground bred disease and decreased fertility, resulting in reduced yields. Farmers this year are describing a good harvest but one less than in previous years. If this trend continues, the value of his farm and his ability to receive top-dollar rents will be reduced in the future.

When he sees a dark cloud forming in the west, he cannot be sure if the approaching storm is rain, snow or locust. Three years ago, a plague of grasshoppers stripped the wheat fields bare in the southwestern corner of Minnesota. Terrible stories of families starving to death after the green insects devoured all of their food and livelihood were on the front page of every newspaper in the state. Every year since, the black clouds of locusts moved farther east. This year they reached the eastern borders of Steele County, less than thirty miles away. If their eastward march continued, they would reach Olmsted County in 1877, potentially wiping out the value of his farm. The businessman who had escaped the potato famine as a young man recognized the danger and decided that now was the time to make a profit on the sale of his farm.

The humidity was thick and the mosquitos deadly the afternoon that Albert and Auguste met John Young. Their first impression of the farm was not good. After years of revolving tenants, the buildings and fences were poorly maintained. As Albert Mueller had warned them, one branch of the Whitewater River flowed from a spring past the property boundaries through the steep hills along the driveway past the house and barn to another branch of the river just across the road. Behind the buildings, the hills were so rugged that the surveyors could not place the road on the township line. Instead, they moved it a half-mile to the east for two miles in front of the farm.

Albert wandered the entire 160 acres asking questions in his thick accent about the quality of the soil and the abundance of the crops. The current tenant, who had been born in New England, could barely understand the prospective buyer and gave only brief *yes* and *no* answers. When the trio of men returned to the farmyard, Albert looked south past the large weeping willow trees that had grown on each side of the creek and saw a flat field of more than twenty acres with a beautiful crop of golden wheat that seemed to be waving welcome to him.

Albert and Auguste walked away from the curious ears of the seller. They found a large rock near the bank of the creek where they sat to make their decision. The farm was not the perfect place they had dreamed of owning when they left their parents' less-than-perfect farms. They now faced the same choice their parents had when the good land had already been claimed. Was this the best they could do?

With the same words his father used to assure his skeptical mother thirty years before, Albert assured his skeptical wife that he saw the farm's potential. "The soil is a little tired, but it is still fertile. The barn needs a few repairs but is big enough to house cows, horses and pigs. Those forbidding hills will support a large dairy herd as productive as my father's and grandfather's herds back home." Pointing at a flock of ducks flying overhead, he said, "Even the small swamp in the far corner of the farm has potential."

Auguste got caught up in her husband's optimism. They would have a diversified farm whose success would not be dependent on the whims of grain buyers or vindictive landlords. The young mother ran after her mischievous, nearly two-year-old son after nodding her approval to purchase the farm.

Albert stood, leaving his wife and son behind as he walked back to John Young. The negotiations were quick. Young wanted $10 an acre: "I have many prospective buyers, and I am not willing to negotiate." Albert countered that he would need help financing the purchase. Young agreed to a contract for deed if Albert made a downpayment of $400. He was willing to wait four years for the balance of $1,200. The Irishman and the German reached out their hands to shake on the deal.

With their hands still clasped together, Albert looked over John's shoulder. Across the babbling creek, he again gazed at the field of golden wheat. Next spring, he excitedly thought, he would celebrate his thirtieth birthday in this exact spot watching the tender shoots of his first crop of winter wheat begin to rise from winter dormancy. At that moment, he felt like he, too, was coming out of dormancy.

The oppressive heat and humidity on the day he agreed to the purchase were replaced by cool, clear air blown by a refreshing light breeze. For the next hour, Albert will not be able to enjoy the weather. Instead, he is inside the dark courthouse with air thick from smoke. With his dream only a signature away, he now has second thoughts. What if the grasshoppers continue their march east next year? What if the wheat blight is worse? Could they lose everything they have worked for?

His negative thoughts are interrupted by the sound of the office door below slamming against the plaster walls. Thomas Brooks, the county's Recorder of Deeds, whose voice is hoarse from overwork, mispronounces Albert's name when he calls him into the room.

The two immigrants push their way through the crowd that is blocking the steps and then through another surrounding the door. Once inside the room, they are ushered to two chairs across the desk from Brooks. With an overly dramatic flourish, the man organizes the inkwell, pens and stamps before him. John Young removes the bill of sale, the deed and the mortgage from his worn brown leather case and places them on the desk.

It has been a long morning for Brooks, and there is still a large crowd gathered outside his office requiring his attention. He does not have time to review the papers in depth. Instead, he briefly skims them to confirm the property description and the mortgage. When he is done, he lays them before the two men, waiting for their signatures.

Albert's hand is shaking, and his chest feels as if it is about to explode when he picks up the pen. It requires all of his concentration to successfully dip it into the inkwell. He places his left hand on his right to steady it as he stiffly signs his name on the most important document of his life. When he finishes and slides the papers to Young, he feels the intense pressure and pain in his chest magically disappear.

Young dips the pen into the inkwell and signs his name next to Albert's. He then spins the papers around to face Brooks, who signs his name and affixes his stamp. Brooks and Young then stare impatiently at Albert, waiting for him to give his $400 of hard-earned money to Young. Once the money passes hands, the two men congratulate the new landowner.

With the transaction completed, the men are quickly ushered out of the office. The reality of the past twenty minutes seeps into Albert's consciousness as he stands on the courthouse steps. Overhead the first flock of geese of the season begins their journey south for the winter. Albert is also ready to begin his journey to a new home.

Two days later, Albert and Auguste are finishing their breakfast when they hear the rumbles of old wagons, the braying of horses, and the snap and jingle of harnesses that are tying the former to the latter. They greet their friends who will help them move to their new home.

The men spread throughout the house and barn, loading the few assets the young couple has acquired into the wagons. Once all the wagons are filled, a final inspection is conducted to ensure nothing is left behind. Then the men and women climb up to the hard wooden seats of the wagons for the trip to the new farm. Patiently the other farmers wait for Albert to help his wife and son into his wagon. He gives Auguste a brief smile before cracking the reins to start their journey.

Reaching the road, they maneuver the familiar left turn toward the church, whose bright white steeple is a beautiful contrast to the blue sky. They can see the blades of the flour mill leisurely turning in the light breeze as the parade turns south on the county line road a mile from the church.

The husband and wife are silent for the next five miles, lulled into their own thoughts by the horses' hooves rhythmically clopping on the hard dirt road. When they get closer to their new home, they pass by farms whose occupants do not share the same language, religion or customs. Yankee farmers come out of their houses and barns to watch another of their neighbors being replaced by Germans. From their wagons, the farmers can see disapproval in the faces of those who think their country is being invaded by foreigners.

After eight miles of bone-rattling travel over rutted roads, the couple is finally at the entrance to their dream. Albert snaps the reins, and the horses pull the wagon forward, creating a small cloud of dust. His back stiffens. He throws his shoulders back. A small smile of satisfaction appears on his normally expressionless face. Auguste thinks he looks like a strutting rooster. He doesn't care—this is an occasion for a little ungodly self-congratulation. Nine years ago, his feet dangled off the back of a wagon as he left the farm where he spent his youth. Today he is in the front of the wagon driving to the farm where he will spend his adulthood.

December 25, 1882 – Grafton, Dakota Territory

A blast of cold air follows August into the house he built last summer on the Dakota prairie. While stoking the iron cook stove, Minnie wraps her shawl tight around her shoulders, expecting an onslaught of wind and snow when their rickety door swings open. As she tends to the small blaze growing in the firebox, she thinks that having the door open or closed makes little difference. She is sure the Dakota wind has not stopped blowing for an hour since the family stepped off the train in Grafton last spring. It is always able to find a crack in the walls, bringing subzero temperatures and snow into her house.

This is the family's first Christmas in the Dakota Territory. Minnie has been frantic for days, making sure their holiday dinner is perfect, but controlling the temperature of her new stove in this cold room with a small amount of expensive hardwood to burn is a challenge. She continually adjusts the dampers to regulate the heat. Baking in the oven is a *Weihnachtsstollen.* Since she was a little girl barely able to see over the table, she has helped make this traditional bread from her mother's recipe. A month ago, she was sure this would be the first Christmas the family would not enjoy because the nuts and fruits for the bread were an unaffordable luxury. Then a letter from her stepsister Ottilie arrived, telling her that their mother had died on July 19—the day they had moved into this house. In her grief, she insisted to August that they had to buy the ingredients for her mother's bread. Burning it now in this inconsistent oven would be a tragedy too great for her to contemplate.

The fresh aroma of the bread conflicts with the smell of the manure-stained clothes of her husband and sons. In the corner, the crock of sauerkraut is pungent. August sits in his chair on the other side of the room and smokes his pipe, adding to the mix of smells.

One night after the summer heat broke, the couple celebrated their new home by conceiving another baby. Minnie takes a deep breath of the competing odors in the ten by twelve-foot room, grateful that the morning sickness she had been suffering the past couple of months had finally ended.

Observing the chaos, August takes a large puff of his pipe. The smell of the familiar bread reignited memories of Christmases when he was a boy. His childhood home was no bigger than this one, and it also overflowed at Christmastime with people, noise and smells. One difference then was that it was not just his brothers and sisters making the noise but also family and friends who went from farm to farm eating, drinking and exchanging greetings. On Christmas Eve, his father would disappear into the woods to cut a tree. After decorating the tree, they would open the few simple gifts their family could afford. The next morning, the family would crowd into the church to pray and sing—and scratch the lice from their hair and clothes. After the service, they returned to the farm to eat a massive dinner whose main course was a goose they had spent the summer fattening for the special day.

When they moved to Minnesota, their holidays were not as festive, although their children's first Christmases were magical. August never had trouble finding a tree to bring into the house. There were churches nearby where they could worship. Extended family and friends stopped to exchange traditional baked goods and to drink a mug of warm *Glühwein.* Just as his mother had done, Minnie spent the summer pampering the unsuspecting Christmas dinner main course.

Last night, there were no pine trees for miles that he could sneak out to cut. Arriving too late last spring to harvest a full crop, they could only afford clothes that Minnie made as gifts for the children. There are few German families in their neighborhood to exchange traditional pastries and drink. The weather this morning is too cold and snowy to travel safely to the German Lutheran churches in St. Thomas or Acton for services. Their worship today will have to be August sitting by the stove reading the Christmas story from the Bible to the children. Rather than a fat goose for their meal, a chicken who could not survive the bitter cold will soon replace the bread in the oven. As they fell asleep last night, Minnie said to him, "I feel like this will be a lost Christmas."

August assured her, "This Christmas may not be the same as the ones we had as children, but we will make it a happy memory for our children."

Many times this year, Minnie had the feeling of being lost. Their small house is surrounded by a flat endless nothing for as far as she can see. When she looks across their land to the north, she can see the homes of fellow homesteaders four or five miles away. To the east, the view is the same. She is thankful that the buildings two miles away in Grafton break the horizon when she looks to the south. Her view to the west is the same as the other directions except for the tracks the Great Northern Railroad is building next to their house and barn. She is almost glad that her view in that direction will be clouded by the black smoke of a locomotive next summer.

In contrast, when August looks across the open prairie, he is excited. Finally, he is sure he is going to provide the permanent home that Minnie wants. Every afternoon, as he sits next to the fire waiting for his farm to emerge from its winter hibernation, he plans for the new year. When a blast of cold wind whips through the wall, he makes plans to plant tree seedlings to the north and west to protect the farm from the harsh winds. On the days when the walls of his house and barn begin to close in, he designs additions to both buildings. At the table on the back of a discarded envelope, he draws his land. Nine-year-old Emil is fascinated as he watches his father plan from the sketch how much seed he will need to buy this spring. Owning a prosperous farm has been August's dream since he was a boy—it is why he came to America. After a series of rented farms, he is confident that his dream is now within reach.

During the first years of their marriage, they lived in a house buried in a steep valley next to a dangerous stream that swelled during the spring melt and heavy summer storms, several times nearly washing away the house and barn. The fields, while fertile, were scattered on the top of the hills. August lost count of how many plowshares and sickle sections he broke when his plow or mower hit the limestone rocks scattered across the fields. He tried to be industrious with the rocks. To earn extra money, he would gather them on a skid and then sell them to his neighbors who were building new barns and granaries.

In the spring of the country's centennial, Henry Schaeffer, the husband of Minnie's sister Amalie, purchased the farm. August and Minnie decided to follow the Priebes to better land in the developing

German communities south of Rochester called Pleasant Valley and High Forest. They began renting a series of farms south of Pleasant Valley near another pleasant-sounding town, Grand Meadow. The land was flat and fertile. August thought that he had finally found a place to succeed.

Prosper they did. That first fall, Minnie gave birth to another son, August Carl. Two years later, another girl, Mina, joined the family. The last child born in Minnesota is little Ida. She has just turned two and is running around the house with an energy and determination that only someone her age can muster.

They prospered not only inside the house but also outside it. Within four years, August was plowing one hundred acres of the quarter section he rented west of Grand Meadow. On warm summer evenings, he would look out from the barn where he housed his three milk cows and two horses at sixty acres of wheat, six acres of barley, five acres of oats, and small patches of corn and potatoes. As he walked across the yard, Minnie's twenty chickens would scatter while his pigs squealed in the background. Before entering the house, he admired the impressive collection of farm machinery he had purchased.

The family still maintained their connections to their homeland through the German Lutheran church in Pleasant Valley. For the first time, however, August and Minnie were living in a neighborhood where none of the neighbors shared their past. When they needed help, they turned to native-born Americans, Irish, Scandinavians and even the wife of one neighbor who had been born in Hungary. In Potsdam, there had been Irish and Yankee neighbors, but the large community of families from Gembitz Hauland made homesickness impossible. After an initial hesitancy, August and Minnie found they enjoyed living in the melting pot.

They had one big problem. Land was too expensive in Mower County. Minnie's uncle Michael Wanke had purchased for speculation 140 acres nearby, paying $25 an acre. With the price of wheat falling and the weather so uncertain, August could not afford to pay those prices. Shortly after they moved to the rental farm, Albert purchased his own farm for $10 an acre. That farm was not as flat as the land August rented, but Albert had inherited their mother's love of cows, and he saw an opportunity on the hills. August grew up admiring the plains on the road to Gramsdorf. He always wanted to own a farm with an endless view of golden wheat like those of his uncles. The two brothers were establishing themselves in their own ways as successful farmers, but Albert was building equity, and August was not. After ten years, he thought he was never going to be as successful as his brother.

Shortly after Ida was born, August and Theodore Lehmann worked together to complete the season's butchering. When they finished their work, they toasted the recent births of their two daughters with mugs of beer. As they drank, Theodore told August that he was moving his small family to the Dakota Territory in the spring. He was excited: "Free land is available there. There is a place in the Red River Valley flatter than any board planed by a master carpenter. The undisturbed prairie grass is as tall as my chest. If you want to own good land, you should join us."

When August told Minnie that he wanted to follow the Lehmanns to the Dakota Territory, a loud argument broke out. Just like he did when his father and mother argued about emigrating to America, his children hid behind the barn as their parents fought about their futures. Across the farmyard, they heard their mother tell their father over and over again, "I don't want to live alone in a shack on the prairie far from my sister and family. I am tired of chasing your dreams." It took him a year, but unlike his father, August won the argument with his strong-willed wife. For the second time in their decade-long marriage, they packed what little they could carry, sold what they could not, and set off for the unknown.

After leaving a bouquet of flowers on little Mina's grave, Minnie boarded the train for Dakota. She made the long journey with her head pressed against the window as she once again listened to a big black locomotive pull her away from her comfortable life. At every stop, as the landscape turned more barren, Minnie would remind her husband, "It is time to put down permanent roots."

As the Great Northern train chugged north across the Red River basin, August watched the tall prairie grass sway in the wind, creating brown waves that resembled a fierce ocean. The flat landscape reminded him of the endless horizon when they crossed the ocean. Then the large ocean waves had been both intimidating and inspiring. Watching the grass sway in the wind from the passenger car rekindled those feelings.

The train's whistle broke not only nature's silence but also the couple's when it announced that they had reached the new end of the line in Grafton. Metal-on-metal screeches joined the sounds of the whistle as the brakes brought the train to a stop. The brakes had a big job as the train was pushed forward by its heavy load of lumber, farm implements, household goods, farm animals, and, most important, immigrants who were willing to settle this imposing landscape.

Theodore Lehmann greeted the family at the train depot. The building and platform still smelled of newly cut lumber, having been built only months before. The entire town of Grafton had the same fresh smell. Theodore enthusiastically told them, "Only four years ago, the land where the town is being built was open prairie. Several months earlier, a fire raged through the town, burning down the bank and several other businesses. But it is just a small bump for your new neighbors. The railroad is also expanding. Grafton is now the end of the line, but not for long, as the Great Northern is expanding its tracks to Canada."

August staked his claim two miles north of the village on a quarter section that was dissected by the future tracks of the Great Northern. Before the family left Minnesota, they were told that they would need at least $1,000 to start over here. Every day the trains were delivering supplies for the settlers, but they were still expensive. August went to the lumberyard next to the tracks to purchase lumber for their new house and barn, then he went to the livery stables to purchase horses and cows to replace the ones he had sold in Minnesota. At the livery stable, the owner told August, "Oxen are better for breaking the prairie turf."

August replied, "I remember how happy my father was when he didn't have to use oxen anymore. I'm not going backward. I want two strong horses."

It was slow, but August's two new horses pulled his new plow through the grass, turning over rich black soil that had never before seen the light. With the help of Minnie and the children, he was able to plant a small crop. It was not enough to make a profit, but it produce enough to feed the family through the winter.

For the first months, the family slept in a large white tent. As a blast of arctic wind whistles through a crack in the house, August remembers the hot wind that blew through that tent last spring and summer. The children thought it a great adventure. Their mother did not.

The landscape shocked Minnie. Their farms at Grand Meadow were also flat. On a clear day, she could see her neighbors' houses two or three miles away. Here it appeared that there was no end to the horizon. As she planted potatoes and cabbage, the wind would pick up her hat and carry it far out in the prairie grass. It was an exciting game for the children to retrieve it, but she worried they would get lost in the tall grasses. Waiting for them to return, she would straighten her back and stare across the endless landscape, feeling as small as the ants scurrying in the fresh dirt.

August staked his claim on the southwest quarter of section 36 of an as-yet-unnamed township where the Lehmanns lived. He was told that if he lived on the land, improved it and cultivated it, he would be eligible to receive 160 acres free from the Homestead Act. Because the railroad and a parallel road sliced across the land, his claim would be thirteen acres short. The surrounding land was being claimed quickly, and he settled for the smaller acreage to be near the town, road and tracks. He planned to set up a brick business as his father had done, and the infrastructure to move the bricks was worth being short a few acres that he did not have the time to cultivate. Later, when he met one of his new neighbors, he was distressed to learn that when the Dakota Territory became a state, his section would be reserved for the new government to establish schools. He was told not to worry, as only a small portion was needed for the school, but it did worry the couple. When their proof period ended, they wondered if they would receive title to the land.

Once August finished planting, he began to build the house. With no trees to shade it, the sun was beating down hard as he pounded the last nails into the roof on a hot, late July evening. When he came back down to the ground, he stood with Minnie and the children to admire his work. When he asked her what she thought of her new home, she said, "I am so happy we don't live in that tent anymore."

As the summer progressed, the family settled into their new surroundings. They maintained ties to the German settlers in St. Thomas and Acton, worshipping with them when they could. Day to day, though, as they had in Grand Meadow, they socialized with a smorgasbord of new neighbors.

During the summer, August made extra money laying tracks for the Great Northern, which was passing the house as it expanded to Pembina. He established his brick business, selling bricks to carpenters who were expanding the Grafton main street. That fall, they harvested their first crop. When the first flakes of snow blew across their farm, the fear of failure the couple felt at the train station last spring was replaced by certainty. They were confident they would survive the winter and thrive in the New Year.

The aroma of the roasting chicken, the sauerkraut cooking on the stove, and the potatoes bubbling in the pot fill the room. August helps the boys to pull the table from its place against the wall to the center of the room. Minnie opens the old trunk that traveled with her to America and removes a tablecloth crocheted by her grandmother. After she covers the table, Hulda sets six plates. The family then takes their seats, which are assigned by age. The chicken is placed in front of August. He leads the family in a short prayer to thank God for their health and success this extraordinary year. After the "Amen" and before the bird is carved, August announces to his family, "We are home."

July 7, 1883 – Gembitz Hauland

Far in the distance, a black cloud starts to form as Pauline Westphal cleans the dishes from the family's dinner. Tomorrow will be Sunday, a day of rest, but today there is work to do. Bread needs to be baked, eggs need to be gathered, cows need to be milked, gardens need to be tended, and a baby needs to be changed and fed. As she does her chores, she looks to the west at the forming rainstorm, and unexpectedly, her mind, as it does for all of us, begins replaying the scenes of her life.

She breathes a sigh of relief. It is always welcome when the wheat, potatoes and pastures have a fresh thirst-quenching drink of water the first week of July. Her husband August farms the same land whose combination of sand and swamp frustrated her father. They do not have a large section of land, but rather small patches divided between more than eighty families spread over almost twenty-five square miles. If you could look down from the sky, the land would look like a thousand-piece jigsaw puzzle. The farms can barely support the large families, even in a good year. If there is a bad harvest, starvation always follows, forcing more families to leave for America. This welcome rain will hopefully delay her family's decision for another year.

Their land is less fertile than that along the Netze River and the other open flat plains surrounding the community in Budsin, Sarben or Radam. Consequently, no one stays here long. A few families, like the Wankes, have lived here for generations, but most families are like hers, just passing through for a generation or two. When the opportunity here is extinguished, people move to another place. As each family comes or goes, the land is divided or stitched back together like the cutting and sewing of fabric for a patchwork quilt.

Pauline was thirty-two when she finally married the neighbor she had had her eyes on since she was a toddler. She and August began their married life without the approval of the government or the church. They finally married six months after the birth of their daughter Bertha. Pauline was the fourth girl in the village to have a child before marriage that year. A child born out of wedlock did not make Anna happy, but she accepted that her daughter wasn't the first, nor would she be the last in that situation. Because of the military service and the financial requirements the government placed on marriage, Anna knew that romance could not always wait for the wedding day. After the wedding, Pauline and August started their own farm nearby, and every two years added another child to work it. She thought that is what you need marriage for.

Seven years ago, Pauline's youngest sister Maria married August Erdmann, the third August in the family. The family calls them Pauline's August, Maria's August, and Our August, for Pauline and Maria's brother. After their wedding, Anna transferred the ownership of her farm to the newlyweds Maria and August.

Rain did not come that first year or the second, and Maria's August began talking about joining his brothers-in-law in America. Anna worried that the farm that had been her home for almost forty years would fall into the hands of a stranger, and she convinced her daughters to swap farms. The two families and their possessions passed each other on the path crossing the Ryga five years ago.

The farm has not changed since Pauline was born. In the center is the house her father built of orange brick with a steep roof that the snow and rain easily run off. On each side of the house are the barns and granaries for the animals. On this hot July day, the closeness of the buildings gives the entire farmyard a particularly foul smell. Whenever she complains about the smell, August teases her that it smells like money to him.

The flat land that opens from the farmyard in the opposite direction of the approaching storm is a very good place to raise the large orange and white cows that produce rich cream-filled milk. Taking care of the cows is an important job for the farmwife: they are the difference between wealth and ruin.

Their community has three main roads running north and south, with the farms dotting the way. Where the middle road and Czarnikau Strasse intersect, there are old buildings made of open beams and plaster and new ones made from the same materials as Pauline's house. That crossroad has always been the meeting point of the community. On the northwest and northeast corners are stores where business is conducted to sustain them in the present. On the southwest corner is the school, where the children are educated for the future. On the southeast corner stands the church, where they ask forgiveness for their past. Most of those who have left the community saw only poverty and disease at that crossroad. Pauline, however, loves the security and familiarity of that place.

Her church is not only the pride of the community but also of her. She does not miss an opportunity to brag that she was a member of the parish's first confirmation class. Before that, when the sacraments of birth, marriage or death needed to be performed, families traveled to Gramsdorf, a long trip on a horse. No matter how much faith you have in God, the cycle of life does not always neatly fit into the schedule of a faraway pastor.

Before she was born, three bells were given to them by King Friedreich Wilhelm IV and hang in a special bell tower outside the church. Every time those bells ring, Pauline thinks, "What an honor for our small little farming village!" Her cynical neighbors tell her, "They were presented to quiet our dissent when the king's father forced us to abandon our Lutheran prayer books for his new Evangelical ones." Pauline always walks away from those negative people, shaking her head in disgust. "They should just enjoy the beautiful sound of the bells when we worship on Sundays or when we celebrate a new life coming into this world or an old one leaving it."

The slow tolling of the bells sets a somber mood when families and friends slowly carry a departed one from the church a half-mile away in the direction of the setting sun to the cemetery in the tall thin pine trees. Too often, the life that has just left the world is not old but rather someone for whom the bells were rung in joy and welcome just a few days or months before. That sad half-mile is the walk all parents fear.

Twice during their nine-year marriage, August carried the casket of a child on his shoulders. They are lucky: five of their seven children are healthy. Her brother-in-law Ludwig has lost six of his eight children. Pauline says a quick prayer that their luck will continue.

No matter the age of the deceased, when the mourners arrive at the cemetery, they turn ninety degrees to the left and enter between two brick spires with an iron cross gracing the top of each. The gate is attached to these spires, and after they pass through the gate, they make another ninety-degree turn at the awaiting grave to be sure the inhabitant of the pine box will face the resurrection of the sun.

Each grave has a stone border, inside of which bright red geraniums are planted to celebrate the life that had been lived. Every year, in addition to the graves of her children, Pauline plants flowers on more and more graves of people whose families have left for America. Walking out of the cemetery, the loss of family and friends across the blue sea of the Atlantic always overwhelms her with new grief.

That grief always surfaces when she sees her children play with their Westphal cousins. She longs to meet her ten nieces and nephews born in America. Today, the impossibility of that thought is accented by the rumble of thunder in the distance.

She looks up at the black cloud on the horizon. Five times her mood has been as dark as that cloud as she stood next to her mother and watched another sibling disappear through the trees. First, it was Albert, who is permanently etched into her mind as a young and enthusiastic nineteen-year-old. Then it was poor Ottilie, who, like a seed planted on hard, dry soil, never had the opportunity to take root in her new country. She was followed by August the day after his wedding and Julius two years later. Finally, two years ago, she watched her baby brother Adolph leave with one of Ottilie's in-laws to avoid the military draft.

Her two oldest brothers have written that they are becoming successful farmers. Albert says he owns a farm nearly as large as the whole southern section of the Hauland. She thinks her brother is exaggerating. Thirty families are being supported here in that area, not just one.

The letter from August last Christmas was even more unbelievable. He and Minnie moved to a place he says can be so cold that if you spill your hot coffee, it will freeze in midair. The coffee story fascinated the children, but Pauline found the rest of his letter even more incredible. He said he was receiving a farm as large as Albert's from the government for free if they agreed to farm it for five years. Pauline cannot believe any government would give land to a person just for working hard—and especially to people who do not speak the country's language very well. She and her husband work hard every day, and the government and the landlord just want more.

She worries about Julius. He sends letters as optimistic as his brothers, but after ten years, he doesn't appear to be doing as well as they are. He is married with one daughter and works as a molder in a factory in the city where Ottilie rests, but he doesn't own land or a house. She hopes his life is as good as he says.

Of her mother's eight children, now only three are left here to care for her as the lines of age develop on her face. The letters from her brothers are enticing her last two siblings. Gustav and his wife's brothers have already contracted to go to America in the spring. Earlier this week, after her husband's funeral, Bertha's mother Minnie cried, "There is nothing here for me now. I will leave with the other children."

Maria's August is an industrious man who is outgrowing their community. The letters from America describing free land have kindled a spark of ambition in him. Pauline is sure they will leave soon after Gustav.

Pauline often wonders if her mother will make the same decision as Minnie Redel if she and her August are forced to leave. She is a strong woman, but if she stayed, how would she survive? That is a black cloud for the future.

Pauline witnessed the birth of each of her siblings. If Maria leaves, she will also witness each sibling's departure for America. Will she follow them? Neither she nor August understands why anyone would leave the certainty of the only home they have ever known for a risky gamble to achieve a possibly better life.

Those imaginary black clouds are for another day because the real dark cloud, once in the distance, is now overhead, bringing Pauline back to the present. She must protect her children and cows before the storm arrives.

Suddenly she hears a loud noise, like a bomb. She feels a tingle, starting at her feet and working through her entire body. When the tingle reaches her chest, it changes to a burn. A bright light is in her eyes. Is the light coming from this world or from the world on the other side? She hopes the first but knows it is the latter. She cries out as blackness overcomes her, "Please take care of the chil . . ."

Tornado damage on the road to Albert and Auguste's farm. Photo courtesy of the Olmsted County Historical Society

Part IV
1883 Rochester Tornado

August 21, 1883 – Viola, Minnesota

It is a hot and humid morning. The sun has been up only a few hours, and already it is heating the wet air into a warm soup that, on a winter day, warms you from the inside out. Today, it feels as if you are being heated from the outside in. Adding to the feeling of being cooked alive is a strong hot wind blowing from the southeast across the fields of freshly cut wheat. This is the kind of foul weather that the farmers of the township know can bring ruin.

At the blacksmith shop in the little village of Viola, the weather is not the only thing that is foul. Albert is in a bad mood. He has traveled three and a half miles this morning to have his grain binder repaired. A storm will be coming soon to break this heat, and he still has wheat to cut. He had hoped to finish last night, but he hit a patch of dirt mounds created by the too-prevalent gophers. The impact broke the sickle of the binder, and now he is wasting precious time in town having it fixed.

Lack of sleep also contributes to Albert's bad mood. It has been a busy harvest season. He has 120 acres of wheat, barley, oats, hay, and corn to harvest. Eight horses pull his new farm machinery, four milk cows produce the rich butter he sells, plus steers and pigs for slaughter—all need to be fed and cared for every day. Auguste has a flock of chickens that produce eggs and a fine chicken dinner every Sunday. Such is the life of an ambitious immigrant farmer. When Auguste tells him to rest, he tells her there will be plenty of time for that in the winter.

This weather has made sleep even more precious. His farm, tucked into the hills alongside the north branch of the Whitewater River, protects his family from the arctic northwest winds in the winter. To the southeast, the farmyard opens to forty acres of the black prairie soil that produces Albert's best crops. Today that open expanse is allowing the hot wind to blow directly into the farm with a hard stop into the limestone hills directly behind the buildings. Last night the house felt as hot as Auguste's cast iron oven when she bakes bread.

Adding to the misery, Albert's youngest son, sixteen-month-old Walter, is cutting a new tooth. Last night he was hot, in pain and could not sleep—and he decided everybody in the house would be miserable along with him. His endless crying kept his brothers, Ed, Willie and Albert Junior, awake. This morning the two oldest boys were so tired they did not want to do their chores, adding to Albert's foul mood.

Albert is hesitant to visit the blacksmith in Viola. Usually, he would have taken his part to Frederick Meyer's shop in Elgin, but that had been destroyed by a tornado one month ago. There are other German blacksmiths in Potsdam or Rochester, but that trip would take too long. His reward for all his work this spring and summer is now standing in the field. An unfamiliar blacksmith today is less risky than the thunderstorms that may be brewing.

The variety of weather in America was a big surprise for the immigrants. There had been tornadoes, droughts, floods and blizzards in Germany but not with such ferocity as in Minnesota. Every farmer knows that they are one storm away from being wiped out.

Albert decides to use his wasted time to walk to the general store. When he left home this morning, Auguste gave him a list of supplies they needed. Because of the harvest, no one in his neighborhood has been to the store for a couple of weeks to pick up mail, so when the clerk returns with his mail as well as that of his neighbors, the stack is high.

Mixed in the letters is one that just arrived from his sister Maria at home. After leaving the store, he eagerly opens the letter, expecting good news from the family. The last letter he received at Christmas said that his sisters Pauline and Maria and sister-in-law Bertha were all expecting babies. He quickly rips open the envelope, eager to learn if they had girls or boys. His dark mood begins to lighten.

As he sits on the wooden bench in front of the store, the darkness of Albert's mood returns multiplied by ten. Tears well in his eyes as he reads, "With great sadness, I write to tell you that last Saturday, our sister Pauline was struck by lightning and died." Albert starts reciting the Twenty-third Psalm aloud to himself in German: "Der Herr is mein Hirte." Two old Yankee settlers at the other end of the bench begin grumbling, "If these Germans want to live in this country, why don't they learn to speak English."

As he continues reading, homesickness overcomes Albert. His imagination returns him to the village he left, wearing rose-colored glasses then as he looked toward his future. He looks now at the tall green pine trees across from the store as he remembers similar trees on the edge of the cemetery down the road from his childhood home. An intense regret overcomes him. "I should have been there to help dig the grave for my sister," he thinks. Then he thinks of his mother, whom he left sixteen years ago for a better opportunity in America. Until today he has never looked back. Now he wishes he could have been standing next to her as the orange dirt was shoveled on the coffin of her oldest child.

Then Albert says to himself, "I *did* find a better opportunity here." This is the seventh season since he purchased the farm. Within three years, he has doubled its value. He added tillable acres and increased the number of animals. There are new buildings to store the crops, animals and farm machinery he had purchased. Under the house, he dug a cellar to store the vegetables during the winter. He is developing a reputation among not only the Germans but also the Yankees and Irish in the neighborhood as an industrious, modern farmer with a great future. These thoughts bring the young farmer back to his normal, determined self. His success has not happened by feeling sorry for himself while sitting on a bench with a couple of snobby Yankees. He needs to get home to finish his harvest before the storm comes.

When he stands, he has a sly smirk on his bearded face and a twinkle in his eye. He turns to wish his seatmates a good day in perfect English. Embarrassed, they mumble a return greeting to Albert's back as he walks down the street to the blacksmith shop.

When he arrives at the shop, the part is completed. Climbing into the seat of his wagon, he feels the air getting hotter and the wind getting stronger. The horses' hooves tap a soothing rhythm on the road while the squeaking wagon wheels accompany out of tune. The sad letter returns Albert to a reflective mood as the wagon bounces over the train tracks. Looking at the rich black farmland and gently rolling hills, he thinks of the sandy and swampy land that Pauline's August will now farm alone. His brother-in-law's farm will never be able to produce half the profit his farm does.

After crossing the railroad tracks, Albert travels up a hill. At the crest to his left stands Viola's simple wooden schoolhouse. To his right, at the ridge of another hill, is the house of Wendell Vine. While his family was trying to eke out a living as tenants of Polish nobles, Wendell Vine's ancestors were fighting for this country's independence. Nine years ago, in the Vine pasture, the Yankees started an annual festival celebrating the trapping of the pesky gophers that broke Albert's reaper. The German farmers have not joined in this yearly celebration. Just as with countries, there is a border with a fence separating where Yankee and German farms meet. The Yankees have their churches and community in Viola or Elgin. The Germans have their own in Potsdam or Rochester.

For the next mile and a half after the Vine farm, the road sits on the top of the hill. Albert is able to see for miles in every direction. He thinks the landscape is beautiful: fields of golden grain stacked into neat shocks, green pastures, spotted cows of multiple colors, and industrious Yankee, Irish and German pioneers working their fields. Ahead toward Rochester, a gray haze begins to form.

Descending a steep hill, Albert crosses a small creek and climbs back up the next hill to the road that will take him home. This road has developed into a neighborhood of German farmers. On the corner is the farm of August Fratzke, followed on the left by Albert's neighbor, the only farmer on this road who is not German, Irish immigrant John

Buckley. Albert stops to deliver mail at the next farm, owned by Albert Mueller and his son Gustav. The Mueller farm is small but well organized. All summer Albert has admired their crops. After greeting the Muellers, Albert shares the news of his sister. Albert Mueller's wife died a year ago, and the news carries him back to his grief. To break the sad tension, the conversation is quickly changed to the weather. Gustav mentions that the birds are flying out of the tall trees to rest in the lilac bushes that surround the farmyard. This weather will break soon.

Albert looks to the southwest at his farm nestled in the valley below. At the bottom of the hill is his wheat that needs to be cut. That field is the best he has grown this year. If he doesn't get that grain cut, the storm could ruin it. That would be lost profit. He quickly snaps the reins of his horses, shouting goodbye to his neighbors over his shoulder.

Entering the farmyard, the boys come running, hoping their father has bought them a treat at the store. Albert is angry at their foolishness. Frightened, they hide behind the large skirt of their mother.

Albert gives Auguste his letter before he unhitches the horses from the wagon and leads them to the tank of cool fresh water. Reading the letter, tears roll down Auguste's face even though she can barely remember Pauline. Their mother's tears also scare the little boys, and they begin to cry. The noise startles the horses, causing Albert to reprimand the boys, and the scolding from their father makes the boys cry louder. Albert mutters to himself.

Knowing that her husband is hungry but too busy to come into the house for a proper meal, Auguste prepares a lunch of warm bread, smoked ham and fresh fruit grown in the orchard behind the outhouse. As Albert fixes the binder, he wolfs down the lunch.

After hitching the horses to the binder, Albert goes down the dirt driveway that runs along the creek bank. At a shallow spot, he crosses into the field and begins to cut the wheat. In the field, nine-year-old Ed, six-year-old Willie, and the hired man are busy standing up and leaning together eight bundles of wheat into a shock. This process ensures that the precious grain will not mold on the ground. The combination of hot sun and strong wind makes the job almost impossible for small boys barely taller than the shocks they are trying to make. Across the road, the

Hemshrot boys are having the same struggles. Suddenly a contest breaks out between the two families as to who can build the most shocks.

The sky is no longer blue. A sun-blocking haze develops as the humidity increases. The leaves on the trees along the creek begin to show their underside. Albert snaps the reins on the horses to get them to go faster. They huff and try, but people are not the only ones having trouble breathing and working today.

A darker haze is forming in the distance to the south. The tired workers can see that the black clouds will move east, missing the farm. Knowing they may not be so fortunate next time, everyone in the family is now in the field to finish shocking the wheat.

By four o'clock, the sky turns darker to the southwest over the hill leading to John Buckley's farm. A light rain begins to fall, and lightning can be seen at the top of the clouds. Each lightning flash sends Albert back to the letter he received this morning. For a brief moment, the current panic is replaced by sadness for the past.

Everyone returns to the farmyard in the light rain to complete the evening chores. The horses that worked so hard today are brushed and given a well-deserved meal of oats and fresh hay. Ed, with Willie close behind, goes to the pasture in the deep valley behind the house to bring the cows home to be milked. The cows lying in the pasture do not want to move, sensing the change in the weather. With difficulty, the two boys get the cows up and lead them to the barn.

Auguste prepares supper as clouds form over the hills to the northwest. She believes they are joining the clouds forming to the southwest. To complete her meal, she needs an egg. Dashing into the farmyard to retrieve a fresh one, she sees a flash of lightning. A shiver runs down her spine. Was this what her sister-in-law was doing when she was struck?

As he leaves the barn, Albert looks to the sky and sees danger to the west. The sky that was turning black when he entered the barn is now black in the center, with green and bronze at the edges. The green and bronze colors alternately jump over the top of one another, much like schoolchildren playing one of their silly games. The clouds to Albert's right are crashing into the clouds to his left, forcing the clouds on the left to rise over the right-hand ones.

Knowing they are in trouble, Albert and the hired man run to the house to lead Auguste and the four boys to the cellar. With all of the canning that Auguste stored there this summer, it is a close fit for seven people. Adding to the tension, the two youngest boys are scared and begin crying. They have good lungs and can cry as loud as any child, but the noise outside drowns them out.

Later, some would say the noise was as loud as a freight train. That would be true if you were lying on the tracks waiting for the train to run you over. The noise over the family was not like any they had ever heard before. They could hear within the roar a hard rain, hail and wind that was snapping the buildings and trees. There were huge crashes as doors, windows and roofs blew off. Horses whinnied, cows bellowed, pigs squealed, chickens squawked and children howled in fright. Suddenly the door to the cellar blew off. The family huddled tighter together for safety, and Albert peeked out to see branches, small animals and bundles of wheat fly by.

After a few minutes, which felt like hours, quiet returned to the farm. A steady rain was falling as they looked out of the cellar. To the west, they could see that the sky was beginning to clear. Slowly the family leaves the shelter to survey the damage. The house and barn are still standing, but several smaller buildings are now piles of rubble. As they walk among the broken branches and recognizable materials from their farm, they also see items that do not belong to them.

The fast-moving creek floats a host of materials that, less than a half-hour ago, were a neighbor's house or barn. Among the debris in the yard, Ed finds a letter, which he brings to his father. The address is Rochester. The children are less afraid now and make a game of picking up the papers littering the yard. With pride, they bring their newfound treasures to their father. Many of their findings have Rochester addresses, and Albert wonders, "What has happened in Rochester?"

After his initial shock passes, Albert looks across to the field he worked and worried about so much that day. The wheat that they rushed to get into shocks only a few hours before is gone, replaced by branches, lumber, and a strange fence. His gaze moves up the hill to the Mueller farm. The neat farm buildings he had admired earlier that day are now a pile of wreckage. Fear wells up in him, and Albert wonders if, for the second time today, he will be forced to face a human tragedy caused by Mother Nature. He jumps on his scared horse to rescue the Mueller family.

As Albert heads to the road, he looks to his left at his large field of wheat on the hill. The shocks that only an hour ago had been standing in neat rows are strewn across the field. At the end of the driveway, he meets his neighbor Gottlieb Hemschrot, who is surveying the damage to his farm. Like Albert, Gottlieb feels sick after losing several buildings and his crops, but he is thankful his family is safe.

From the north, Otto Baum and John Boie ride down the hill to see if their neighbors are safe. The tornado had traveled at the edge of the valley that is cut by the creek, and their farms sustained no damage. The four men look up the hill and say a silent prayer as they start the half-mile trip to the Mueller farm.

When they arrive at the farm, they are greeted by the family, looking like they had seen the devil and barely escaped his grasp. There is no house, no barn, no granary, no shed for the machinery—which is not a problem because the machinery is also gone. Looking to the north, back toward the Hemschrot farm, having no granary is also not a problem because the seventy acres of crops that separate the two farms are missing. The group stands in disbelief, taking it all in, when August Fratzke and his wife Pauline arrive. Their farm is only a quarter-mile to the south and, incredibly, sustained no damage.

As the men talk, they look to the west at the farm of their Irish neighbor John Buckley. Normally they cannot see his farm, which is located a half-mile back from the road. But this evening is not normal. His buildings are spread over his fields. Knowing now that the Mueller family is safe, Albert leaves to check on his other neighbor. When he arrives at what had been the Buckley farm, he finds that the family is not hurt, but the buildings, like at the Mueller farm, are gone. Both the Mueller farm and the Buckley farm were in the direct path of the tornado. John Buckley, a survivor of the potato famine in Ireland, stands in what had been a field of potatoes. The storm dug them out of the ground and left them on top of the soil, ready to be picked up.

Assured that all his neighbors are safe for the night, Albert heads for home across fields littered with debris. Standing next to his neighbor's uncut wheat field on the tall hill overlooking his farm, Albert observes that there will be no need to cut it now. The tornado removed all of the grain, leaving only the stalks standing.

He looks over his shoulder at the destroyed Mueller farm and then behind him at the Buckley farm. He looks down into the valley and says a silent *thank you.* A slight variance in the path of the storm, and he would have lost everything.

August 22, 1883 – Olmsted County, Minnesota

The first rays of the sun shone directly into the eyes of Paul Priebe. He quietly slides his lanky twenty-two-year-old body out of the bed he shares with his nine-year-old brother Max, trying not to wake him. In the bed across from him, his twenty-four-year-old brother Emil is doing the same, trying not to disturb their two-year-old brother Walter who recently started sleeping with him. Both brothers think they are too old to have to sleep with their younger brothers, but their only other option in this small house would be to sleep with each other. That is even more unappealing. They must accept the situation until they start their own families, as their four older stepsiblings have done.

As the brothers descend the steep stairs to the kitchen, they hear activity in the bedroom across the hall: their five younger sisters are getting dressed. Paul and Emil rush outside to beat their sisters to the outhouse. As they run through the kitchen, their parents, August and Wilhelmine, are drinking their first cup of coffee at the large table in the center of the room, planning the day.

Yesterday was oppressively hot. In the middle of the afternoon, a dark cloud passed overhead, providing some relief from the sun's heat. Paul watched the dangerous storm strike near Pleasant Grove to the east as he made shocks in his uncle's wheat field. His mind was less on the storm and more on his wish that he was working in one of the stores in nearby High Forest or, even better, in Rochester.

Later the family ate their supper outside—it was too hot to eat inside. Tables were set up under the large tree that shaded the north side of the house. As they ate, they watched dark rolling clouds move across the sky in the direction of Rochester to the north. It was a rare moment when no one in the Priebe family spoke or ate as they watched the rolling multicolored clouds. Their father broke the silence to lead the family in a prayer for the safety of those in the storm's path.

Paul and Emil quickly finished their dinner and the evening chores. Then they left the farm for the beerhall in High Forest three miles away. The saloon, off the public square of the little village, founded with ambitions as big as its name but slowly slipping in importance to fast-growing Rochester, has never been described as elegant. Last night the humid air lowered the respectability of its business even further. The combination of heat and humidity turned the beer-soaked sawdust on the floor to a foul smell that took the brothers' breath away when they entered through the broken screen door. The smell and the large horseflies it attracted were quickly forgotten as thirsty, excited patrons arrived from the north. They said a monstrous tornado had struck Rochester. The Priebe brothers were finishing their second beers when they heard that telegraph messages were coming in that said the tornado may have continued on to Viola. That is where their oldest sister Auguste lives.

The boys finished their beer and rushed home. When they told their parents what they heard, fear filled the simple farmhouse. The stern old stone mason reviewed his children like a general preparing for war. "Emil and Bertha, you will stay here tomorrow to finish the harvest. Paul and Alwine, you will leave at first light for Albert and Auguste's farm." The father had raised good soldiers. No one was brave enough to question why the old man had chosen his twenty-two-year-old son and seventeen-year-old daughter for the trip or why he was not going. Everyone went to bed for a long, sleepless night.

Now as Paul leaves the two-hole outhouse, the nearly full moon is touching the horizon to the west, and the bacon his sisters are cooking is sizzling on the iron stove in the summer kitchen. He enters the barn to get two chestnut-colored horses that he hitches to a wagon. Two paths to the wagon are cut in the tall grass damp from the morning dew: one is to the summer kitchen where the girls are preparing crates and bags loaded with bread, meats, vegetables and other cooking supplies Alwine will bring to her sister's family, and the second path has been cut by his brothers to their father's blacksmith shop. Hammers, nails, saws and axes that Paul and Albert may need today are loaded on the wagon.

The moon has nearly disappeared, and the sun is now a bright orange-red circle on the low horizon of the eastern sky when Paul and Alwine climb onto the hard seat of the wagon. They look at the full wagon bed and understand why only two of them can make the trip today. Paul snaps the reins, and the horses tighten the harnesses. As the wagon rumbles out of the yard, the rest of the family stands by the house, wishing their brother and sister a safe journey.

The fastest route to Auguste's home is north to Rochester and then northeast to the farm. Today will not be a normal day. As they approach Rochester, the roads become clogged with people going into the city to help. In the opposite direction, victims of the storm are escaping, telling unbelievable stories to the northbound travelers along the way.

Paul hopes the stories are exaggerations. As they enter the city, the destruction appears minimal. Some roofs are missing, and branches from trees are strewn about, but there is no evidence of the mass devastation they heard about on the road. With each passing block, though, there are more and more branches, roofs and dead animals on the road, making smooth travel nearly impossible.

When they arrive at the center of town, the steeples of the Methodist and Congregational churches are blown off. The cupola and most of the roof of the courthouse are gone. At Fourth and Broadway, George Stocking's new grocery store is totally destroyed. Businesses on Broadway that previously had shiny metal roofs are now as bald as the siblings' stepbrother August.

When they reach the Rommel Dance Hall, they give the horses a rest. Paul has spent many nights at the hall drinking good German beer and dancing with the pretty German girls. Today the activity at the hall is not festive. On the large open dance floor, Dr. Mayo and the other doctors of Rochester have set up a hospital. Entering the hall, Paul sees something he never witnessed at the dances. The Sisters of Saint Francis are dancing across the floor between the cots to give nursing care to the victims. The women with their funny-looking clothes appear to Paul to be floating through the hall smoother and more gracefully than any of the girls he danced with last week.

When the horses are sufficiently rested, the duo continues north on Broadway. At the railroad tracks are the grain elevators where their father sells his wheat. This year he will have to find somewhere else to sell it. Mr. Cole's mill is totally destroyed except for the machinery inside. The elevators of G. W. Van Dusen have their roofs blown off, and Tondro's mill is blown away as if it never existed. Lying on the main railroad track is what is left of Horton's elevator. The machine works, creamery and coal warehouse, all businesses necessary for the financial health of the area farmers, have been destroyed. Looking at the mess on the railroad tracks, Paul cannot decide which building is the greatest loss to the community. Then he hears that Mr. Cole had been picked up by the tornado and thrown to the ground: he was killed instantly. Paul thinks, "The buildings will return. Mr. Cole will not."

Paul skillfully navigates the wagon among the wreckage, continuing north to the neighborhood called lower town. Yesterday it was home to immigrants like him. Now more than 150 houses are missing. The beautiful canopy of trees that cooled the simple houses is mostly gone; the leaves of the few surviving trees have been shredded off their branches. In the hot sun, dead animals strewn among the furniture, household goods and parts of homes are beginning to bloat.

Among the wreckage, Paul sees a flock of healthy chickens with no feathers. The owner, with an empty look on his face, stands amid these strange birds. Paul yells, "Where did you buy those strange birds?" For the rest of his life, he will be haunted by the answer. "Yesterday, they were normal. Their feathers were blown off by the winds."

The brother and sister continue northeast through the destruction of lower town to Geisinger Hill. Reaching the top of the hill, they stop for a minute to look down on the destroyed buildings, dead animals, and lost people. They pray they will not see this devastation going forward.

Their prayer is not answered. They follow the path of the tornado on the eight-mile trip to their sister's farm. Every farm they pass shows some destruction. The Geisinger family, for which the hill is named, lost their house and barn. Two miles later, they are told that Mr. Canter was killed and every building, all machinery and the crops on his farm were destroyed. Hearing that death struck one of the farmers scares Paul and Alwine. They now travel faster among the damaged barns and houses, mangled machinery, and destroyed crops. With every mile, their worry about their sister's family increases.

Three miles from Rochester, they arrive at the Haverhill town hall. At a picnic last year Paul remembers he entered the building from the south. Alwine gives her brother a quizzical look: now the entrance is facing north. Paul answers, "The tornado must have picked the building up off its foundation and turned it around." Alwine rolls her eyes and shakes her head, thinking that her brother having too much to drink is more believable.

Even those who were already dead were victims of the storm. When they passed a little cemetery, every stone was tipped over. The destruction and despair overwhelm Alwine, and she begins to cry. Paul snaps the reins to get the horses to move faster.

To the east of the town hall is a large expanse of prairie where some of the best farms in the county are located. Now the houses, barns and crops have been destroyed, returning them to the uncivilized state they were when the settlers arrived twenty-five years before. In the middle of this destruction, Fling School has magically disappeared, with no trace of bench, book or blackboard remaining.

After they pass the Adler farm, the damage becomes less. They hope that their sister's family has been saved. Approaching the Fratzke farm, their optimism turns to terror. Looking south, they see the wiped-out Mueller farm. Paul again snaps the reins hard on the backs of the tired horses. Their fears from last night may be true, and there is no time to waste.

When they reach the crest of the hill by the Mueller farm and can see the Heyn farm standing, Paul pulls back the reins to stop the overworked horses for a moment. Relieved, Alwine begins to cry again. The surrounding fields are filled with volunteers cleaning up the mess. Paul recognizes helpers from Potsdam, familiar faces mixed among unfamiliar ones. Yesterday, the German Lutherans, the Irish Catholics, and the Yankee Methodists who lived along the north branch of the

Whitewater River had lived separate lives. Last night, though, the tornado had favored no nationality or religion, and today the residents of the area were not Germans, Irish or Yankees but Americans who all needed each other's help.

When he sees his in-laws enter the farmyard, Albert pauses his salvage efforts to greet his visitors. Auguste, preparing lunches for the men in the fields, runs from the house. After a few minutes of talk, the group hears Walter, who has awakened from his nap. Auguste and Alwine gather up the food that was packed this morning and walk to the house to check on the wailing baby.

Albert is exhausted. He took advantage of the light of the full moon to repair doors, windows and roofs. Every building on the farm has some damage. Windows in the house are missing. The barn lost doors. Parts of the roofs of the machine shed and granary are gone. Two small buildings are completely destroyed.

Shortly after sunrise, friends, neighbors and strangers from the north and south came to the valley to help with the cleanup. Each visitor shared stories of the storm's fury. On the road over the hill from the Hemschrot farm, where the railroad tracks between Viola and Elgin are located, there is also serious damage. One helper reported, "The Wells farm has been totally destroyed. The couple are both seriously injured and the old man will probably not live. Henry Stanchfield's farm was wiped out like Mueller's and Buckley's. Martin Sawyer and Henry Vine had buildings seriously damaged like yours."

Most of the helpers went to the Mueller or Buckley farms, where the need was greater, but a half-dozen stayed with Albert. Those with carpentry skills continued to repair the buildings. Others went with him to the fields to salvage the grain. Large portions of the fields were stripped clean, with no salvaging to be done there. Stacks of grain that yesterday were standing across the horizon like soldiers on guard duty were now laid flat like the vanquished in a battle or, worse, totally blown away as if they never existed. Albert's top priority is to gather as much as possible before the crop is totally lost.

Seeing that his brother-in-law is ready to collapse, Paul urges him to sit down on a large gray boulder under the oak tree at the edge of the creek. Sitting together, the pair tells each other the events of the past twenty-four hours. Albert starts his story with the letter from Germany: six weeks ago, a storm took his sister's life, and last night another almost took his.

After Albert finishes his story, Paul shares what he saw in Rochester. He tells Albert about the grain elevators, lower town, the bald chickens, and the boy who was picked up by the tornado, carried over the Zumbro River, and deposited by Oakwood Cemetery with only a few broken bones. Albert is suspicious about his brother-in-law's stories. He is not so old yet that he cannot remember how as a young man, he could exaggerate.

Getting up from the resting place, both men return to the field. As they work, Paul entertains the tired coworkers with his stories. All of the men wonder how it is possible to have that much destruction with so few people killed.

As the heat of the afternoon fades, the weary volunteers return to their farms. Albert thinks to himself that at least tonight, he will see the fiery red sunset. He and Paul walk back to the house, tired. It has been a long day for both.

At the door, they are greeted with smells of meat, new potatoes and vegetables roasting. That afternoon Alwine took the boys to the orchard behind the outhouse to pick up apples that had blown off the trees. She cut up the damaged fruit to make a hot apple pie, a sweet ending for a couple of very sour days.

Albert and Auguste look at each other from their places at the far ends of the table. They do not say anything out loud, but together they both think that the damage is only a temporary setback. They and their children are safe, most of the buildings are standing, the animals are safe and farm machinery is not damaged. Their crops were damaged but not totally destroyed. This year will not be as profitable as the last six were, but they will still pay the bills.

Last night at this time, the sky was dark and dangerous. Today it is tranquil. Tomorrow it will be brighter. Before the family eats, Albert leads them in a prayer of thanks. After the events of the past two days, Albert and Auguste are positive they will prosper.

The former Budsin Posen train station, now Budzyn Poland, built in 1879. Fall 2022. Personal photo

Part V
Emigration Ends

July 9, 1885 – Owatonna, Minnesota

Adolph and Louise dance their first waltz as husband and wife to the thumping sound of an accordion and tuba. Adolph ignores the jeers of his brothers, brothers-in-law and friends as he gazes into the pretty blue eyes of his eighteen-year-old bride. His brothers are amazed to see their clumsy baby brother gracefully glide across a dance floor that was cleared in the new hay mow of the bride's brother Gus.

Outside the warm barn, four old friends sit under a large maple tree. They wave homemade fans, rock in their chairs, talk and reminisce. On the outer edge of the half-circle of oak rockers is Gottlieb Radel, the bride's father. He is the head of one of the first families to leave Gembitz Hauland for America. In the other chairs are three mothers who, on a dark, stormy night eighteen years ago, worried about their children's safety on the ocean. Minnie Redel, Christine Wegner, and Anna Beutler were sure that night, as lightning lit the sky and thunder shook their homes, that they had said goodbye to their children forever. But death has a way of detouring life's certainties.

Three years ago, Christine ran away from the angel of death with her daughter Henriette's family. During her life as a farmer's wife on the plains of Polajewo Hauland, she buried one husband, half of her children and all five of her grandchildren born to Henriette. As she talks with her friends, a two-year-old girl jumps into her grandmother's lap. Christine introduces the girl as Amelia, the first child born in America to the Siewert family. She tells her friends, "Louise and Julius have been lucky with my Rosolack grandchildren who were born in America. I hope Henriette and Wilhelm will finally be as lucky here, giving me Siewert grandchildren."

Minnie swats a mosquito. Death has also brought her here. When her second husband died, she quickly married Martin Redel, who was nearly twenty years younger than she was. She was certain then she would never again experience the calamity of widowhood, but two years ago, for the third time, she planned a funeral for a husband.

Her oldest daughter had already purchased tickets to join her brother and sisters in Minnesota when Martin died. Shortly after they left, Minnie's three Redel children decided it was time to follow their Wanke siblings to America. Before her sons booked the passage for their young families, they asked Minnie if she wanted to join them or live with Ernestine, her last daughter in Gembitz Hauland. After this place where she was born had given her seventy years of death and disappointment, Minnie decided she wanted to die with her children in America.

Minnie swats another mosquito. Gottlieb laughs, "Did you get it?" It is one of the first signs of joy the old man shows today. Life has been prosperous for him in his adopted country, but it has not always been easy. Today he sat alone while Pastor Klein recited the marriage vows to his daughter. Thirty years ago, his second wife, Gertie, was almost the same age as Louise when he decided to uproot them. In only a couple of years, the carefree teenager became a stepmother, mother and immigrant. The day their community said goodbye to the family, she was so overwhelmed and withdrawn that the women now sitting with Gottlieb asked Anna Sawall to care for her on the trip. She made it across the ocean, twice created a new home in the wilderness, and gave birth to seven more children. Three years ago, she finally succumbed to the stress and took her own life.

This morning Gottlieb stopped at the small cemetery carved out of a wheat field to place flowers in front of her white stone. Chiseled into the marble base are words from Paul's letter to the Philippians: "Christ is my life. Dying is my gain." Gottlieb told the marble, "You are wrong. A mother should be with her daughter on her wedding day."

Anna occupies the fourth chair. She arrived in the new country only six weeks ago. Four years ago, on a warm early August morning, sweat had run down her back as she watched her baby jump into the back of a wagon to leave her forever. She accepted, as she had four times before, that this would be her last memory of her son. Today, while she watched her mischievous boy marry the daughter of her childhood friend, a new bead of sweat followed the same path down her back. As the water uncomfortably made its way to her waist, she thought that life could follow a similar tortuous route. As it had for the others, death had intruded into her life to alter her destiny.

While the vows were exchanged, she remembered it was the second anniversary of sitting in the front row of a different church, staring at another of her children. But rather than seeing her youngest child joyously plan for his future, that day, she had been looking at the cold body of her oldest, lying in a wooden coffin. The lightning bolt that Saturday afternoon ended her daughter Pauline's life but also altered hers.

Gustav had been indecisive about following his brothers to America, but the deaths of his sister and his father-in-law within a week sealed the decision. Shortly after Pauline's funeral, he met with an agent from the Hamburg–Amerika shipping company and purchased tickets for his family on the same ship as his in-laws.

Before he signed the contract, he sat at his mother's well-worn table and asked her if she wanted to stay or go with his family. Still deep in grief, she emphatically responded, "No. You can go, but I am staying. I still have Maria to take care of me." For Lent last year, Anna gave up her oldest son, his wife, six grandchildren, and one of her best friends, Minnie.

It was the second time she had decided to stay in the place where she had been born, gave birth to her children, created a farm, and built a church. The first two decisions were separated by thirty years. The third time she had to decide was only months later. After the first letter from Minnesota saying that the Redel–Wanke–Hein caravan had arrived safely, Maria's August met with the same agent as Gustav had.

Recalling that thought, Anna stops rocking and turns to Gottlieb. "I had many conversations at the table Friedrich bought at your auction. None was as serious as the one I had the night Maria and August told me they were also leaving. I was out of options. Friedrich and I always thought that some of our children would follow you to America, but I never could have imagined there would be no one left there to take care of me in my old age."

Gottlieb asked, "Could Pauline's husband have taken care of you?"

Anna huffed, and her two friends quietly chuckled. "He has five children and a mother to take care of. Plus, he'll find a new wife. He had no interest in adding a former mother-in-law to his house. I did not want it either." Instead, that night she had gotten up from her table, walked through the door, and sat on her bench to admire her world. Chickens clucked, a cow cried for her lost calf, and the leaves on her favorite tree gently blew in the breeze. She looked across the meadow to see smoke rising from the chimney of her old house. Even though she loved the peace and beauty of that spot, she quietly told Friedrich's spirit, "It is time for me to leave. I'll buy a better bench and have a larger farmyard to admire."

On the first Sunday of April, Anna did not feel joyous that Christ had escaped the tomb. The sun shone in the windows, and the old floorboards of her church creaked under her feet as they always did, but the hope of renewal proclaimed during the service was missing. The dark gloom of Good Friday continued to hang over her.

Usually, the rebirth of Easter would flow out the church doors and flood the surrounding farms. The smell of the freshly plowed soil would mingle with the scent of the purple lilac flowers. Farmers planting the newly plowed fields would enjoy watching cows and horses running and jumping in the fresh green grass of the pasture. In the barns, chickens, geese and pigs would be born to replace their relatives who had fed the family during the long cold winter.

This spring was different. Maria's August did not work his land with his hands but rather with his mouth. One by one, he sold his various parcels to the remaining farmers, including Pauline's August. No new chickens, geese or pigs were needed because no one would be there to butcher them when the leaves changed from green to orange.

There were no new calves with hour-glass markings on their face rollicking in the pasture. The fruits of Anna's dowry given by her father to Friedrich now belonged to her former son-in-law and several other neighbors who would not appreciate their importance. On the day her last cow was led away with its empty udder swinging lazily between her legs, Anna cried. Her life as a farmer's wife began the day her father led that cow's great-great-grandmother to her farm. As the cow disappeared, so did that part of Anna's life.

She took only a few items to America; everything else was sold, given away or just left to decay. Maria told her they were just objects they could replace in America. The daughter had inherited her mother's logical mind. But Anna was not logical at that moment. The cradle in the corner, the dishes on the shelf, the broken stool by the door or the saw hanging by the barn door were not cold objects to be replaced. Each was a happy, sad or angry memory for her.

As they always did after the last church service of members soon going to America, the community threw a farewell party for Anna, the Erdmanns and the Schroeders, who had booked passage on the same ship.

Anna tells Gottlieb, "My party was not nearly as large, loud or festive as the one we threw for you. There was still sausage, sauerkraut and potato dumplings, but the tables did not bend from the weight. The men sat around the beer kegs discussing the same subjects you did but with less enthusiasm. There were children running and playing, but they were much quieter and sadder. Every time we had one of those parties, they knew that their circle of cousins and friends would get smaller. Even that old tree where our parents and grandparents always sat observing the activities has more room in its shade now."

The memory of their aging parents and grandparents sitting under that tree, freely offering their critical opinion of the food preparation, the quality of the men's farming techniques, and the children's behavior brings a smile to the quartet. After she criticizes her daughter's sauerkraut, Minnie chuckles. "Our children are lucky they will never have that experience."

Just like it had for her other six children, Anna's trip to America began with final goodbyes. This time she was the one who climbed into a creaking wagon and disappeared. Pauline's five children took Anna's usual place by the door with tears on their cheeks as they bravely waved goodbye. Before she climbed in the wagon, Anna gave eleven-year-old Bertha a yellowed lace veil she had made long ago for Pauline's confirmation. Her request was simple, "Please wear this at your confirmation so that your mother and I can be there with you."

At that moment, Anna had secretly hoped that time would stop. Instead, Pauline's August snapped the reins, and the wagon rolled forward. The spring mud squished under the wheels as his older children ran alongside the wagon calling final goodbyes to their cousins. As the last branch of their mother's family disappeared through the trees, their father bellowed at the children to return to their other grandmother.

Anna begins to cry, remembering these grandchildren she will never see again. Again, the three women sitting under the tree share a common bond of grief: they all have grandchildren back home they will never see again. Anna continues, "I took my mind off my Westphal grandchildren by turning my attention to my Erdmann grandchildren." For weeks their emotions had alternated between sadness, excitement and fear. When the train blew its whistle at the station in Budsin announcing the beginning of their adventure, Amandus was withdrawn as he already missed his cousins Arnold and Emil. When the train pulled into the next station at Ostrowke, they had traveled less than three miles, but Ottilie and Elizabeth already were asking if they were at the boat. Adolph, sensing the disruption to his usual life, was by then expelling an amount of energy that only a toddler has. Anna tells her friends, "The children's chaos distracted me from my own sadness. When we arrived in Hamburg, I could not believe the sea of people. There were not enough hotels in the city for everyone. We shared a dirty boardinghouse with other German, Norwegian, Polish and Russian families. Each family was speaking their own language. It sounded like the chickens on my farm when a fox got into the coop. We spent most of our time trying not to lose one of the children. Maria and I were sure that if one of them wandered away, we would never see them again. That worry played over and over in my mind the first night as I tried to sleep in that small room of snoring men, crying children,, and women saying strange-sounding prayers."

After several days in the cramped rooming house, the shipping company agent came to August to tell him it was time to prepare his family for the voyage. "We repacked clothing and food and walked to the dock. A small boat called a tender took us down the Elbe River to Cuxhaven. Suddenly for the first time in my life, there was no ground under my feet. My stomach began to move up and down in rhythm with the water." Anna laughed as she continued. "It did not take long for me to lose my breakfast."

Arriving at the port, Anna saw the SS *Frisia* at its berth, ready to take her to America. At 360 feet long and 43 feet wide, the ship was the largest object that Anna had ever seen. She asked August if he was sure that the ship could really float on the ocean. He reminded her that Gustav and his family had traveled on the same ship last year, and they were now safely in America waiting to greet her. Minnie chuckled, "I asked Gustav the same question. Probably in the same spot."

They stood in endless queues, answering the same questions over and over about their health and finances. Finally, the family boarded the ship. They were guided to the between decks where they would be sleeping and eating for the next two weeks. Entering the small room, Anna did not believe her eyes: before her were sixty beds stacked three high floor to ceiling, four rows across the width of the room and five rows the length of the room. For the next two weeks, Anna would have to maneuver her ample aging body into one of those bunks in this room that she would share with a potpourri of Germans, Poles, Russians and Scandinavians. Anna says, "The rooming house in Hamburg suddenly seemed luxurious."

Gottlieb responds, "The *Frisia* sounds grand compared to the *Helen McGaw.* I spent seven weeks sleeping on straw with my family when we sailed for America."

May 6, 1885, is not a date many people remember. For most, it was just another Wednesday in a lifetime of forgotten Wednesdays. For Anna, that Wednesday, when the ropes of the *Frisia* were untied to separate her from the only country she had ever known, will be a day she will never forget. As she had done every day of her life, she rose with the sunrise and then went up on the deck. Standing a safe distance from the rail, she watched the familiar and known become smaller and smaller until it disappeared.

The Hamburg–Amerika shipping line provides three good meals a day, but for the first several days, the Erdmann family did not eat much. Farmers' stomachs are not accustomed to the rolling of the sea. The sounds and smells of her fellow passengers' stomachs losing their battle with the sea added to Anna's misery as she helped Maria care for the sick children.

After seven nights of feeling the bed move with the sea, Anna became brave enough to venture again to the top deck. She felt the cold air sting her face. Out on the endless sea, large pieces of ice floated in the water. Several of the crew members told Anna that the sight of the white ice floating in the dark blue ocean was beautiful, but she would rather look at her orange and white cows standing knee-deep in green grass back home.

Unlike Gottlieb's trip of seven weeks, she had to endure the sea for only twelve days before the ship finally glided into New York harbor. Anna had been amazed by the buildings in Berlin, but the sight of New York was even more incredible. She saw buildings four or five stories tall built as close together as the overcrowded pine trees in the woods north of her farm. Towering over the buildings was what appeared to be a church steeple. Who, she wondered, was brave enough to build these buildings, and how did they stand so tall?

On an island in the harbor, a small square building was being built. One of the crew members, who made this trip every month, said that the building was the base for a statue that France gave to the United States to celebrate America's centennial. Thinking of the few statues she had ever seen, Anna thought the crew member must be exaggerating. Why would they need a base that size for a small statue?

The *Frisia* sailed up the Hudson River past New York to a dock in Hoboken, New Jersey. May 19, 1885, became another memorable date for Anna when she wobbled on American soil for the first time. After almost two weeks at sea, she was surprised when she could not walk a straight line. This scared her. Rumors had been spread by the ship crew that passengers who had trouble walking would have to have a medical examination and may be forced to return to Germany.

Standing in the courtyard of the Castle Island office, Anna thought it was impossible that the world could have this many people. As the crowds pushed and shoved, occasionally, a polite person said they were sorry in a language Anna could not understand. The huge crowd scared Anna's grandchildren, and they clung tightly to the skirts of their mother and grandmother.

Maria's August directed his family through the confusing crowds and lines. After hours and hours of standing in the queues, both mind and body numbed, they finally stood before a tired government agent whose pen controlled the family's fate. The agent with a perpetual scowl looked up from his desk to greet the exhausted, scared family. He asked several questions in English. The family answered in German. A standoff was developing until a nearby German translator stepped in to quickly diffuse the situation. With a disgusted look on his face, the agent stamped the necessary documents and motioned the family to exit through the door behind him.

Walking through the door, Anna stepped into the new world and her new life. Around her, other families were greeted by family members they had thought they would never see again. No family was at the office to greet them. Instead, they relied on a travel agent to help them purchase train tickets to Troy, New York, where Julius and his family lived.

The agent patiently directed them the four miles through the city to the Grand Central Railroad Depot. Along the route, Anna saw the great wealth of her new country but also the poverty of the tenements that housed immigrants like her. She tells her friends, "At that moment, I thanked God I was not going to be one of those unfortunate souls stuck in that horrible city." Her friends nod in agreement.

When the train arrived at Union Station in Troy, happiness returned to Anna for the first time in months. From the train window, she saw Julius standing on the platform. The skinny boy who could barely grow a beard thirteen years ago was now a man. Next to him was a woman Anna assumed to be his wife and also a young girl. "This is why I made this trip," she thought. "As soon as this train stops, I will meet the first of my nine living grandchildren who were born in America." Anna's first impression of six-year-old Julia was that she was so similar to her at that age—she looked proud and determined to live her life on her own terms.

Julius took the travelers to his cramped rental house on Tibbetts Avenue. Houses in Gembitz Hauland were also small, but this house was different. At home, when the walls of the house crowded her, Anna would step outside to breathe. In this house, when she stepped onto the porch the road was only ten feet away and full of wagons, buggies and horses. Anna wondered how Julius and Gertrude ever had any peace. Maybe that is why her maternal intuition told her that the couple was having some troubles.

After two short nights, Maria's August told everyone it was time to finish their journey to Minnesota. Before they left, Julius walked his mother and sister down the hill to place white and purple wildflowers on Ottilie's grave. A light breeze rustled the trees as Anna looked at the depression in the ground, which was the only physical mark that her daughter had existed. For a few moments, she remembered the lively little girl who always tried to keep up with her older brothers. She told Maria and Julius, "My neighbors always envied me that I never lost a baby. I felt lucky. Now in my old age, my luck has run out. Standing at the graves of adult children is worse than losing a baby."

At the train station, Julius told them that he was planning to move to Minneapolis next year. Waving goodbye from the train, Anna saw a tear running down Julia's cheek. Quickly the little girl wiped it away and waved goodbye to her grandmother, aunt, uncle and cousins. Anna felt like she was looking into a mirror when she looked at Julia.

After one month of traveling in a wagon, three boats and multiple trains, the 12:40 train carrying the Erdmann family screeched into the new train depot in Elgin five minutes late and emitted a long, loud whistle and a cloud of white steam. From the window, Anna saw the six grandchildren she shares with Minnie cheering her arrival. Once she was off the train, she marveled at how much they had grown in a year. Martha, the baby, was just beginning to stand the last time Anna hugged her. Now she was a chatty but shy two-year-old. Bert and Elizabeth would not talk to their forgotten grandmother. Anna thought about her grandchildren in Gembitz Hauland and wondered, "Is gone and forgotten how I will now be to Pauline's children?"

Standing next to Gustav's two oldest boys were three of Albert's four sons. Anna arrived too late to meet one of her grandchildren born a citizen of the United States. Last year Albert's second son, Willie, was stabbed in the abdomen by a pitchfork. An infection developed, and on Maundy Thursday, while Anna took communion, grieving the loss of Gustav and his family, Albert and Auguste stood at a grave grieving the loss of their son.

Anna pushed the thoughts of her four dead grandchildren and the five she had left behind out of her mind. There were thirteen living children, ranging in age from a year and a half to thirteen years old, seeking her attention here. As Anna walked to the waiting buggy, the cousins stayed in a close circle around her. Cousins who had never met each other and cousins who could barely remember each other were forming friendships that would last their lifetimes. When Anna rode away from the train station, a smile suddenly appeared on her face like a rainbow after a storm.

Until Maria's August can find his own farm, they are living with Gustav two miles west of Potsdam. On their first Sunday, the two families met Albert's family at the wooden church that stands at the village's highest point. As she walked up the steps of the church, she was welcomed to Minnesota by Hoffmanns, Wankes, Christine's brother Fred and her daughter Louise, plus many others. Each person pointed east, west, north or south toward their new home, asking Anna to visit. Looking at their farms from the church steps, she thought how much more successful they looked compared to the ones at home.

Anna tells her friends, "I want to own land that good." Minnie and Gottlieb both think that that is an ambitious goal for a woman her age.

The elderly quartet's conversation pauses as they observe the wedding guests. To their left are the little girls from thirty years ago now sagging the long tables with the weight of their sausage, ham, sauerkraut, red cabbage, cakes and pies. To the right, the rambunctious boys of the past, whom the adults were convinced would never be successful, sit around their own barrel of beer, bragging about their families and farms. Mixed with the grown girls on the left and the grown boys on the right are their children, who run between the legs of their mothers and sneak beer from their fathers. The proud grandparents remark on how much they look like the children they remember. Anna says this sight confirms her decision: "The community I thought was dead back home is alive and well here." Minnie and Christine nod in agreement.

Anna's story is interrupted by the cheers of the wedding guests. Louise and Adolph have left the dance floor in the barn to prepare for the old tradition of working together to saw a log in half. The guests form a circle around the newlyweds, and the four old friends join them. Surrounded by her children, grandchildren and old friends, Anna feels the homesickness that sometimes overwhelmed her during the past several months pass. At this moment, she recognizes that home is not a particular structure or a familiar place but rather the people who fill the buildings. Many of the people important to Anna are no longer where she gave birth to them. They are here. She is home again.

Street Car 132 at Layman's Cemetery on the corner of Lake Street and Cedar Avenue in Minneapolis 1887. Photo courtesy of the Minnesota Historical Society

Part VI
Murder in the Hub of Hell

July 26, 1887 – Minneapolis, Minnesota

It is nearly midnight. The air in Minneapolis is filled with heat, rain, smoke and tension. In the light of day, the wealthy businessmen who run the city faced two fires that could have destroyed the downtown. In the dark of the night, the excitement of the fires and the hot, humid air incites the passions of the city's various outlaws who prey on the lives and properties of the businessmen's employees.

Two mules are slogging through the mud of Cedar Avenue. Harnessed to a streetcar owned by the Minneapolis Transit Company, they need almost no direction from the driver, John McKinnon, as they near the end of the line at Lake Street. One passenger waits to exit at the rear of the streetcar. He is Julius Heyn, a clean-shaven young man with a particularly large nose.

At the streetcar turnaround, Julius steps down the two rear steps of the car and wishes the driver a good evening in his thick German accent. As he staggers the 130 feet south to the simple wood-framed, two-story house at 3009 Cedar Avenue he shares with his brother's family, he feels the effects of the beer he enjoyed this evening. After they left New York last year, Julius, his wife Gertrude, and daughter Julia moved into the second floor of the house Adolph had been renting since his marriage.

Five people live comfortably in the narrow house now, but soon it will be too small. Every morning this week, Julius has heard his sister-in-law vomiting her breakfast, and he assumes she is suffering from morning sickness and sometime this winter, he will have another niece or nephew. They are still grieving the death, only four weeks ago, of Adolph and Louise's six-month-old daughter Emma. Soon it will be time for Julius's family to move to their own house, which Julius has promised Gertrude for the entire ten years of their marriage. As soon as he saves enough money, he will buy it for her, but saving is hard in this rough section of town they call the Hub of Hell, especially if you spend too much time at the numerous saloons the city has to offer.

Julius steps onto the front porch and gently opens and closes the door, trying to avoid waking any of the house's sleeping family. Slowly he climbs the narrow wooden stairs and enters his bedroom. Today's oppressive heat has warmed the room so much that it feels like he stepped into an oven. Gertrude lies in the iron bed Julius spent a week's wages to buy.

Desperate to avoid another fight, he tries to remove his coat, hat, vest, shoes and stockings without waking his wife, but he is unsuccessful. She is awake, and the couple soon starts another of their many arguments concerning Julius's late-night activities. Adolph wakes up downstairs.

Julius defends himself. "I was working late."

Gertrude responds with a familiar refrain. "I can smell the beer on your breath. I agreed to move here last year from Troy because you promised to change."

Anger spews from Julius's mouth. "I have a good job as the assistant superintendent of the Metropolitan Life Assurance Company. I come home with a clean suit now, not one covered with the soot of the ironworks of Troy."

Familiar tears stream down Gertrude's face when she responds with equal anger. "That may be true, but it looks like you haven't lost your appreciation for the many saloons and brothels of the city."

Tired of this endless battle, Julius puts on his slippers. He descends the back stairs to go outside to relieve his full bladder.

The smell in the privy, intensified by the heat and rain of the evening, assaults Julius's large nose, sobering him up faster than a pot of strong coffee. No longer able to hold his breath, he quickly shakes off the last couple of drops of beer and shoves his penis back in his pants. Suddenly, just as he turns to push the door open, the quiet of the night is broken by a deathly shriek heard only when a human or beast experiences a painful, terrifying death. He looks across the yards of his two neighbors in the direction of the streetcar turnaround. The darkness of the rainy night is shattered by a flash of light followed by the blast of a gun. Julius thinks he hears the cry, "Murder!" Forgetting about his pants, he runs the full length of the yard to the street.

At the front porch, his loose pants begin to fall, and he stumbles. He stops to button them. Then he sees three new flashes of light and hears the cracks of three more gunshots. This time the shots are not followed by cries of pain or fright.

Julius's heart is racing from a combination of exercise and adrenalin as he sprints to the slowly moving streetcar. Just before he reaches the back steps of the car, two dark figures leap out of the front of the car and run north toward the city. Julius jumps onto the back platform of streetcar number 132. Breathless, he looks through the glass door to see that the mules are pulling the car down the track without a driver.

Julius assumes that one of the running men is the driver. Thinking the driver will need help to apprehend the shooter, Julius quickly jumps off the platform. He runs alongside the driverless car until he reaches the Cedar Avenue gate of Layman's Cemetery. The mud from the afternoon rains is slippery, and he falls. His knee is the first to hit the pavement, and a sharp pain radiates from it as he lies in the mud. He stays in the muddy street to examine his bloody knee through the fresh rip in his pants. Looking up, he sees two men jump the fence of the cemetery—a large man in dark clothing is chased by a smaller man. Once back on his feet, he looks into the dark cemetery, but they have disappeared.

To his left, the frightened mules now pull the driverless streetcar faster down the street. Soon they will be at the Hastings and Dakota train crossing. If an evening train comes at the same time the leaderless car arrives at the tracks, there will be a disaster. Julius abandons his chase for the men and thinks, "I will go back to help the driver when the streetcar is under control."

As he begins to run, Julius discovers that he not only ripped his pants but also lost his slippers when he fell. The mud squishes between his toes as he runs barefoot after the streetcar. The feeling is as liberating as it was when he was a small boy chasing his sisters through their mother's garden. Those happy thoughts of youth return a vigor to his body that he thought he had lost years ago.

He athletically leaps with the grace of a buck deer back onto the streetcar's rear platform. His foot lands firmly on the platform, and his arm grabs the rear door handle in one swift move. He opens the door, runs past the five windows of the passenger section, and shoves open the door to the driver's platform. When he steps onto the driver's platform, the refreshing sensation of the fresh cool mud on his feet is replaced by the texture of coarse, scratchy fabric. Julius looks down, and his heart stops. It was not the driver he saw chasing the tall man into the cemetery—the driver is sitting on the floor, dead, his body held up by an arm draped over the iron handrail of the car, one leg under his body and eyes covered by his hat.

Looking up from this horrific scene, Julius can see that one of the reins is hanging over the rail, but the other is being dragged on the ground. He cannot stop the mules with just one rein. Before he jumps off the out-of-control car for the second time in five minutes, he takes a deep breath. This time without his slippers weakening his balance, he lands squarely on the street and races toward the mules. It is a short dash that ends when he grabs the bridle of one of the panting animals, pulling them to a stop. At the finish line of the race, both Julius and the mules stand in the rain, quietly calming their breathing and cooling their overheated bodies.

Julius looks over the mules' heads to see that they have stopped just past Twenty-eighth Street in front of the home of Charles Peters. He runs up the front steps and furiously pounds on the man's door. Angry at being awakened, Charles yells for Julius to go away. Julius does not stop his pounding and breathlessly shouts, "I need help! The street-car driver has been murdered!"

With those words, the sleepy woodworker bolts out of his house and runs with Julius to the streetcar. As they stare at the dead man, the two thirty-three-year-old German immigrants discuss in their native language what to do. Even though crime is not unusual in this tough neighborhood on the edge of the city, they know that finding a policeman at this hour of the night will be impossible. Instead of waiting, they decide to drive the body back to the transit station stables eight blocks north on Franklin Avenue.

Charles observes Julius's hands shaking and takes the reins from him. He shouts a command in German and snaps the leather to get the mules' attention. The mules, who understand only Norwegian commands, do not react to this strange language and won't move. The stubborn animals do understand the next hard snap of the reins, and they begin pulling their load down the muddy street.

After two blocks, the streetcar suddenly hits several twelve-foot-long wooden planks. The six steel wheels of the carriage jump the track, causing the mules to bray again in fright. This time Charles maintains control of the terrified animals, and the car comes to a screeching halt.

The two men are pulling the planks out from under the car when they see Peters's neighbor, Edward Mitchell, walking home from his job as a nurse. The black man who lives with his widowed mother and seven siblings asks, "What were the noises I heard several blocks ago?"

Julius responds, "The driver has been murdered!"

Mitchell jumps on the back platform and runs through the car to the body. Looking at the corpse, the nurse tells the others, "The body is becoming stiff. We should move it to the passenger section so that it can be laid flat."

In unison, Charles and Julius disagree with him. "We don't care how difficult it will be for the undertaker to lay the body out for burial," said Julius. "It is going to be in this position when the police and the coroner conduct their examination. The best way for the dead body not to freeze into its current unnatural position is to get the derailed streetcar back on the tracks and finish our trip."

The three men create a lever with one of the planks, and their combined brawn lifts the car. Quickly the car is back on the tracks.

Edward continues his walk home, and Julius and Charles snap the mules to attention, promising them no more stops on their sad journey to their stable. It was a false promise.

After a couple of blocks, Julius sees John McKinnon, the driver who gave him a ride home less than an hour ago. He is walking down the street with Patrolman Hans Burlie. Charles Peters pulls the reins to stop the mules, allowing the two men to board the car. John McKinnon's face turns white when his concerns about the driver, whom he identifies as Thomas Toffelson, are confirmed. Over and over, he moans that it is his fault that the square-jawed, burly thirty-year-old Norwegian immigrant, married only five months, is dead.

He cries, "Earlier in the evening, I saw three men lurking in the shadows behind the trees at the corner of the cemetery. I ignored the danger until I struck some planks—then, I was sure it was an ambush. I whipped the mules, forcing them to pull the derailed streetcar in the mud. After several blocks, when I believed it was safe to stop, I struggled to put the car back on the rails when Tom stopped to help me. I didn't warn him! Instead, I just waved goodbye. After I put the car and mules away for the night, I started to walk home. As I left the stables, I noticed that Tom's car had not returned, which worried me. On my way home, I met Patrolman Burlie and told him my suspicions. We started down Cedar Avenue to find him." Totally dejected, McKinnon moans, "Tom was murdered protecting a cashbox with no more than twenty dollars in silver."

Patrolman Burlie, a five-year veteran of the Minneapolis Police Department, takes control of the situation. In a thick Norwegian accent, he orders that the streetcar should continue to the stables.

When the four breathing men and one nonbreathing corpse arrive at the Franklin Avenue stables, a crowd begins to gather at the streetcar. In the chaos, each man tells the assembled crowd his version of tonight's events as he remembers them.

Standing in the middle of the excited crowd, Julius looks down at his bare feet. Embarrassed, he asks Patrolman Burlie if he can go next door to the home of Adam Disper, a shoemaker, to get some stockings and shoes before a police wagon arrives to drive him home. With the officer's permission, he knocks on Disper's door. Sophia Disper, a proper fifty-year-old German woman who works as a clerk for C. M. Douglas Company, answers the door and is more disturbed by an indecent barefoot man standing on her porch than by a murdered man in a streetcar at the stables. She takes pride in maintaining proper German order in this ungodly city, and she quickly finds Julius stockings and shoes before the reputation of her house is permanently stained. While he sits on her porch putting on his new footwear, he tells Mrs. Disper in German what happened. Before he can finish, the police wagon arrives.

About a half-hour after Julius saw the first flash from the gun, Gertrude was sitting on the steps of the porch of their home, shaking with fear. When her husband first angrily descended the back stairs on his way to the privy, his equally angry wife was glad that he wasn't in the room anymore. Then she heard three or four shots and the howling of what sounded like a wounded dog. When Julius did not return after a few minutes, her anger transformed into fear.

She went to the door and called out for him. After several cries with no response, she ran back upstairs, sure that he had been shot. She put on her shoes, threw a wrap around her shoulders, and woke up nine-year-old Julia. The mother and daughter took the back stairs into the yard. They called for him in unison. They peeked into the water closet, went into the shed, searched behind the shed, and then looked around the large stone pile at the rear of the house. When they found or heard nobody, they left the yard and walked in the direction of the turnaround—where Gertrude thought the shots had come from. They went as far as the band shell when fear overcame the girl, and she began wailing. They returned home, and Gertrude assumed her spot on the steps.

When she heard the clock strike one, she was convinced she had become one of the city's countless young widows. Desperate for help, she pounded on her brother-in-law Adolph's door.

Adolph also was awakened earlier by the shots and screams. He had looked out the window and saw a figure without a coat running across the turnaround toward the streetcar. Sure someone had shot a dog, Adolph simply went back to bed.

Now the young man reacts to comfort his frantic sister-in-law. Louisa leads her niece to a bed while Adolph wakes their neighbors, Frank Storey and John Erickson, to help search for his brother. The three men and Gertrude walk to the turnaround.

George Fassett was standing on the corner. They told him they were searching for Julius. He said, "I saw a man without a vest or coat jump on the streetcar that was heading up the street."

With that news, the group continued north on Cedar Avenue. When they arrived at the cemetery gate, Frank Storey picked up a pair of slippers that Gertrude immediately recognized as her husband's. Her fear that had subsided when they talked to George Fassett now returned.

Frank Storey offered to hitch up his wagon to continue the search up Cedar Avenue to the intersection with Franklin Avenue. While he hitched up his team, Gertrude went upstairs to get clothes for Adolph to give to his brother when he was found.

Gertrude watched the two men and the wagon disappear into the darkness. She returned to her sentry post on the porch to wait for the return of the man who had made her so angry a few hours before.

Julius is relieved to see the police wagon pull up to the Disper house. He walks with Charles to the common-looking wagon that can be used to haul wheat, freight or people. The side of the wagon, where other companies advertise their products, is painted with the words Police Wagon and the bed of the wagon, rather than being open to maximize the amount of hard goods to be hauled, has two rows of benches along the walls for the police department to haul its human goods. Climbing into the back of the wagon, which had a tent canopy to protect the benches, each man takes a seat and looks forward to the trip home. The wagon is as uncomfortable bouncing across the rough Minneapolis streets as any wagon Julius has ever ridden.

Halfway home, they meet the springboard wagon driven by Frank Storey. Standing behind Frank with both hands tightly gripping the back of the seat to maintain his balance is Adolph. The stone-cold fear on Adolph's face quickly changes to relief when he sees his brother.

Frank Storey turns his wagon around and follows the police wagon back to the turnaround, where a crowd has assembled. Julius jumps out of the wagon and is greeted by a less angry wife, curious neighbors and possibly one policeman, Henry Krumweide. The exhausted Julius wants only to cross the street and climb the stairs to bed, but the crowd wants to hear the story of his adventure—and the man always in search of an audience does not waste an opportunity to entertain. Encircled by his neighbors, he tells them about the four gunshots, the two men he saw running away, and the poor man driver in the streetcar. Almost everyone around him had heard the shots and screams. Most agreed with Julius's story, but some thought they heard only two shots and concluded that Julius was embellishing his story.

When the crowd begins to disperse, Julius takes Gertrude's hand. Feeling closer to her than he has for a long time, they cross the street to return to bed. Before falling asleep, she tells her husband how scared she was. Then for the second time tonight, she scolds her husband, but now there is no anger in her voice. "Don't be that brave again. Widows with small children in this neighborhood have only a few very unpleasant choices to support a family."

Two days after the murder, Julius sits in a courtroom preparing to testify at the coroner's inquest. In the chairs around him are reporters from both the Minneapolis and St. Paul papers, Tom Toffelson's fellow transit drivers, and citizens curious about the events two nights ago. Before Julius is called to the stand, Deputy Coroner Spring testifies to the gruesome details of Toffelson's autopsy: "One bullet had torn through Toffelson's leg above the knee and the second into his chest under his right nipple, tearing through his lung and aortic artery, lodging in his left shoulder blade." Julius hears the coroner state, "I think the first shot was the chest wound that stopped his heart instantaneously because I found little blood around the leg wound. My opinion is that the heart was not beating when the leg wound was inflicted."

Hearing the coroner's testimony leaves Julius confused and relieved. "If there were only two wounds, what happened to the other two shots I heard?" he wondered. Hearing that the man died instantly relieved him of dark thoughts. During every quiet moment since the murder, his mind kept asking, "What if I had not stopped to button my pants? Could I have saved Tom Toffelson?" Trusting the words of Deputy Coroner Spring, he is satisfied that would not have made a difference.

When the coroner finishes his testimony, he steps off the stand and the judge, with a stern look on his face, asks Julius to step forward. At first, Julius does not respond to the judge, who mispronounced his name, and he is called a second time. Julius stands, straightens his coat and tie, walks to the front of the room, raises his right hand and swears to faithfully tell the truth. The county attorney methodically questions him about every step of the deadly evening. Julius tells the same story that he has told many times since he stood before the crowd at the turnaround thirty-six hours ago. He adds that he is not sure but thinks that one of the cries he heard was the word "murder."

When he is dismissed from the inquest, Julius rides a streetcar home. At the turnaround, a large crowd has gathered to witness Tom Toffelson's funeral procession. Julius, Gertrude and the other neighbors solemnly walk to the spot where two nights ago the man was murdered. Looking into the cemetery, which was too dark on Tuesday night to see the perpetrators, Julius can see the new grave that was dug in the southwest corner. In the distance, he hears the rhythmic sounds of the black funeral horses' hooves on Cedar Avenue, pulling the hearse from the Swedish Lutheran Church. As the procession turns into the gate of the cemetery, where Julius lost his slippers, he sees through the side glass panels of the dark hearse the fully draped and fringed casket with oxidized silver handles.

People in the crowd whisper that the Minneapolis Transit Company is paying for the funeral. Julius wonders if his employer would have done the same—bitterly, he thinks not. Slowly the casket is carried to the grave, orienting the victim so that he will spend eternity looking away from the spot where he met his earthly fate. The somber, quiet moment is interrupted by the cries at the grave of Thomas Toffelson's young widow, Lena. Shivers run down the spines of those who had heard the frightened, painful cries of her husband before he died. Lena Toffelson, kneeling at the grave of the man who was going to be her future but now is her past, moans cries as loud and as piercing as those heard two nights before. Men, women and children all have tears running down their cheeks as they share the unimaginable grief of the young widow.

Every morning and evening since the funeral, while waiting for the streetcar, Julius looks at the mounds of dirt that cover the graves of his niece and Toffelson, watching as the graves slowly settle and the grass begins to cover the bare ground. Julius thinks what a waste it was. Unfortunately, the death of a six-month-old baby can almost be expected, but a thirty-year-old man dying at the hand of another cannot. The murderers have not been found, and many in the neighborhood fear they will commit more hideous crimes.

Life can be hard in the Hub of Hell. The temptations are great, and the opportunities can be few. But for one night, the citizens of this neighborhood, born all across the globe, banded together to help another working man.

January 4, 1888 - Minneapolis, Minnesota

A ten-year-old paperboy stands on the corner of Washington Avenue and 2nd Street, repeating the front page headline over and over. "Tim is Guilty!" Julius buys a paper and enters his office. Sitting behind his desk, he reads the story and replays the events of the past five months.

About three weeks after the streetcar driver's murder, he noticed the first weed sprouting up on Tom Toffelson's grave. The same morning, he read an article in the *St. Paul Globe* that exposed the corrupt dealings between city hall and the city's illegal saloons. Multiple bold print headlines enticed his curiosity.

Henry Barrett, the owner of a blind pig, as saloons operating without a license in Minneapolis are called, described the various payoffs to city officials and political contributions he had made to keep his illegal business open. Barrett, the son of Irish immigrants, is called Reddy because of his bright red hair and mustache. He is malicious and dangerous and rarely looks anyone straight in the eye. His blind pig had a couple of simple tables, a few chairs, a bar and a pool table in the front of the family's house at the corner of Twenty-eighth Street and Fort Road, less than a mile from Julius's home. It was a mean place that attracted some of the most dangerous people in the city. Over the door was a crudely painted sign welcoming customers, appropriately, to the Hub of Hell.

The Barrett family was dysfunctional. Reddy's parents had once owned a large, successful farm in Mills County, Iowa, that they were forced to sell when their marriage ended. Reddy whined to all his customers that after the farm was sold, his mother took all of the money and moved to Omaha with her favorite children, leaving her least favorites to follow their father to Minneapolis. She was not shy about using her wealth as a weapon against her unruly offspring.

One night a customer of Barrett's blind pig was robbed of his gold watch. When he returned to get it back, a huge brawl broke out. After that, neighbors gathered a long list of signatures of people who supported the closure of the blind pig; the petitions were ignored. The article in the *St. Paul Globe* said Reddy was paying off Licensing Inspector Smith and had been making campaign contributions to corrupt politicians for at least the past three years to keep his business open.

Within weeks, the embarrassed city leaders, along with the police and inspection departments, arrested Reddy for running his saloon without a license. He got thirty days in jail and a fifty-dollar fine. If he did not pay the fine, he would spend another thirty days behind bars.

It was a busy summer for Reddy. He married a fifteen-year-old girl, and earlier in the summer, his mother purchased two tickets for her sons Tim and Pete to visit their family in Minneapolis. Tim is a year older than Reddy, and seventeen-year-old Pete is the youngest of the family and reportedly their mother's favorite.

The three brothers, who had not lived together since Pete was a boy, quickly bonded, with Reddy as the ringleader. Shortly after they arrived, rumors spread about the trouble the Barrett brothers were creating in the neighborhood on the edge of the city. At night they would menace unsuspecting strangers on the street. The next morning, they would fight among themselves over money or the affection of their parents. In the afternoon, they would fight about Tim or Pete's romantic interest in Reddy's wife or her sister Chloe. When night arrived, they would start the cycle again.

While Reddy was in jail, visitors to the parks around Minnehaha Falls were being robbed by a highwayman. In November, while a woman and her daughter were visiting the picnic area above the rushing water, a handsome red-headed man with a long blond mustache and a nickel-plated .38 caliber long barrel gun approached. He pulled a gold ring from the finger of the little girl. Until that day, the police had no suspects for the robberies, but the description given by the mother and daughter matched Tim Barrett.

When the police arrived at the Barrett house, they found Tim there with Reddy's wife Minnie and her sister Chloe. When the police handcuffed him and started to lead him away, Chloe suddenly gave him a hug. One of the policemen noticed that during the embrace, they held hands for a second. The police forced Chloe's hand open and found the stolen gold ring. They then searched the house and found many other items that had been reported stolen during the past couple of months. For the next several days, Reddy and Tim shared the same address at the jail.

The two brothers were together in jail only for a couple of days. Despite not working for two months, Reddy suddenly had the money to pay his fine. At the city's numerous saloons, the patrons were convinced that Reddy borrowed the outstanding $3.75 of his fine from Deputy Sheriff Johnson—most thought it wasn't a coincidence that this happened the same day Tim Barrett became a suspect for the murder of Tom Toffelson. Then several days later, the police left town to arrest a second suspect. They returned from Omaha with Pete, the youngest Barrett brother.

When William Donahue, the expensive defense attorney the brothers' mother had hired, met Pete for the first time at the arraignment, he saw a clean-shaven, nervous teenager wearing patched pants that barely touched the top of his thoroughly worn shoes. He turned to the prosecutor and asked, "Is this the terrible desperado we have been reading so much about of late? Dangerous-looking man, is he not?"

After the confused Tim was brought into the courtroom, both brothers were arraigned. Donahue requested that they be tried separately and, even though this was the first time he met the men, that the trial start that day. The prosecutors requested a ten-day extension to find and prepare their witnesses. Julius, the witness to the crime, was sure he would be one of the men the prosecutors would prepare for the trial.

Tim's trial was first. It began slowly as the prosecutor used his presumptive challenges to remove Irishmen from the jury while the defense did the same with Scandinavians. When a jury was finally selected, testimony began.

After two days of jury selection, the first witness was John McKinnon, the streetcar driver who drove Julius home on the night of the murder. His testimony left the impression that when he met Toffelson's missing streetcar, he found it empty except for the dead man. That testimony contradicted what he told a reporter the day after the murder, that the streetcar was being driven by Charles and Julius. He also said that he had found Toffelson lying on his back, his head in the corner of the driver's platform, with his mouth and eyes open. Julius had found the dead man sitting upright against the platform railing, his leg crouched under him, his head bowed and cap pulled over his eyes.

The next witness was Deputy Coroner Willis Spring. At the coroner's inquest, Dr. Spring testified that the first shot had immediately killed Toffelson. Now the doctor just stated the facts about powder burns and directions of the wounds but said nothing about whether the leg wound or chest wound struck Toffelson first.

Prosecutor Davis stunned the courtroom when he called his next witness—Henry "Reddy" Barrett. Defense attorney Erwin immediately jumped to his feet to object. He eloquently argued that a potential defendant in a crime could not testify against another being tried for the same crime.

A slight smile could be seen behind Prosecutor Davis's mustache when he explained that Reddy was not a potential defendant. Reddy had agreed to help hang his brothers in exchange for full immunity.

When Julius heard Reddy's testimony, he was sure that the police and prosecutors were changing the facts to fit Reddy's story. There were major differences between what Reddy said happened and what Julius had seen that night. Now he knew why he and Adolph were not being called to testify even though they both were in the courtroom.

Reddy testified that after an evening of drinking downtown, he and his brothers jumped on the Riverside streetcar but got off early at Franklin Avenue. Then they walked down Cedar Avenue. Needing money, they decided the quickest way to get some was to rob a streetcar driver. They placed several planks on the tracks to stop the next car. Their plan was foiled because the driver became scared after seeing them earlier, lurking in the shadows by the railroad tracks at the corner of the cemetery. Rather than stopping, the driver snapped the reins hard, and his mules continued to pull the car down the street with its back wheels off the tracks.

Reddy then said they continued to the Lake Street–Cedar Avenue turnaround, determined not to fail again. As the streetcar navigated the turnaround, he and Tim jumped out of the rainy darkness to stop the mules. Reddy held them while Tim and Pete ran up to the driver's platform with their guns pointed at the driver, demanding the cashbox. The large Norwegian refused. He placed the cashbox under his left armpit and grabbed the barrels of both revolvers, raising them above his head. Everything went wrong at that moment when Pete accidentally fired his gun, hitting the driver's leg.

Reddy said that after Pete shot the driver, the man's deafening howl scared him, Pete and the mules, and they started running. When the two brothers reached the cemetery gate, they heard another shot. After the second shot, Tim ran to rejoin his brothers, carrying the cashbox. Excited, he told his brothers that he had shot the driver in the head. Reddy testified that Tim ran east on Lake Street to the south entrance of the cemetery, not north on Cedar Avenue to the west entrance where Julius had lost his slippers.

Adolph and Julius sat next to each other in the courtroom that day. Both brothers knew that the fiend was lying. Julius whispered in Adolph's ear, "I was within fifty feet of the streetcar, buckling my pants when the second, third and fourth shots were fired. After the shots, I ran north chasing two men. Tim did not run past me to the east."

Adolph whispered back, "After the first shot, I looked out the window. The only person I saw was you, running north without a coat toward the turnaround. I did not see anyone running to the east."

The expensive defense team did their best to defend Tim Barrett, but neither Tim nor Pete was an even match against their brother on the stand. Reddy answered his questions easily and engaged with the onlookers in the courtroom. Tim rarely looked at anyone; when he did, it was only with a strange vacant smile. He was clearly mentally slow and gave awkward answers to the questions.

Pete was slightly more eloquent than his brother, but he still was not nearly as engaging as Reddy. Julius thought Pete's account of the events from last summer was believable, especially his last statement that his brother Reddy was a liar.

William Erwin presented numerous witnesses who testified that Tim and Pete Barrett were not with Reddy that night. He called Dr. Heflin to the stand. The doctor testified that he was with the two brothers at the home of their sick sister when the murder happened. The testimony was impugned when the prosecutor forced Dr. Heflin to admit that he had recently been prosecuted for mailing pornography.

Louis Riel, a former Minneapolis policeman, was the next defense witness. He swore he had overheard three men at the Minnehaha pavilion talking about robbing a streetcar driver. Then he pointed directly at Reddy when he was asked if the man who threatened him with a pistol that day was in the courtroom. When he was asked why he had not reported the encounter, he responded that he had told Officer Henry Krumweide. Krumweide told him to forget it. "The prosecutors do not want him ruining their case," Riel said Krumweide had said.

The defense presented two other witnesses who also said they had heard and seen Reddy, before and after the murder, conspiring with two men to rob the streetcar. But it did not matter. After only two hours, the jury convicted Tim Barrett. Hennepin County will have its first execution since the legislature reinstated capital punishment.

February 8, 1888 – Minneapolis, Minnesota

Julius is usually not a man of prayer. Today, though, he is praying that his nervous stomach and bowels continue to hold his breakfast. It is not just his digestive system that is groaning but also the floor timbers of the packed Hennepin County courtroom, struggling to carry the weight of the large crowds gathering daily to witness the second trial of a Barrett brother.

From the back row of the courtroom, Julius stares at the back of Peter Barrett's small neck. He thinks, "He is just a boy." He shudders. Whether a rope snaps that fair neck in half will depend on whom the jury believes. Julius, whom the *St. Paul Globe* described last July as an honest man, or the boy's brother, Henry, who admitted in the same paper three weeks later that he had paid bribes to city officials for years. The thought causes another painful cramp deep in Julius's stomach.

When Julius arrived at the courthouse early this morning, his feet were numb from walking in the subzero temperatures. Now it is almost noon, and he has lost the feeling in his legs again—this time not from the cold but rather from sitting for almost three hours on the hard wooden courtroom chairs listening to attorney William Erwin present the summary of his upcoming defense of Pete Barrett.

Nearly a month ago, shortly after the historic double events of a crippling blizzard and the issuance of the death sentence for Tim Barrett, a large gust of bitter Siberian air rushed into Julius's office at the Metropolitan Life Assurance Company. A well-dressed, obviously successful man followed the cold air into the room. He asked to speak with him. Julius recognized his prospective client as the "Tall Pine," the infamous defense attorney William Erwin. After being offered a hot cup of coffee, Erwin told Julius that he was not there to buy insurance. Instead, he wanted to talk to him about the night Tom Toffelson was murdered.

The joints of Erwin's chair cracked loudly in protest as he leaned back to begin what to Julius sounded like one of his famous summations for a jury. "The one thing that bothered me at the end of the trial of Tim Barrett was why the prosecution had not called the partially dressed man who stopped the mules that night. I think I know now.

"On the Sunday after Tim's conviction, Reddy visited his father at the Gault Hotel. He must have had an attack of conscience. He blurted out to his father that there was one honest man in the city the police had not bought. The aged father begged his son to talk to me. He initially agreed. However, when the prosecution heard of the meeting, they threatened to revoke his immunity.

"The threat against his son did not stop John Barrett from reporting the strange comment to me. My curiosity was aroused, and I read the newspaper accounts of the night of the murder and the coroner's inquest. Are you the Julius C. Heyn who discovered the body of Tom Toffelson?"

Julius nodded yes. Erwin then asked him to tell his story. When Julius finished his version of the events, Erwin asked, "Are there other witnesses who can confirm your story?" Julius wrote down the names of the people who, he said, would be able to corroborate his testimony.

Erwin's coffee cup was empty by the time Julius finished his account of the murder. He refused a second cup and instead prepared to leave the warm office. Before opening the door, Julius stretched his short neck to look into the eyes of the tall lawyer. Erwin said he was determined to save his second client from the same fate as the first. The powerful attorney and simple insurance agent shook hands in agreement.

As the first month of the year 1888 came to an end, the numerous winter storms and subzero temperatures of January were still raging. At the courthouse, the same judge, lawyers and spectators filed into the same courtroom, all expecting the same quick result at the trial of the younger Barrett brother. Most anticipated that they would be observing a double hanging by the time the spring sun melted the record mounds of snow piled throughout the city. Yet defense attorney Erwin asked his questions of prospective jurors with a vigor and enthusiasm that surprised his opposition.

On the third day of Pete's trial, the prosecution finally began to present the same witnesses they had in Tim's trial. To a casual observer, it seemed a second performance of an enjoyable play, except that one of the lead actors, Bill Erwin, was delivering a more impassioned performance. He forcefully questioned Deputy Coroner Willis Spring about the dead man's wounds. "Why," he asked, "if Toffelson had been first shot in the leg, as Reddy had previously testified, did the wound not bleed?" He received a vague nonanswer.

Ole Byorum, the mortician who had undressed Tom Toffelson the morning after the murder, was the next witness. A minor witness in the previous trial, he was surprised to be questioned about blood and powder burns he had observed on the body. Byorum was beginning to relax as Erwin walked back to the defense table, appearing to conclude his questions. Suddenly he spun back toward the mortician and said, "May I see the dead man's clothes?"

The embarrassed undertaker's Norwegian accent became thicker and almost unintelligible when he responded. "De var accidently give til rag man." Erwin dramatically posed before the witness stand for a minute, allowing the jury to comprehend that one of the primary pieces of evidence had been sloppily destroyed.

Erwin's confidence was even greater when Reddy was called as the next witness. In contrast, the courtroom was shocked that Reddy's confidence and swagger from the earlier trial were gone. His wife, Minnie, had given birth to their first child the day before, but the newborn had died. Today the court saw a man exhibiting the combined emotions of grief and regret that were missing at his other brother's trial six weeks before.

As Reddy delivered his carefully prepared testimony, he clasped his hands together, attempting to slow the constant motion of his fingers as his pent-up nervous energy sought escape. Under cross-examination, he said he confessed to the crime after being released from jail because his conscience bothered him.

The highly skeptical Erwin asked, "Were you immediately granted immunity? Are you expecting to receive the reward?"

To both questions, Reddy emphatically answered, "No."

Erwin then suddenly turned his questioning to what Reddy knew about Julius. "Yes. I met my father at the Gault Hotel. No, I did not tell the old man that there was one honest man who knew the truth."

Erwin asked, "Do you know Julius Heyn?"

Reddy quickly answered, "No."

Last Saturday at the trial, Erwin made one final attempt to shake the confidence of the man the city newspapers were now describing as Cain, the man in the book of Genesis who committed the world's first murder against his own brother, Abel. Erwin shocked both the court and Reddy with his next question. "Did you not tell your father at the Gault Hotel that the reason you were so angry with Tim was because he had sexual relations with your wife and sister-in-law while you were in jail?"

Suddenly Reddy's quiet sadness turned into the raging fury that customers of the Hub of Hell knew well. He clenched his fists and screamed, "I will not answer such a vile question!"

In contrast to the witness, Erwin calmly turned to Judge Lochren. "Please instruct the witness to answer the question," he said.

When the judge told Reddy he must answer the question, the man angrily shouted, "No!"

It took two days for Reddy to complete his half of the agreement to send his baby brother to the gallows. He left the stand, never wavering from his previous testimony but also not displaying the same cocky enthusiasm as he had at his other brother's trial. That Saturday afternoon during the lunch break, he was observed standing alone staring out the window, deep in solitary thought. Some spectators wondered if they were witnessing his grief after losing his son; others were sure he felt anger from the damage to his wife's reputation. Erwin was sure Reddy was contemplating a guilty conscience.

Before the court adjourned that Saturday afternoon, John McKinnon was recalled to the stand. This time he admitted that Julius had been standing in the doorway of the streetcar when he found his lost coworker. When questioned if he remembered any blood on the floor of the car, he answered, "I do not recall it, but I think I would have remembered if it were there."

The trial resumed on Monday with the final witnesses for the prosecution repeating the testimony they had given at Tim's trial. The one exception was Officer Krumweide, who previously had told Louis Riel that the prosecution did not want to talk to him. Suddenly the officer remembered meeting Julius at the streetcar barns as he helped move the body.

Julius arrived at the courthouse this morning expecting to lose only one day's work. The large clock on the wall is now just a couple of pendulum swings away from striking noon. Julius spent the morning studying a mole on Pete Barrett's neck. He wonders, "If I fail today, will the noose tear this mole loose from his neck?" The gruesome image snaps Julius back to reality. John T. Byrnes, the third member of the defense team, is still attacking not only the character of Reddy but also the justice system of Hennepin County. "If Peter Barrett was the son of one of the rich men who owned the city's flour mills rather than a poor broken-down Irish immigrant, would he have been charged with a crime with so little evidence? Would a jealous rich brother who had admitted to participating in the crime, had threatened to kill his mother, and had attempted to kill his father been granted immunity to testify against his brothers? I think not."

Near the end of his oratory, Byrnes asked the question Julius had been wondering for months. "Why did the prosecution not call the one eyewitness to the crime?" Byrnes answered his own question in a loud accusatory tone. "The prosecution knows that the testimony of the one living eyewitness to the crime from whom you will soon be hearing contradicts their star witness." Then, turning away from the jury, the attorney pointed his long finger toward his client and asked again, "Would this happen to a millionaire's son?"

Byrnes finally ends his speech and calls Julius as the first witness for the defense. Julius feels a jolt of energy surge through his body. He feels all the eyes in the room fixed on him, curious about this new character in the drama. The pressure in his chest begins to release as he stands before the court clerk and raises his right hand, placing his left on an unfamiliar English Bible, and promises to tell the truth.

The first questions from Byrnes are easy.

"Were you at the coroner's inquest over the remains of Thomas Tollefson?"

"Yes."

"Where were you born?"

"In Germany."

"How old are you?"

"I am thirty-three years old."

"Where did you live on July 26?"

"At 3009 Cedar Avenue."

"What is your occupation?"

"My occupation is assistant superintendent of the Metropolitan Life Assurance Company."

"How long have you lived in Minneapolis?"

"About one year and two months."

"How long have you lived in this country?"

"About sixteen years."

The nervous energy that had been dissipating from Julius's body returns. He notices several jury members leaning forward, struggling to understand his thick German accent. His stomach twists tight when he remembers Erwin telling him he had lost Tim's trial because Reddy was so engaging with the jury. If Julius is going to save Pete Barrett, these twelve men have to believe him and not Reddy.

Byrnes begins to lead Julius through events of the dark, rainy evening of July 26, 1887. Methodically, Julius starts with hearing the first shot and the scream as he left the outhouse. Then he is emphatic. "As I buttoned my pants, I saw three more flashes of a pistol. The time between the first and the last three shots probably might be a minute." Julius then raises his arm to demonstrate how the three shots were fired.

He continues, "I was a few feet away when I saw two men leave the front of the car on the right. Because I was so near the streetcar, the two men started running up Cedar Avenue."

Byrnes asks, "Can you describe the two men?"

Julius responds, "From what I could see, I thought they were well-built men, one taller than the other. The man running ahead was taller than the second. They both were wearing dark clothes. I could not describe them."

"Reddy has testified that Tim ran east on Lake Street to the south cemetery gate after the fatal shot. Did you see him as you ran to the streetcar?"

Julius's English is perfect when he answers. "No, I did not. I ran alongside the streetcar chasing the two men from the turnaround until I slipped and fell near the Cedar Avenue gate to the cemetery." He points to the gate on the map and then continues, "I do not exactly recollect where the two men went. Whether they jumped over the fence on the right side of the gate or ran in through the gate I am not positive." Again, he points to the Cedar Avenue gate on the map.

Julius's accent becomes thicker when he turns toward the jury to tell how he raced to stop the streetcar and then describes what he saw when he found Toffelson's body. Byrnes's final questions ask Julius to describe his encounters with Charles Peters, John McKinnon, Edward Morrison and Hans Burlie after he had discovered the body.

Then a battle of legal wits breaks out between Byrnes and Prosecutor Davis.

Byrnes asks his witness when he first was connected with someone for the defense. Davis objects, and it is sustained.

Next, Byrnes asks Julius if he had talked with the officers prosecuting the case. Julius quickly answers yes, but Davis again objects, and the answer is stricken from the record.

Byrnes asks next if it is not true that Julius had talked about the case with Assistant Prosecutor Jamison before Tim Barrett's trial. Before Julius can answer, Davis again objects, and the judge sustains the objection.

The next two questions are also objected to. "Were you in the courtroom at the trial of Tim Barrett? Isn't it true that the prosecutors knew you were in the courtroom?"

Again, the judge sustained both objections, and Julius was not allowed to answer.

Frank Davis begins his aggressive cross-examination of Julius by reading his inquest testimony. He asks, "Why did you begin most of your answers that day with the statement, *I think*?"

Julius looks confused.

Davis, with a menacing flick of his hand, gives Julius the inquest affidavit and quickly asks him, "Are these not your words?"

Determined not to be intimidated by the theatrical prosecutor, Julius slowly reads the document. When he is finished, he looks Davis directly in the eye before answering. "I think it has been altered."

This is the second time in the trial that Davis's integrity has been questioned. He is willing to accept that from an expensive slick-talking defense attorney but not from a Kraut immigrant who can barely speak God's English. Davis angrily points his finger at Julius's signature at the end of the document. "Is that not your signature?"

Tension is high in the courtroom as Julius examines the document. Then he responds, "Unless I was very excited that morning, it is not."

Davis begins a series of questions asking Julius why he told different stories on the night of the murder at various times and places to Mr. Bowditch, Mr. Fassett, Mrs. Disper, Mr. Disper, Officer Krumweide, Charlie Peters, Mr. Littleton, and others in the crowd at the streetcar turnaround. Each question was simple. "Did you not tell them you heard one shot when you were in the privy and then another when you arrived at the street? Also, did you not tell them you saw only one man running from the streetcar?"

Julius's answers were equally simple. "No, sir."

The tension in the courtroom caused by that statement is broken as the judge pounds his gavel to end this long day.

The next morning Julius is back in the witness chair and quickly becomes frustrated by the continual legal challenges of the competing attorneys that interrupt his testimony. Under re-direct examination, the defense attorneys attempt to walk Julius through his coroner's jury testimony and clarification of the prosecutor's questions. Each question is challenged by Davis and sustained by Judge Lochren, whose ruling is noted by exception by the defense for a future appeal. Each challenge is delivered by competing attorneys with fiery fake indignation, which tests Julius's patience. These interruptions will not imperil the finances of the bickering lawyers, but he is a working man who is losing income each hour he sits in this chair.

Davis makes one of his more strenuous objections when a snide comment by the defense implies that Reddy's testimony had been purchased. With all the drama that only an experienced actor or politician can muster, the county attorney cries that the defense is impugning his reputation. "If it is true that Reddy's testimony had been purchased, then it was me who authorized the bribe."

A sly smile is seen behind Judge Lochren's pepper-gray goatee as he rules. "I think the jury is smart enough to make that decision."

After almost ten hours of responding to the questions of the intimidating legal teams, Julius is excused. As he walks to the back of the room to sit next to his wife and brother, he thinks that while that was not easy, he is proud of himself. Amid the courtroom chatter, his mind also hears his mother: "I raised you to always tell the truth. I am proud that you did not let a slick-talking lawyer trick you." Those spectators, with their eyes still on Julius, see a contented smile cross the contemplative man's face.

After Patrick McLaughlin, who as a boy had escaped the potato famine in Ireland and then bravely served to protect his new country in the Civil War, completes his testimony, Gertrude is called to the stand. As she makes her way to the front of the courtroom, she stumbles. Julius, who has noticed that this occurs regularly, thinks he may have a new worry when this trial ends.

The jury, who had struggled for two days to understand her husband, relax in their chairs when Gertrude tells them, with no accent, "I was born in New York and have been married going on twelve years. On the night of July 26, I was living at 3009 Cedar Avenue. The night Tollefson was killed, I went to bed about nine o'clock. I suppose my husband was downtown when I went to bed. I think he came home about twenty minutes to midnight. After he took off his clothes, he went back downstairs to go to the privy. He was gone about five to ten minutes when I heard a shot and a terrible scream, which I thought was a wounded dog. Then I heard two more shots coming from the direction of the front of the house. When he had not come back to bed after a few minutes, I went to search for him. I am not sure how long I searched."

She ended her testimony by telling the jury, "Later that evening, when Julius came home in the back of a police wagon, a small crowd had gathered at the turnaround. I remember him telling the same story of the murder that he told in court this week."

Adolph is then called to the stand. Jurors listen with difficulty to the earnest, hard-working young family man whose accent is thicker than his brother's. The third member of the Heyn family confirms that there had been at least three shots and that the cries ended after the first shot. He is also very clear that he had observed from his bedroom window only one partially clothed man running across the street toward the turnaround after the first shot, directly contradicting Reddy's testimony.

Following Adolph, Mary Storey testifies next. She bluntly states, "I heard three shots that night."

As she is being cross-examined, Julius, who has tangled with his feisty neighbor on more than one occasion, smiles as he listens to her exchanges with the pompous Davis.

Davis asks, "Did you ever tell anyone that you had heard more than two shots?"

Mary answers, "I told about a dozen people at the turnaround that night."

"Did they disagree with you about there being more than two shots?" Davis asks.

Mary snaps back, "They agreed on the number of shots better that night than they do now."

Julius, Gertrude and Adolph all smile at the response of their tart-tongued neighbor. At the end of her testimony, the court adjourns for another day.

When court reconvenes on Friday morning, there is hope that the day will be warmer than the previous two. While the morning temperature is still well below zero, there is also a black sky to the west, signaling that more snow may be coming, welcome relief from the subzero weather.

Today's first witness, Julius's sister-in-law Louise, is within weeks of giving birth to her second child. At the breakfast table, Julius reassures his brother that the weather this morning will be manageable. After the death of his first daughter last summer, Adolph is very worried for his wife and unborn child. Normally a woman in Louise's condition is confined to bed at this stage of pregnancy rather than venturing out to testify at a murder trial when the temperature is twenty degrees below zero with the threat of snow visible in the western sky. Adolph does not want Louise to leave the house, but Julius, Gertrude and Louise herself assure the panicky father that all will be fine.

Later when her name is called in the courtroom, the pluckiness Louise expressed at the breakfast table is gone. As she tries to find a comfortable spot on the undersized witness chair, she hopes the stabbing pain in her stomach is tension and not the beginning of labor. She looks into the eyes of her very masculine husband across the room and smiles. "How strong would he look if I went into labor in front of the entire courtroom?" she wonders. In a rare act of humanity, neither attorney asks her many questions. She quickly confirms the testimony of her husband, Julius and Gertrude. As she walks back to her anxious husband, Louise feels the baby give a swift congratulatory kick.

The courtroom is overflowing in anticipation of Pete taking the stand. Louise's dramatic entrance and exit provide the audience some early entertainment, but they quickly become bored. Frank Storey, Edward Mitchell and John McKinnon are called by the defense to corroborate a portion of Julius's testimony that contradicts Reddy. It was clear to all of the observers that either Reddy or Julius was lying. The fate of the boy would be decided by which one the jury believes.

If the men and women who had stood in long cold lines for hours to hear Pete on the witness stand were expecting new and exciting revelations, they would be disappointed. His attorneys lead him through his version of the events of that night, and he does not vary from the testimony he gave six weeks earlier at his brother's trial.

After Pete Barrett finishes his defense, his father is called to the stand. While not yet sixty years old, the man walks to the witness chair with the bent frame and withered face of a man at least twenty years older. In a soft, unsteady voice, he confirms his conversation with his prodigal son at the Gault Hotel. "My son seemed repentant that day. He said he was willing to identify to the defense team the one honest man in Minneapolis who knew the truth."

The defense team then calls another series of witnesses to confirm the boy's testimony. George Coleman, Pete and Tim's new brother-in-law; William Pettman, a saloon keeper; George Robinson, one of Pettman's customers; and Pettman's wife all provide alibis for the brothers on the night of the murder. When Pettman was asked why he had not testified earlier, he responded, "When I told a police officer about seeing Tim and Pete, I was told that I had better keep my mouth shut. To operate a saloon in Minneapolis, you have to maintain friendly relations with the police. I was afraid to tell what I knew."

Frank Davis is now given an opportunity to refute the case presented by the defense. It is clear that he does not plan on wasting that opportunity. He knows that Julius's testimony contradicting Reddy may have sown the seed of doubt in the jurors' minds. His first task is to refute Julius's version of the facts.

George Fassett, Adam and Sophia Disper, and Officer Krumweide are called to the stand. Each testifies that Julius told them on that dark, rainy night that he had heard two shots and saw only one person run away from the streetcar. When they are cross-examined, they all admit that they never spoke directly with Julius. Rather, each had either overheard him at the turnaround or had read the newspaper account of his coroner's inquest testimony.

The next morning the defense rests its case, and the trial moves to closing arguments. A quiet relief fills the room before defense attorney Bill Donahue rises to his feet and faces the jury. For the next hour, he makes a passionate defense of his client and an equally passionate indictment of the Minneapolis Police Department. There is no fear in his voice as he describes the malfeasance of the department. "Members of the department intimidated witnesses so that they can supplement their income with a share of the reward they think they will receive when the Barrett brothers are convicted." A great sigh of disappointment can be heard in his voice as he says, "But that is the way justice is meted out in this city."

Donahue then turns his attention to Reddy. He raises his eyes upward as if he is asking God, then says, "Why is the testimony of a man who already admits to murdering one man and is now willing to do the same to his own brothers carrying more weight than that of the honest citizens the defense has presented?" As he pauses to let his final words register with jurors, he appears to say "amen" as he lowers his head and walks back to the defense table.

It is now Frank Davis's turn. Worried that the jurors are focusing on the unsubstantiated claims of Donahue against the police, he attempts to bring the jury's minds back to Tom Toffelson. He tells the jury, "There is no marker standing in the cemetery to remember the man. The monument for this working hero must be the conviction and punishment of his murderers." The long day comes to an end. Davis is satisfied that his remarks will be on the jurors' minds as they fall asleep tonight.

Davis starts the next morning trying to refute Julius's testimony. He is very careful not to call him a liar but rather a confused man. Davis points out, "He began every answer at the coroner's inquest with the words 'I think.' If he had heard three or four shots, why was no evidence found of the extra bullets in the body or the streetcar." Davis concludes by implying that the extra man Julius saw running away that night was a figment of his imagination.

When Julius hears Davis make that statement, he thinks to himself, "It is true that sometimes when I have too much to drink, I might see double, but the dual vision always stands side by side and is the same size." He shakes his head in disgust.

Davis then, after praising the character of the working man Toffelson, questions the reputations of the working men and women who defended Peter Barrett. After doubting the honesty and intelligence of the potpourri of businessmen, laborers, immigrants from every corner of Northern Europe, a veteran of two of the bloodiest battles of the Civil War, and a man freed by that war, Davis praises the conscience of Henry

Barrett, the serial felon and confessed accomplice to a murder. Several spectators in the packed courtroom raise their eyebrows in disbelief when Davis tells the jury, "It was a guilty conscience that caused Reddy to testify against his brothers, not greed or revenge. It was his heavy heart, not police corruption, that forced him to seek justice for the poor streetcar driver whom he had conspired with his brothers to rob and accidentally kill." After this unbelievable statement, Davis rests the state's case against the second Barrett brother.

William Erwin, the famed attorney whose eloquence Davis had warned the jury the day before had returned many a guilty man to the street, immediately rises, bows his head to Judge Lochren, and turns to the jury. In a quiet voice that the jury can barely hear, he starts by reminding them it is their duty to fairly judge this poor boy and that they cannot find him guilty if there is a reasonable doubt. He then spends the afternoon explaining this reasonable doubt step by step, walking through the truth his team presented at the trial. "After all of the obstacles the prosecution and police have placed in my path by restricting access to my clients, evidence, witnesses and interrogation documents, I am confident that I have given you the basis of reasonable doubt."

Erwin then begins a sordid condemnation of Reddy. "I am convinced that it was Reddy who committed the crime with the two men that Riel overheard at Minnehaha Falls. These two trials are simply a masterful plot of revenge by Reddy against his mother. He was angry that the woman manipulated his brothers against him to take away his home and business after he married a young girl his mother did not approve of. After she succeeded, he contrived to get arrested and then for the prosecutor to grant him immunity without confirming his testimony and involvement in the crime.

"The only remorse Reddy has ever shown was when he met his father after Tim's conviction. That day he was prepared to speak the truth, but that burst of conscience was quickly snuffed out when the prosecution threatened his immunity. His guilty conscience gave way to the fear that he would replace his brothers on the gallows."

Then Erwin turns his attention back to the jury and asks once more, "Why is this man who has terrorized his neighborhood for the past five years to be believed over the honest citizens who testified for the defense the past two weeks?"

With those words, William Erwin rests his defense. The jury has heard the testimonies of sixty-one witnesses for the state and thirty-nine witnesses for the defense, plus days of lofty oratory. Their verdict will be determined by which of two witnesses they believe: the prosecution witness who says he was an accidental accomplice to the crime or the defense witness who saw the heinous crime unfold.

The jury finds that it is not a hard decision. Like the jury in Tim Barrett's trial, after only three hours, the twelve men return a guilty verdict.

Two weeks later, everyone reassembles in the courtroom for the sentencing. Judge Lochren then reads another lengthy statement, just as he had at Tim's sentencing. He says that Minnesota statutes are clear that unless there are extraordinary circumstances, he has no choice but to rule for capital punishment. He asks Pete to stand and make a statement.

Pete simply says, "I am innocent, and time will prove it."

At that, Judge William Lochren issues his unsurprising sentence. Eighteen-year-old Peter Barrett is to join his brother in one of the death-row cells on the upper floors of the courthouse. The grim judge tells the boy, "Use the next three months to prepare to seek your maker's forgiveness after your short life concludes at the end of a rope." With those harsh words, the shackled Pete is led out of the courtroom.

Within days after Pete Barrett was sentenced, William Erwin prepared an appeal, asking the Supreme Court for new trials for both of his clients. For each defendant, he cited twenty-eight serious judicial errors made in each trial by Judge Lochren. His most significant argument was that the prosecution's failure to call Julius to testify unfairly affected the results of Tim Barrett's trial.

Prior to the filing of the appeals, Julius, Gertrude, Adolph, Louise, Mary Storey, Peter McLaughlin, and Edward Morrison all returned to the courthouse to swear to what happened the night of July 26, 1887. Methodically each again told their stories to a court reporter and signed an affidavit that their testimony was true.

On a cold January night before the one-year anniversary of the start of Pete's trial, the Supreme Court issued its opinion rejecting all of the defense's arguments. Their logic for rejecting the testimony of the sole eyewitness of the crime at Tim's trial was particularly infuriating to Julius. The court concluded that since the testimony had been presented at Pete's trial and he had been found guilty, the twelve men in the first trial would also not have been persuaded. When Julius read that conclusion, he was so angry that Julia ran and hid under her bed. He roared that if he had been able to refute Reddy's testimony at the first trial, Pete's jury might not have been prejudiced by Tim's conviction.

After the Supreme Court issued its ruling, the brothers' last chance to live was a pardon by the state's new governor. Many in the city agreed with Julius that the trials had been unfair, and they worked hard to convince Governor Merriam to spare the men's lives, especially the boy, Pete. Bill Erwin and his team made direct appeals to the new conservative governor. When those direct appeals were not convincing the man, petitions circulated requesting the governor reconsider the sentences.

An infatuated fifteen-year-old teenager, Ada Boyd, announced that she had collected five thousand signatures on a petition to save her dream lover, Peter Barrett. When she went to St. Paul to personally deliver her petition to the governor, his secretary saved his boss from having to meet with the smitten girl.

William Donahue, the Barrett brothers' other attorney, traveled to St. Paul for a meeting with the governor, carrying a petition signed by three hundred citizens, one-third of whom were attorneys or judges, asking that Pete's sentence be commuted to life in prison because of his age. When Donahue presented the petition to Merriam, he was disappointed when the governor glanced at the first page and then laid the document on a pile of papers.

Ellen Barrett's expensive legal team made one final effort to save at least one of her sons before the governor issued his final decision. John Byrnes, the third member of the team, with the support of an assistant, began a journey of two hundred miles across the vast rural areas of Hennepin County asking the members of Pete's jury to sign a petition requesting that his life be saved. What started as a long shot to ask the long-suffering jurors to admit they may have made a mistake turned out to be successful when they secured ten of twelve signatures. Several jury members admitted that their decision would have been different had they known the boy was going to be sentenced to death.

Not everyone in the city thought that the brothers should be saved. An ugly split developed between those wanting the governor to show Christian charity and those who wanted revenge for Toffelson's death no matter what. Several nights before the scheduled executions, a group of Scandinavian immigrants from South Minneapolis said that they did not care about any new evidence in Pete's favor. "He is a Catholic, and that is all the evidence we need to decide that he should be hung."

The petition of the love-struck Ada Boyd, the appeals of the legal community, and the remorse of the jury had no effect on Governor Merriam. At ten o'clock the night before the brothers were to be hung, the governor left his irritated wife, who could not understand why anybody cared about those two ruffians, to face the reporters on his porch. No one expected that he would save Tim, but there was still hope for Pete. That hope ended when the large affable man took his cigar out of his mouth and the corners of his handlebar mustache drooped, changing his look from confident happiness to respectable solemnity. He flicked ashes from his cigar and then confirmed that he would not be commuting Pete's sentence. After the passing of an appropriate minute or two, the jovial look returned to the governor's face as he answered several questions about the current legislative session. When the questions on his favorite topic were over, he turned his back to the whole sordid affair and flicked burnt ashes onto the floor of his porch, exactly as he had just done to Pete's life.

On the afternoon of March 22, 1889, downtown Minneapolis returned to normal. The clock in the courthouse's tower announced the quarter hours, streetcars rumbled down Washington Avenue, and the Milwaukee Road depot bustled with action as travelers arrived and departed from the city. On the corner outside Julius's office, a paperboy hawked the special edition of his paper, which described the Barrett brothers' last hours before they reached the end of their ropes at eleven o'clock that morning.

Julius sits in his office wondering what would have happened if he had taken streetcar 132 that night. Would he and Tom Toffelson now be rotting next to each other in Layman's Cemetery, or would they enjoy a beer together tonight at Lally's saloon? Would Pete Barrett have continued on the road of crime, or would he have transformed into a productive citizen?

Julius shakes his head to throw these thoughts out of his mind. There is no longer any reason to dwell on that steamy July night when the fates of the young Norwegian, Irish and German men tragically collided at the corner of Lake Street and Cedar Avenue.

Trinity Evangelical Lutheran Church Bremen, Minnesota circa 1909. Anna's grave is in the center. From the "Geschichte der Synod von Minnesota und andern Staaten" published in 1910

Part VII
Anna's Final Homes

October 17, 1889 – Bottineau, North Dakota

A new two-row buggy appears to be gliding between the tall brown prairie grass and the golden black-eyed Susans of Bottineau County. Homesteaders stop their work to rest their backs when the elegant vehicle passes their farms. For most, seeing a buggy pulled by two prancing horses is rare. Since they moved to some of the last land available for settlement in their new country, the only vehicle they see on the road to the county seat is a broken-down farm wagon pulled by oxen.

Anna sits behind her son-in-law, August, and twelve-year-old grandson, Amandus, unaware of the envious stares of her fellow settlers. The steady beat of the horse's hooves on the dirt road, the meadowlarks singing in the grasses, grasshoppers rhythmically creaking in the wheat stubble, and the October sun shining on her black dress cause her head to bob down to her chest as she falls in and out of a deep sleep. While she slumbers, vivid dreams replay the past four years in her mind. Then when the carriage bounces over a fox den, a flock of geese squawks overhead, or a cool fall breeze makes her shiver, her head violently jogs back up. During those miles, she worries about declaring her intention to become a citizen of the United States at the end of this eighteen-mile trip to Bottineau.

Anna's first two years in Minnesota were satisfying. She loved traveling from one of her children's houses to the next, telling her grandchildren stories of the "olden days" back home. Determined that the children would not forget their heritage, she sternly required them to speak only German when she was with them.

By the end of her first winter in the frozen tundra of Minnesota, Anna eagerly anticipated teaching five more grandchildren. The first was a boy, Otto, born to August and Maria on the first anniversary of the day she looked over the ship's railing at the unfinished Statue of Liberty. Two weeks later, Albert and Auguste added a second Otto to her family. While Anna was planning her second Christmas in America, daughters-in-law Bertha, Minnie and Louisa, the daughters of her neighbors in Germany, gave birth to three granddaughters within two weeks. The bounty of the harvest and the expansion of her family that year created a strong immune response to the homesickness that she was still suffering.

After the baptism of little Otto Paul Erdmann, christened in memory of his two deceased aunts, Ottilie and Pauline, Anna stepped out of the church at Bremen Corners into the humid, late-spring air. She stopped at the door to enjoy the brief coolness of the breeze. Her thoughts were interrupted when a deer sauntered across the cemetery that surrounded the building. The long-legged animal's ears stood straight up when it saw Anna, then it took a bite from a bouquet of flowers that a grieving mother had left that morning on her child's new grave. As the brazen animal lobbed away across the rolling hills of wheat, Anna turned to Gustav standing next to her. "I could spend eternity here," she told her son.

That feeling did not last. Maria's August had purchased eighty-five acres one mile from the church shortly after they arrived. He found the land just as hilly and rocky as Our August had found his first farm. Every time his plow pulled up another limestone shelf rock, he swore that he was going to join his brother-in-law in the Dakota Territory, where he could receive free land by homesteading. He told himself that he was born to be a farmer, not a stone mason like Gustav, who was content with his small rock farm on the road to Hammond.

During the short window of time between planting and threshing, the Erdmann family took the train to Grafton to visit Our August and his family.

On her first night in the Dakotas, Anna sat on her son's new porch and stared across the endless horizon that was broken only miles in the distance by the black cloud of smoke of an approaching train. As the train rumbled past the house, carrying farm supplies north from Minneapolis, it momentarily drowned out the ear-splitting screams of play of the newly acquainted cousins.

Taking advantage of the temporary calm after the train passed and the children found a quieter activity, Our August told Maria's August, "German families from the area are moving west to a new railroad stop called Willow City."

Maria's August said, "I've heard of the town. One of the Kitzmann brothers from Potsdam staked a claim there."

The two Augusts decided to take a 150-mile trip west to explore the area. When the train chugged into the depot at Willow City, they were met by Theodore Lehmann, whom Our August had followed from Pleasant Valley to Grafton. As the men traveled in the wagon five miles west to Lehmann's dugout house, the two brothers-in-law looked across the flat plain that was only occasionally interrupted by trees that appeared to be weeping along the banks of snaking Willow Creek as it flowed north, south, east and west before merging into the Souris River, its waters then flowing out of the country into Canada.

The next morning, Lehmann took the two Augusts to an available piece of land near his claim by the creek. Maria's August grabbed a shovel from the wagon and used it to cut through the prairie grass and then dug another two feet into richer and richer soil. He looked up at Lehmann and held out his hand. "It looks like you will have a new neighbor."

Later the men sat by the door of Lehmann's dugout, drinking beer and watching the sunset. The host said that the area's families were trying to organize a church. "My former pastor at the church in St. Thomas north of Grafton has been traveling here to deliver sermons at Friedrich Kitzmann's and my houses. In three years, I think we have grown enough for a full-time pastor. We asked Pastor Feulling to fill the position. Unfortunately, he accepted another call." Lehmann assured Maria's August, "We are not giving up."

The first Sunday after they returned to Bremen, Maria's August leaned on a large tombstone halfway between the church and the parsonage and, excited, told the other men of the congregation about the vast land available in the Dakota Territories. He was not alone in his enthusiasm as the Schroeders, Kitzmanns and Rothgarns said that they were also planning to join brothers, cousins and former neighbors on the wind-swept prairies near Willow Creek. Maria's August quickly sold his farm to Friedrich Hoffmann and prepared to move his family for the second time in two years.

It has been only eighteen months since the family made the grueling trip from the relative comfort of Bremen to the claim less than thirty miles from the invisible border between the United States and Canada. When Anna, Maria and the five grandchildren, ages eleven to almost two, first arrived, they all thought that August was joking. On their way to the claim, they saw tired-looking shacks made from the deep roots of the prairie grasses that had been undisturbed for centuries. Women stood in front of these haphazard houses and looked exhausted from overwork. Dirty children were next to their mothers, appearing not to have bathed in months. Anna saw those forlorn souls and wondered, "Have I made a mistake?"

Once at the claim, the two women learned that they, too, would live in one of those pitiful houses. First, they would have to help August build it. Neighbors who had made the same struggle one or two years earlier came to help. August cut from his new fields large slabs of grass and dirt as he cleared the land to plant his first crop. His neighbors helped him to drag the heavy slabs back to the building site and stack them to create the walls of their first house. Those dirt walls were then wallpapered with old newspapers. The ground between the walls was packed hard to make a floor. Anna, who had always been proud of the cleanliness of her family and home, again doubted whether she had made the right decision.

Only one window and one door brought light into the dark house—which did not matter, as there was not much to see outside. Rather than a blooming apple tree or an orange and white cow with an hourglass mark on her face grazing peacefully in a pasture, all Anna saw was grass as tall as her waist, shrub trees growing by the creek, and a faraway horizon. She sadly thought that the thatched-roof, timber-hewed cottage where she had been born was finer than this sod and log shack where the six of them now lived.

Life changed quickly during the first summer near the banks of Willow Creek. The heat baked their walls into concrete. Maria let out her dresses to accommodate the next child. August broke more sod with his team of oxen while staring hopefully at the cloudless western sky and praying for rain. Anna and the older grandchildren walked the land, picking up the bones and droppings of bison that had once grazed here. On baking days, Anna heated the oven with the large dried buffalo chips. In the evening, as the family enjoyed her fresh bread, she had to force from her mind the fuel she used to bake it.

The rains that August prayed for did not come. Last year's most profitable crop was the bones that Anna and the grandchildren collected. They piled them to overflowing in the wagon. August then traveled to the train station in Willow City, where he sold them for sixty dollars a ton.

Another call was made for a pastor for the local church. This candidate, Pastor Huber, accepted. Later in the summer, when it was clear that the harvest was going to be bad, the farmers sadly had to withdraw the offer, which distressed Anna greatly. She had always lived within walking distance of a Lutheran minister. Finally, two months ago, at the farm of their neighbor August Hinz, Anna watched Pastor Zagel be ordained and installed as the first pastor of Immanuel Lutheran Church. After the new pastor's long, first sermon, Maria's August stood with seventeen other tanned farmers to sign the charter for their new church on the prairie.

Watching him glide his pen across the paper, Anna recalled that Friedrich had signed the charter of their new church in Gembitz-Hauland. Memories of her old church had returned to her at Christmastime while she watched August and Maria's new son become one of the first children baptized into this new congregation. Maria stood by the basin of water used during the sacrament, and Anna remembered that the baby's mother had been one of the first baptized children at their old church.

Several weeks ago, the farmers of the congregation built a small church and parsonage. The picnic to feed the hardworking men was as abundant as any Anna had organized back home. After the meal, she sat in the warm Dakota sun and felt her first real connection to this land.

Over the past two summers, Anna often sat on a bench looking across August's wheat field at a piece of vacant land. She was told that to receive the free land offered by the Homestead Act, she would have to declare her intention to be a citizen. For other elderly immigrants who were forced to follow their children to the new country, denouncing the nationality of their birth may have been difficult. Anna, however, thought that governments come and go, but the opportunity for free land was an occasion that happened once in a lifetime. To the surprise of Maria and August, one day Anna announced that she wanted to apply for citizenship.

All of her children were surprised. They had heard the story of Anna's initially attracting the attention of their father by "accidentally" tripping as she left the church. When he died, leaving her with a farm and young children to support, she did not hesitate to find a new husband in the community. When their sister Pauline suddenly and unexpectedly died, she bought a ticket to America. Anna wondered, "Why would they think the simple act of renouncing a king to own land would stop me now? I'm not dead yet."

The piercing sound of a train's whistle startles Anna awake as they enter the village of Bottineau, with its fewer than forty buildings. Her resolve weakens for a minute when the buggy stops in front of the courthouse.

While Anna waits for her grandson Amandus to help her out of the buggy, she looks at the building that was a saloon until the county went dry. She thinks how simple and unimpressive it looks, with only one door and three windows in the front. She wriggles her face in disapproval when she sees the roof line. The center trusses of the building were not placed down the center of the building but rather to the side, creating a steeply pitched roof on one side and a long flowing roof on the other. As Amandus takes her hand, she tells her grandson, "In the past, when I made a major decision, I went to a grand building made of large timbers, stone or brick that usually had a high tower for a bell. This wooden building where the men of the town once wasted their family's money on liquor is not grand enough for the momentous act I am about to do."

The old floor creaks and the door screeches as Anna, August and Amandus enter the building. Inside there is a buzz of activity. Bottineau County is growing fast, and the nearly organized government is bustling every day, resolving disputes, recording transactions and accommodating immigrants who want to become citizens.

Anna and August are at a language disadvantage in this building. Twelve-year-old Amandus has come along today to serve as his grandmother's interpreter. With broken English, he explains to a disinterested clerk why they are here. The man huffs at the indignity of dealing with a boy and simply points to the county's courtroom. In the room, District Court Clerk John Bennett and his deputy, the former Probate Judge Dana, sit behind a table that used to be a bar and now serves as a judge's bench.

Bennett scowls when he sees not only a barrel-chested German farmer, whom he assumes wants to declare his intention to be a citizen, but also an unnecessary old woman and young boy. "Why is this short, wrinkled German woman in a black dress with white hair pulled tightly back in a bun and a blond, blue-eyed boy whose pants don't reach the tops of his worn-out shoes in my courtroom?" he wonders. He starts to ask August questions but is shocked when Amandus says, "No. It is my *Oma* who wants to declare."

Dana rubs his white goatee and grins when he sees that Bennett's disapproving Yankee stare is not intimidating these three. After clearing his throat, Bennett proceeds with the questions he asks every immigrant who seeks citizenship in the United States. When the form is completed, he asks Anna to raise her hand. She stares awkwardly at him until Amandus whispers to his grandmother to raise her right hand. The boy whispers "*Ja*" when a question requires his grandmother to answer the judge affirmatively and "*Nein*" when a negative response is necessary.

After a couple of questions, Anna is startled when the room echoes from the crack of the judge's gavel. Her breathing stops as she notices a flurry of activity at the desk before her. Amandus whispers, "Put your hand down. You just renounced the Kaiser and swore allegiance to the Constitution of the United States." A satisfied smile spreads across his *Oma's* face.

The activity at the desk ends with the clerk handing Anna a paper she cannot read. She feels a tug on her sleeve from her grandson. His finger, black with prairie dirt, points to a line on the paper. "*Oma*, put your mark here," he says. In a space between two words on each side and two words above and below, Anna makes her ***X***. Judge Dana stiffly signs the document and then offers his hand to the new American.

Back on the wooden sidewalk, dust is thick as more and more wagons come to conduct business. Across the street to the northwest, farmers carry the money they earned from this year's crop into the Bottineau County Bank to pay their mortgage. While husbands do their business with Banker Harmon, the women gather in the middle of the block to purchase supplies at the town's two general stores.

Before the trio joins their neighbors, they carefully examine the document Anna has just received. Anna is again embarrassed by Amandus's dirty fingernails as he moves his index finger across the words that he says confirm that she can now own government land. She leans against the wall and breathes a sigh of relief. It has been a long journey, but she is now one step closer to realizing her dream. Although she cannot read the words on the page, she runs her slightly bent arthritic fingers across the signatures of Bennett and Dana. Watching his grandmother, Amandus recognizes her steely no-nonsense expression. He takes a deep breath. He knows she is planning her next adventure.

December 26, 1891 – Devil's Lake, North Dakota

It is the first day of the Rauhnachte. Ancient traditions hold that the twelve days between the birth of Jesus and the attendance of the Magi at his baptism is a dark time when evil spirits attempt to take over the world. As a little girl, Anna cowered in fear that evil spirits would take her during the night.

Today, she is a passenger on a Great Northern train that is chugging through new snow drifts created by a Christmas Eve storm. She smiles as she recalls childhood memories of those magical twelve days. One of her earliest memories is breathlessly hanging over the edge of the farm's well as her youngest uncle was lowered on a rope to clean the devil from the structure's stone walls. The sight of her wet, shivering uncle and her father's quick actions to cover the well to prevent the vanquished spirits from returning to their water is still vivid in her mind.

During Rauhnachte, Anna was not a debutante observer sitting on the crest of a hill watching others fight deadly battles in the valley below. She was a foot soldier in the battle for her family's souls. Her mother supervised the children as they thoroughly cleaned the evil out of walls and floors, like Friedrich the Great leading his troops into the Battle of Mollwitz. As soon as she could, Anna would escape to the barn to watch her father spray the animals with a pungent incense to ward off spirits.

But it was a time of fun as well as fear. On the first day of the year, the numerous children in the neighborhood would band together, marching from farm to farm as they banged metal pots and sang ear-splitting songs to scare the devil away. Finally, after twelve days, the battle would be won and celebrated with an Epiphany meal. Everyone thanked God that they had survived the dark time. As she looks out the train window at the snow blowing across fallow fields, Anna fondly thinks that those twelve days of the year were among the scariest and most magical of her long-ago childhood.

As she always did on Christmas night, Anna sat in her rocker by the wood stove with her grandchildren circled around her feet. From her perch, she warned them of the danger the family faced for the next two weeks. The younger boys sat cross-legged with mouths gaping open and eyes popping out. Her older grandchildren simply rolled their eyes as their blunt grandmother began her familiar story. The old woman wagged her finger at the small boys and warned them of the evil that had overwhelmed the family twenty-three years ago. She tells the boys it was on a Christmas night just like tonight when their step-grandfather was sitting in his rocker by the fire digesting his Christmas feast feeling strong, healthy, and happy. By the end of Rauhnachte, he was sick with typhus and dead within two weeks. Fear overwhelmed three-year-old Ernest, the first child of the family born in the Dakota Territory, and he ran screaming to his mother.

The large barrel chest of the children's father shook from laughter as he witnessed the traditional annual chaos his mother-in-law brought to his house. While calming her petrified son, Maria scolded her mother, as she did every year, to stop scaring the children. Teenage arrogance seeped out of the mouths of the older children as they joined in the scolding.

They tried to be adults as they told their grandmother to forget the old superstitions from across the ocean while they also secretly enjoyed the tradition.

When she woke up this morning, Anna was glad to see that the Christmas storm had moved east. Winters on the North Dakota prairie are hard and too often deadly. She has been looking forward to boarding the train in Willow City to spend the rest of the winter with her sons' families in Minnesota. Her arrival in Minnesota, though, needs to be delayed one day. She and Maria's August have an important stop to make at the Devil's Lake Land Office.

Before Anna left the home she had built with Friedrich in the woods of Gembitz Hauland, she was told by the travel agent that the government of the United States would give her free land. Two years ago, after declaring her intention to become a citizen, she stared at the unclaimed land next to the Erdmann farm, ready to claim her bounty.

The Homestead Act did not make life any easier on the prairie. Anna learned that the Homestead Act required her to build a house and continuously live on the land for seven years. After her first winter, she knew that living in a shack alone on the wind-swept prairie without trees or a family to protect her was impractical for a woman her age. Like many of the other settlers, she wanted to escape the long winters by traveling south to Minnesota. If she did, her claim for a homestead would be invalidated. She was convinced that the travel agent who sold her the ticket to America was a lying con man, and she was angry. Bitter complaints against this man were as common as discussions about the weather when she greeted friends at the farm, at her church or at the stores.

One day a bachelor farmer heard one of her outbursts. He told her, "I have been able to leave my claim during the brutal winters by taking advantage of a previous act of Congress passed in 1820. You can claim 160 acres by paying two dollars an acre and improving the cultivation of the property."

Certain that this was another false promise, Anna rejected the advice until August confirmed it was true. Maria's August told her that if she purchased the land, he would agree to rent it and make the necessary improvements.

Anna is shocked back into the present by the train whistle as it shrieks its warning to the residents of Devil's Lake that it is arriving. While the whistle blows, August whispers in his mother-in-law's ear, "The evil spirits do not appear to be as strong this year."

The old woman scoffs at the man who brought her to America. She sharply tells him, "No one knows how strong the spirits will be until the season is over."

Other passengers see an unusual amused grin on the normally impassive German man's face.

Anna and August carefully step out of the passenger car onto an icy platform and into subzero air. The wind is blowing the new snow into their faces. Anna bundles her heavy buffalo-skin coat around her body and pulls the collar around her face. It does little good as they climb over the small snow drifts on Kelly Street. For four blocks, they pass a checkerboard of vacant lots, livery stables and rooming houses as cold winds freeze Anna's face. The old woman doubts if she will survive the trek when she hears the bell in the imposing tower of the new, three-story brick courthouse gently rung by the howling wind.

Her fingers are tingling when they arrive at Cairn's Hotel to reserve a room for the night. Tomorrow August will take the train back to Willow City while Anna continues to Minneapolis. First, though, they must conduct their important business across the street.

It has been a long morning, and they both are hungry. Before returning to the cold to complete their mission, they order hot coffee and a meal of potatoes and roast beef in the hotel's dining room. Anna bows her head when the meal arrives, praying that the evil spirits stay away until she completes her business.

When they finish eating, they go back out in the cold air for a couple of minutes before entering a large room with high ceilings and dark heavy wood. August steps to the counter. In halting English, he tells the agent that they are there to complete a claim for 160 acres in Bottineau County. August directs the transaction as maps and papers are spread across the counter.

The clerk mistakenly assumes that August is the buyer. He asks the farmer for his citizenship declaration, ignoring the old woman by his side.

Land Recorder Roberts is curious when the farmer in front of him speaks to the woman in German, and she removes the document from her bag. He is surprised again when he asks for the money to complete the Land Patent; again, the short, square, white-haired woman gives him the three $100 treasury notes with the picture of Admiral Farragut and the one $20 note with the picture of Chief Justice Marshall. He removes from the drawer behind him the Land Patent form. As he does many times each week, he begins to complete the form to transfer the ownership of a quarter section of land from the United States to Anan Beutler as written on the citizenship declaration. To Anna, it seems an eternity passes before the man gives August a copy of the document. Her son-in-law gives the paper to her, and she quietly puts the document into the pocket of her bag, now empty of money.

Anna does not examine the paper until she returns to her hotel room. She sits in the only chair and carefully removes it from its hiding place in her bag. Taking a deep breath, she stares at the paper and recognizes that her dream of owning land in America has come true.

On the second day of Rauhnachte, Anna gets up early and eats a hearty breakfast of eggs, smoked ham and fried potatoes in the hotel dining room. She then wraps herself again in her warm buffalo coat and walks four blocks back to the passenger depot. Exactly twenty-four hours after she had stepped off the train in Devil's Lake she hears the distinctive whistle of the Great Northern train in the distance as it arrives on its way to Minneapolis.

Maria's August helps his mother-in-law to her seat in the passenger car. As he leaves the car he tells her, "When I see you in the spring, I will be planting your land."

Once the train pulls away from the depot, Anna sits back in her seat. Within moments of feeling the forward motion of the chugging train, she looks out the right window to see men cutting big blocks of ice on the large lake the town is named for. It is hard for her to believe on this cold morning how refreshing the ice cream made with that ice will taste during an oppressive heat wave next summer. First, though, she is looking forward to tonight when she will see her sons Julius and Adolph and their families before she continues to Gustav's home for the rest of the winter.

Hours later, when the train pulls into Union Depot along the Mississippi River in downtown Minneapolis, Anna is overwhelmed by the crowd. Panic overcomes her when she sees the sea of people. Then she sees Julius standing on the platform. The sight of her son in a fine suit and a proper black bowler hat with a large cigar poking out of his mouth makes Anna proud. Those warm feelings do not last long when she steps out of the car and is assaulted by the cold winds blowing through the tunnels of the covered rail platform. Her maternal pride also quickly ebbs when she greets her son and smells whiskey on his breath. She gives her wayward son a disapproving look.

Anna does not want to spoil the moment by scolding the boy, who has been a challenge since he was a baby and screamed relentlessly throughout the night. Instead, as they walk through the large brick building that expands along almost an entire city block, she admires the cavernous waiting area, the wooden benches, the porters moving trunks, and the din of passengers coming and going. The mother and son step out of the large double doors into the late afternoon tussle of the city. They walk two blocks on the icy sidewalks of Hennepin Avenue to the streetcar stop on Washington Avenue.

The mules pulling streetcar 132 stop at the corner. Julius tells his mother, "This is the car where Tom Toffelson was murdered." He immediately recognizes that sharing that fact with her was a mistake. The woman, whose greatest danger usually is a lost skunk wandering into the house, breathes heavily and starts shaking, certain that she will be gunned down in this dangerous city.

Julius finds his mother a seat on one of the car's wooden benches. Her hearing is beginning to fail, requiring him to talk loudly over the din of the car and the city. "We are going to Adolph's house. Gertrude and I are moving again and don't have room for you to stay with us. Plus, I am worried about her. She has more and more difficulty walking and has started to use a cane."

Julius changes the subject to his daughter, Julia. He proudly tells his mother, "She is becoming a very independent teenager. She has been doing most of the housework plus finding odd jobs at many businesses in the city."

When the streetcar arrives at the turnaround at Lake and Cedar, Anna sees her youngest son standing at the corner, smoking a cigar. He helps her descend the two back steps of the streetcar. Then Anna proudly walks south on Cedar Avenue, supported by a son on each arm.

Climbing the steps of Adolph's porch, she is greeted at the door by her daughter-in-law and two shy girls hiding behind their mother's skirt. Anna is distracted from greeting the shy toddlers by the little bump in Louise's dress. Almost every year for the past twenty, at least one grandchild has been added to the family, and she is excited that 1892 is not an exception. The second day of Rauhnachte is almost over. As she steps over the transom of Adolph's house, Anna thinks the family will beat the evil spirits this season.

When the family finishes the meal Louise and Gertrude prepared, Anna's sons ask to see the paper that says she owns land. She does not understand what the boys are saying as they read the document. Suddenly the dark feeling that the evil spirits have tricked her overwhelms her.

Seeing their mother's distress and unable to convince her that everything is okay, Julius and Adolph give the paper to thirteen-year-old Julia. She sits on a stool next to her panicked grandmother. Just like her cousin Amandus when Anna became a citizen, she runs her finger across the paper, reading and translating the words. With a voice of authority, Julia reads, "According to the provisions of 'An Act making further provision for the sales of the Public Lands,' passed by the Congress on the twenty-fourth day of April 1820, the southwest quarter of Section 36 in the Township One Hundred and Sixty north of Range Seventy-Six west of the fifth Principal Meridian in North Dakota has been purchased by Anan Beutler."

The grandmother does not notice that the girl quickly skipped over the line that read, "do give and grant unto the said Anan Beutler and to 'his' heirs." Julia quickly decided that it was best that her nervous grandmother did not know that the agent not only misspelled her name but also misrepresented her gender.

On Epiphany, Anna is eating another large family dinner at the home of her oldest son, Gustav. She is relaxed: she survived one more Rauhnachte without serious calamity. She is still fixated on the validity of the piece of paper she received on the first day of the darkness. She is convinced that she has lost her money. No amount of assurances from her four grown sons and their wives can permanently remove the fear from her mind.

That afternoon Gustav's seventeen-year-old son Max decides to step into the family fray. A huge confident smile is on the face of the serious young man when he attempts to calm his grandmother. "Even though your first name is spelled wrong and the paper says you are a man, it is legal," Max says. He moves his grandmother's finger to the signature of the U.S. President. "President Harrison says you now own a piece of land as big as the farms of the Leppkes, Westphals, Nickolais and Wankes plus all of the pastures, fields and forests. Do you remember how long it took us to walk all those pastures, fields and forests when I was a little boy, *Oma*?" That pleasant memory relieves Anna.

Rauhnachte ends like it began. Anna's aging mind hopes that her dream has been realized, but she is still not convinced that anything good can happen during this season. She tells her assembled grandchildren, "Not until I return to Willow City in the spring and see your uncle turning that land black will I believe it is real. I will know then that my dream has come true."

July 11, 1893 – Gembitz Hauland

The acrid smell of smoke burns the nostrils and eyes of the Westphal family as the summer sun begins to set. Bertha Westphal rubs her irritated eyes as she removes several sheets of precious paper from a chest. Earlier, when the family was leaving the smoldering pile of ash that had been their church, her father, August, stopped to look at the red glow one last time. Then he told his oldest child, "I want you to write to your grandmother in America. She must know about this."

While searching for the right words, Bertha gazes out the window. The lingering smoke in the air has turned tonight's sunset bright orange. Admiring the beauty of the setting sun, memories of her grandmother and the church flood her mind. She rubs her red eyes, now more irritated by her memories than by the smoke.

As she dips her pen in the ink she remembers the day she protested going to their Lutheran school. She was afraid as her angry grandmother's eyes narrowed before the scolding. "Every member of the church sacrificed to start that school. We wanted our children and grandchildren to be able to read and write, unlike us. I expect you to appreciate what we did for you and appreciate the education we are providing."

Tonight, as she addresses the letter intended for her grandmother to her aunt and godmother Maria, Bertha is glad she listened to that stern rebuke.

Liebe Tante Maria und Onkel August.

Only two days ago, I received the Lord's blessing at the communion rail that you, my family, and all of my other aunts and uncles had worn smooth from frequent use. Unknown to me, I was praying before that old wooden cross above the altar for the last time. I felt such joy on my way back to my seat when I looked at the pew where Oma always sat. You could still see her outline rubbed into the wood by the many years of her faithful attendance. Now it is all destroyed.

A tear falls from her cheek, smearing the last word.

To regain her composure, Bertha stops writing and recalls the day her *Oma* Heyn left. After the wagon carrying her disappeared, Bertha went into the house and carefully rewrapped the precious gift she was given to wear at her confirmation. Then she hid it from her brothers and sister near the bottom of their old wooden trunk between their mother's wedding dress and the family's baptism gown. On Palm Sunday five years ago, she finally retrieved the package.

Looking across the room, Bertha sees the old trunk and remembers her four-day-old stepsister Hulda was sleeping next to her mother, Bertha's cousin Alwine, on that morning. Bertha now has two more stepbrothers, but she feels a special connection to Hulda. She also was born illegitimate. Bertha was six months old before her father and mother married. Staring at the pen in her hand, she thinks that little Hulda was fortunate because she legally received the Westphal name only three months after she was born.

Bertha had waited until she arrived at the church on the day of her confirmation to unwrap the veil her mother had worn as a member of the church's first confirmation class. When she took her mother's place at the communion rail for the first time, the yellowed lace softly touched each cheek and felt like gentle kisses from her mother and grandmother.

Other memories of the past slow her progress in describing the current events. Today began much like the day ten years and four days ago when her mother was killed. Like that Saturday morning, black clouds were forming to the west past their cows grazing in the pasture. Her father had ended the last meal her mother prepared, saying, "Thank God the crops are finally going to get some rain." This morning, as the clouds began to darken the house, he finished the breakfast prepared by her stepmother, uttering the same words.

Since the day her mother was struck by the lightning bolt, the flashes and booms of a summer storm scare her. This morning, only months away from her twentieth birthday, that fear had not lessened. As the storm struck, she hugged her scared three-year-old stepbrother Adolph since she was too old for a doll. She loosened her grip on the boy when the worst seemed over. Then the horror of electricity struck her life again.

Bertha groans and continues writing.

A summer storm was passing when a large
bolt of lightning fell out of the dark sky.
There was a flash, boom and fire almost
all at the same time. Seeing the flames and
thinking a neighbor was in trouble, Papa
and the boys ran to hitch the horses to the
wagon. Then he snapped the reins hard,
leaving the boys and me running after him.
I am sure the sight was the same as you
saw the day you rolled away from our lives.
When we arrived at the muddy middle
road, we saw it was not a neighbor's house
or barn burning, but the church.

The families who live near the crossroads

were able to save the baptismal font and some furniture before the flames became too strong. By the time we arrived, all we could do was stand helpless in the rain as the roof that once protected all of us fell, creating a blazing bonfire. Pastor Schwerdtseger led us in prayer as the heart of our community turned to ash.

Later this afternoon, as I looked at the glow of the embers inside one of the ancient timbers, I felt that it was not just the building that was being destroyed. That old structure, built before Oma was born, was our connection not only to those who rest in the cemetery down the road but also to all of you who have moved away. As the cinders of our past rained down on my head, I was certain that the fire was burning through the rope that connects me to you.

Now, as I write this sad letter, I know that you will always be with me. Across the room, Emma, who was barely two months old when Mama died, is washing the dishes. Every year she looks more and more like I remember Mama and Oma. In a month, the orchard that Oma tended so carefully will have bushels of plums for Papa to distill into his special brandy. As I near the end of the page, I can hear the gentle sounds of one of her special cows mooing in the pasture. Please assure Oma that neither her memory nor yours burned today. It surrounds me everywhere.

Beste Grüße deine liebe Nichte Bertha.

March 21, 1894 – Bremen, Minnesota

Gustav leans against the door frame of his church. His finest pipe dangles from his mouth as he enjoys the warmth of the second day of spring. Around the foundation of the church, the daffodils and crocuses pop out of their winter slumber. Across the road, the knolls of the hills are beginning to dry. The peacefulness of the moment is broken by a bright red cardinal perched in a pine tree, serenading his mate with a seductive tune.

Seven years ago, on a hot, late spring Sunday, Gustav stood here with his mother, admiring the same view. That day she took a deep breath of humid air before telling him, "I could spend eternity here." The recently orphaned forty-nine-year-old thinks, "Tomorrow, she will get her wish."

His sadness at losing the previous generation is tempered by the joy of watching members of the next one compete with each other to dig their grandmother's final physical home. Even though there is little snow on the ground and the frost has not been driven deep, his sons and nephews are working hard, swinging pickaxes to open the grave; the struggling boys are lucky it has been a mild winter. Normally during the last two weeks of March, there would have been a multi-foot blanket of snow to clear and then three or more feet of frozen ground to chop through.

Memories of his youth flood Gustav's mind as he watches the boys test their physical limits. It was only yesterday when he was young, strong and competing with his brothers to dig a frozen grave for his stepfather. His knee is aching from standing too long in the cold. It is a painful reminder that youth is just a short introductory chapter in the book of life.

Gustav returns to the interior of his simple country church. He smiles: friendly competition is taking place not only outside but also in the building. The women of the congregation are busy scrubbing and polishing. Tomorrow, his mother's funeral is also Maundy Thursday. For the next four days, there will be a flow of visitors to the church. The women are determined that no visitor will leave thinking they are poor housekeepers.

Several women take a break from their work to offer Gustav condolences. Their mothers had taught them that sincere sympathy is expressed not with words but rather with food. Each woman offers him a jar of last summer's vegetables, a loaf of bread or a cake made with the secret recipe they brought to America in their head. He thanks them for their concern while assuring the women that his house is overflowing with not only people but also food.

Three miles away, a buggy pulled by a pair of chestnut roan geldings comes to a stop in front of Gustav's kitchen porch. When she hears the jingle of the harness outside her kitchen, Bertha steps out to greet her expected guests. In the front seat, Albert's pudgy eight-year-old son Otto is squeezed between his slight father and equally diminutive uncle August. In the back seat, wedged tight between the seat's low metal rails, are Albert's wife Auguste and his sister Maria, seven months pregnant with her eighth child. Otto jumps from the buggy before it comes to a full stop, eager to play with his cousins. Albert loudly scolds his young son for his rudeness before joining his brother to help the ladies descend from the buggy.

The past two days have been busy and tiring for Maria and August. It was nearly dusk on Sunday when the telegrams they were expecting arrived at the telegram offices in Grafton and Willow City. That morning as they were celebrating Jesus' triumphant arrival in Jerusalem, their mother had hitched a ride on his donkey before it passed through the gates of heaven.

In each of their homes on the Dakota prairie there was no discussion about if they would attend their mother's funeral at the first church where they worshipped in America. Well-worn train schedules were laid across the table, and suitcases were packed. August took the train south from Grafton to meet Maria's eastbound train in Grand Forks. From there, they chugged together across Minnesota, arriving at 7:30 last night at the depot on the edge of Viola.

After nearly two days of travel the tired siblings were relieved to see their brother Albert standing on the platform. On the road to his farm, illuminated by a large full moon, they questioned their brother about their mother's death. He simply summarized the details into two logical thoughts. "Thankfully, she is not suffering any longer." Then in his typically blunt manner, "The specifics are not important because every creature is born, lives and dies."

Now the two travelers have finally arrived at their sad destination. Bertha directs them to the house's parlor after they enter her spotless kitchen. From the dining room, the trio of siblings can see the cold face of their mother in the adjoining room, lying on a bed of fine silk in a highly polished hexagon coffin surrounded by colorful paper flowers. The two brothers, as they did when they were children, protectively stand on each side of their baby sister as they walk to their mother. At the edge of the coffin, they become lost in their own thoughts and memories.

Albert is tired and reacts the least. Since his mother became ill, he has repeatedly shuttled the nine miles between his farm and his brother's. Contrary to his stark message last night, Albert is grateful that the young undertaker was able to make Anna look so peaceful. That was not how she looked on Sunday. In the morning, she lay in the adjoining room's bed, violently thrashing her arms and legs. Her mouth hung open, her saliva soaking the pillow as she painfully gasped for each breath. Then with almost no warning, there were no more gasps of air or movement in the bed. When Albert returned to the room, her mouth was frozen open, locked in place as her body fought for its last breath. Her eyes were also frozen open as if she were witnessing an unbelievable sight. Albert had thought as he passed through Potsdam that night that the vision would haunt him for the rest of his life. Now he is thankful that it was not his final memory of his mother.

August is thinking about his mother's hazelnut crown cake. In four days, just as he has done every year since he was a little boy, he will eat a slice of the brightly decorated cake after his Easter dinner. Minnie has been baking that traditional cake every year since their first spring in America. He never thought that any of those twenty-plus cakes were as delicious as the ones he remembered as a boy. Two years ago, Anna celebrated Easter at his home. During the visit, she admitted to her daughter-in-law that when she gave Minnie the recipe as they were leaving for America, she purposely omitted an ingredient. Last Easter, after including the missing ingredient, the cake still was not the same as his mother's. Looking at her body, August thinks that he will have to accept twenty years of disappointment. On Sunday, and at all future Easters, there will be no possibility of tasting his mother's moist, nutty cake again.

Maria looks at the mannequin that resembles her mother—and the baby suddenly kicks her stomach hard. The painful punch is a blunt reminder that this will be the first of her eight babies who will not be handed to her by the hands now clutching an Easter lily. This overwhelms the usually strong woman. Her surprised brothers react quickly as Maria falls to the floor.

The brothers help their grieving sister to a chair. Then they pull back the black curtains surrounding the bier on which their mother's coffin rests. Behind the curtains are two silver washtubs used by Bertha and her daughters on Mondays to wash the family's dirty clothes and on Saturday nights to wash the family. Since their mother's death, they have been filled with snow and ice to slow her body's decay until tomorrow's funeral. They are heavy with melted ice. Each man grabs a handle to carry the tubs outside, dump the water and refill them with fresh snow and ice. The family clock chimes twelve times as the two brothers return the tubs to their special hiding place.

At the sound of the clock, Albert remembers it is time for him to go to Elgin to meet the 12:30 train that brought his mother back to him nine years before. This time he will meet his two youngest brothers, Julius and Adolph. Tomorrow the six surviving children of Friedrich and Anna Heyn will be together in a church for the first time in almost thirty years.

Later, a buggy pulled by two horses going west and a wagon pulled by two others going east meet at Gustav's driveway. As the two vehicles approach the porch, six of Anna's grandsons ranging in age from manly twenty-one to boyish twelve pile out of the wagon to quickly greet their uncles riding in the buggy.

Inside the house, the boys politely greet their other visiting aunt and uncle. They are at the ages when they are always hungry, and breaking the ground for their grandmother's grave has made them especially famished. Immediately they head for the dining room table that was extended to full length to hold the mountains of food brought by the neighbors. Each boy loads his plate to overflowing. Bertha and Auguste scold their sons, "Do not take more food than you can eat." The five adult brothers smile, thinking they are hearing the voice of their mother.

Julius and Adolph enter the parlor. Like their brothers and sister before them, each becomes lost in individual thoughts and memories.

Julius looks down at his mother's lips, which the undertaker prepared to appear severe and stern. He saw that look many times when he returned home after a fun escapade. He remembers how much he hated that look then and how grateful he is for it today. While he did not always appreciate his mother's advice, he now recognizes how comforting that security was growing up. His mind flashes for a moment to Tim and Pete Barrett, swinging at the end of a rope at the end of their lives. He recently read that their mother had been arrested in Omaha for fraud. Maybe if those two boys had had a strict, stern mother like the woman in the black dress lying before him, they would not now be decaying in unmarked graves.

Adolph, the youngest, thinks his special place in the family hierarchy has been lost forever. No one will ever again marvel at how much he looks like the father he can barely remember. His older nieces and nephews will have memories of their grandmother that they will pass on to their grandchildren. His three small children will have only fragments of memory that will slowly fade away. The only grandparent his future children will know will be Louise's rapidly aging father. He sighs and thinks that being the youngest may have advantages when you are a boy, but as an adult, it means that your children spend much less time with a benevolent grandparent.

After the impending starvation of the boys is interrupted, the six siblings fill their own plates. Sitting around the table, years of adulthood vanish, replaced by youthful sibling teasing and taunts. Those youthful feelings disappear when they look up from the table to see their mother's lifeless body. The six youngsters put down their knives and forks and quickly return to adulthood.

The sun lowers in the western sky. It is time for the siblings to separate to go to the various homes where they will stay tonight. Julius agrees to sleep in the bed where his mother died. Adolph leaves with his father-in-law and brother-in-law, who arrived this evening from Owatonna, to spend the night with Louise's cousin, Emilie Bartz. August returns to the farm in the valley where he and Minnie started their married life. Now it is owned by the widower of Minnie's sister Amalie, Henry Schaeffer. Maria bounces across the country roads in Albert's buggy to the bed she slept in last night.

The next morning two shiny black horses with braided manes pull a tattered old black hearse to the front steps of Gustav's front porch. The undertaker steps down from his perch after securing the horses' reins and greets Gustav with a jovial German salutation. He apologizes for the condition of his hearse and brags that he recently placed an order for a new hearse that will have curved glass on all sides of the carriage for people to pay their respects from any direction as they stand by the side of the road watching the procession. He marvels that after only two years in the business, he will be investing nine hundred dollars for the new death coach. The man's cheery chatter is a welcome relief to the grieving Gustav, but his thoughts are elsewhere, and he turns and enters his house.

Inside, the parlor is filled with siblings, spouses, grandchildren, neighbors, friends, and Pastor Lindmark, standing in front of the open coffin. The pastor leads the inhabitants of the rapidly warming room in prayer and song. When he is finished, for a final time each sibling takes a turn to look at the body that, as children, they ran to during moments of distress. At this moment of their greatest distress, even in a room full of people, each feels entirely alone, with no one to run to. Then the undertaker replaces his previous jocularity with the required cold solemnity of his profession. He methodically places the lid on the coffin, blocking the family's view of their matriarch forever.

Anna's remains are carried out of the house feet first to ensure that the evil spirits are sucked out of the house with the coffin. Her six grandsons each grab one of the wooden handles of the coffin and slide it gently into the hearse. On the porch, their fathers, mothers, aunts and uncles stand without emotion, watching the coffin decorated with paper flowers disappear.

It is a bumpy ride for the hearse and the long line of buggies following it on the zig-zag three-mile route west and north to the church. The buggies carrying Anna's family are followed by mourners with the familiar faces and names of Hoffmann, Wanke, Wegner, Radel, Fedder, Meitzner, Gehlhar and Siewert. Gustav enjoys a long puff of sweet tobacco before he turns to his wife, who is crying at the loss of her second mother. "Mama's physical circle of life did not meet where it began, but her personal circle did."

The procession turns into the driveway near the parsonage, dodging a flock of fleeing chickens kept by the pastor's wife. Mourners' eyes gravitate to their left at the mound of brown, yellow and red clay left by the boys yesterday.

At the steps to the wooden church on the hill, the six grandsons slowly pull their grandmother's coffin from the back of the hearse. The four oldest each take a corner while the two youngest take their place in the center. They struggle to keep it level as they slowly carry it up the steps. Then each adult child, two by two in order of birth, follows their mother into the sanctuary. Pastor Lindmark, who led the procession, patiently waits for everyone to take their seat before he begins the funeral liturgy.

When the somber service is completed, Anna is carried out of the church. Mourners shiver when a blast of cold air enters the building as her grandsons carry her across the transom of an Evangelical Lutheran Church for the last time. The boys carefully navigate the ice, snow and mud, terrified that they will slip and drop her. Behind them, the church bell tolls, and the adults are singing a German hymn off-key. With each treacherous step the weight becomes heavier. Their arms are aching by the time they arrive at the grave a short distance down the small hill.

They rest the coffin on two boards that were laid across the hole. Gustav and Albert take their place at the center of the grave, flanked by August and Maria to the left of their oldest brother and Julius and Adolph to the right of their next oldest. Cold is being pulled out of the frozen ground first into their feet and then throughout their bodies as another hymn is sung. Pastor Lindmark stands at the foot of the grave and recites the familiar commitment of Anna's earthly remains to the earth while a biting wind nips at their faces. The pastor reassures the siblings that their mother will rise on a cloudless day in the future, but their minds are wandering through a moving picture of the joys, hopes, sadness and failures they experienced with her.

Pastor Lindmark's "Amen" brings the siblings back to the present. The undertaker steps forward and nods his head to the brothers. It is time for them to lower their mother into the ground. The four youngest brothers each grab an end of the two ropes that were laid across the open hole earlier. Hand over hand, they tighten the ropes until they carry the weight of the coffin. Gustav pulls away the now free boards. Slowly the brothers lower their mother to the bottom of the hole.

Each mourner files past the grave and throws a handful of dirt on the wooden box while saying a quick prayer. Then the undertaker gives Gustav a shovel. He throws four shovelfuls of dirt into the hole: one each for his father, stepfather and two sisters, whom he is sure his mother is now with.

The sounds of those four hollow thuds on the wooden lid are her children's final goodbye. Following their mother's example, the six siblings turn their backs on their cold past. They climb into their buggies, snap the reins, and move forward into the warmth of the future.

Six months later, when the hours of day and night are again equal, Gustav and Albert stand before the grave. The mound of dirt left the afternoon their mother was buried has nearly settled back level with the surrounding ground. At Anna's feet, the wooden cross that was left that afternoon tilts at an awkward angle. Now at her head stands a gray marble spire capped with an ornate carving that resembles a lantern.

The two brothers proudly admire the stone they purchased to immortalize Anna Christina Schmidt Heyn Beutler for generations. Albert's eight-year-old son Otto runs his finger across the words written below MARCH 18, 1894.

Ruhe sanft nieweiten oft von uns bis bev-
ereint
der Himmels Frieden uns mit dir vereinen.

Gustav's eight-year-old daughter Laura cries as she proudly translates the words into English: "Rest in peace, never far from us, until heaven's peace unites us with you."

As the families walk away, a flash of red swoops past their heads. Instinctively each person turns to see the bird that nearly knocked Albert's hat off his head. Perched on the highest pinnacle of the stone is a red cardinal. The bird stretches its neck and begins to sing a high-pitched tune. As the Heyn families leave the cemetery, they are serenaded by the love song of a protective male to his partner, who observes the scene from the church's steeple.

First Dakota Memorial, Walsh County Courthouse, Grafton, North Dakota. Personal photo

Part VIII
First North Dakota

October 2, 1899 – Grafton, North Dakota

Black smoke, shrill whistles and the rhythmic clanging of train cars disturb the peace of the North Dakota morning. Charles Hein is on the Great Northern train traveling east. He is lost in thought as the remnants of previous millennia whiz past his window. As the train passes through the marshes and lakes of central North Dakota into the dried-up bed of the ancient Lake Agassiz, he measures his travel through time by months, not a long-ago ice age.

Another Great Northern train took him west last year. That day farmers were carefully maneuvering their horse-drawn cultivators between the barely visible rows of corn. He joined in the cheers when one of his fellow soldiers in Company C of the First Dakota regiment bragged, "Once we liberate the Filipinos from Spanish rule, we'll be home in time to pick that corn." Already homesick, that day he wished the pain on his backside was caused by a long afternoon on the iron seat of the cultivator, not the hard seat of the train car.

After reaching San Francisco, he boarded a troop carrier for his trip across the Pacific Ocean. One night he stood on the deck staring across the vast rolling water at the infinite number of stars in the sky. His eyes stung when the sea breezes blew a mist of salt water at his face. As he wiped the irritant from his eyes, he remembered his father's endless stories about traveling across the Atlantic. That night he figured out that his father was the same age when he faced his great adventure. He sighed to himself. "Papa was traveling west to create a new life for himself, not to risk it fighting a war."

Charles shivers as a cool fall breeze blows through the open window of the train. He remembers a totally different reaction when his carrier, after a brief stop in Honolulu, pulled into Manila Bay. It was the last day of July, and sweat streamed down his back. The air was so thick he could not take a proper breath as he descended the gangplank. He had forgotten the heat as he enjoyed watching his friends jumping and waving on the dock as they were attacked by mosquitos.

The sound of the train whistle shocks Charles back to the present.

The naive farm boy is now a seasoned soldier who skipped one season's harvest. Across the endless skyline, he can see hundreds of columns of black smoke. Each of those columns represents a threshing crew throwing bundle after bundle of wheat into threshing machines. After risking his life in the jungles of the Philippines, he wonders if he will ever again be satisfied spending his day hoisting those shocks of wheat on and off a wagon.

It has been six days since the decommissioning ceremony at the Presidio. After a sharp salute and blast of gun, he was magically transformed back into a civilian. The army that sent him to fight in jungles halfway around the world announced it had no responsibility to pay for his train ticket home. Fortunately, a committee at home raised the necessary funds for two victory trains to carry their heroes home.

His fellow soldiers were loud and rowdy as they left San Francisco. Order and quiet slowly returned to the train as it passed from the rugged Rocky Mountains to the flat plains of Montana. In Dickinson, North Dakota, after a raucous greeting and welcome at three o'clock in the morning, enough soldiers had reached their homes that the passengers of the two trains merged into one. A much shorter train now approaches the Grafton depot.

As the train's shrill whistle announces his impending arrival, Charles is overcome with the same nervous energy he had preparing for battle. He taps his leg, leans his head against the window, and lets out a huge gasp of air.

In Grafton, a trail of cigar smoke follows his father, August, as he paces through the large crowd gathered at the depot. Even though the smoke irritates the ladies and children, August shows little concern. After each lap, Minnie orders him to please sit down. Each time he replies with a gruff "kein problem, alles gut." As she has done for more than a quarter of a century, Minnie rolls her eyes and shakes her head. She turns to her niece, "He was the same way when we traveled to America with your mother."

It has been a long year. Around the dinner table, August complained about losing the labor of his second son. This spring, he could not enjoy the sweet smell of the freshly disturbed prairie soil. Spending his day sitting on his seeder planting his spring wheat normally reinvigorated his soul, but this year dark thoughts about his son's safety constantly invaded his solitude.

For more than a year, their combination world atlas (bookmarked to the Philippines) and county plat book replaced the family Bible in the parlor. They followed their son's battles in the newspaper and then tried to follow the progress on the map. Rarely did they find the exotic locations. Manila was easy to find, but there was not enough detail on the map for Santa Cruz, Paeta, Busta, Barres, and the other sites. The unknown was terrifying to the family. Whenever a letter arrived, it was months old, doing little to diminish their worries about Charles at the present moment. Finally, two months ago, they received word that the ship carrying Company C had left Manila Bay on the one-year anniversary of the company's arrival.

The rumble of community voices on the platform is suddenly pierced by the faint sound of the train's whistle in the distance. August stops pacing. He takes a final puff on his cigar. A cloud of cigar smoke encircles his head as he waves for Minnie to join him.

She struggles to her feet. After giving birth to ten children, her body is no longer slim or spry. When she is next to her husband, he enthusiastically points to a single column of black smoke rising in the distance. The pain in her joints disappears. Once again, she is a nineteen-year-old bride standing next to her groom, who is pointing at the smoke of a train arriving from the neighboring town. When she sees the same sparkle of anticipation in his eyes as on that day, she smiles.

The smoke comes closer and closer. Then all the clamor on the platform is drowned out by the chugging of the engine, a loud steam whistle, the train's clanging bell, and the screeching brakes bringing the town's precious cargo safely to a stop. A loud cheer erupts as families run along the platform to greet the men hanging out the windows.

Charles's brothers and sisters run with the crowd, but they don't see him. When he begins to rise from his seat, the reflections of James Buckley, Frank Upham, Isadore Driscoll, Peter Tompkins, Alfred Almen, and William Lamb look at him from the window. As the other soldiers rush to the door, Charles falls back into his seat to collect his courage.

When the train is nearly empty, he takes another gasp of air to fill his body with courage. He taps his leg one more time before pulling himself up, then he makes his way to the train door.

Suddenly out of the morning shadows, he is visible to his parents. The one year of pent-up worry escaping from Minnie is as loud, jarring and uncontrollable as the steam released by the train engine. The motherly outburst ends when Charles is safely enclosed in her arms. Her joy is cut short when she looks over her son's shoulder at Margaret Driscoll, standing alone with only memories to hug.

After purchasing the train tickets to bring their soldiers home, the grateful community had enough money left to pay for a proper day of celebration. Of course, there will be political speeches but also parades, banquets, picnics, and finally, tonight a fireworks show. But first, the organizers have mercifully given the families a half-hour to become reacquainted.

The reunion of the Hein family is strained. Only small talk comes easy.

They ask, "How was the weather in the Philippines?"

He responds, "Hot. How was the summer here?"

His mother huffs, "You're too thin. Didn't our army feed you?"

He answers, "The food was terrible. I can't wait to eat one of your threshing crew dinners."

Hulda shoves a baby in his face. "Meet Minnie, your newest niece."

"She looks just like you, sister. That is too bad," he teases.

Finally, his soon-to-be-ten-year-old brother Eddie asks the question everyone is thinking, but only a young boy will say, "How many did you kill?"

Pain is visible in his brother's face. He looks past them and responds, "I think it is time to form the parade to the GAR hall." As their son hobbles away, August and Minnie have a wordless worried conversation with their eyes.

Marching to the GAR hall, Charles sees red, white and blue bunting hanging from every building in town. The streets that he thought as a teenager were too quiet are packed with cheering people waving flags. If not for the pain in his leg, the excitement would have pushed the horror of the Luzon jungles from his mind.

Not wanting his mind to wander back to the humidity, mud and bugs of the jungle, Charles avoids being alone with his family for the rest of the day. To evade their prying questions, he slips into a far corner while enjoying lunch at the hall. At the band concert on Hill Street, he becomes lost in a crowd of other young people. After the concert, he marches one more time with his friends in the grand parade. His legs are tired and hurting badly when they arrive at the reviewing stand at the corner of Fifth and Hill Street. Pain wells up from his feet to his legs and finally his back as he listens to the endless speeches.

After the Grand Banquet, the final festivity at sundown is a grand fireworks display. But each blast that lights up the sky returns Charles to the shores of Manila Bay. His concerned parents watch this morning's confident son jump and shake with every blast. After the grand finale, Charles climbs into the family buggy for the last two miles of his two-month journey.

When they arrive at the farm, his mother offers him a piece of the apple pie she baked especially for him. She is disappointed when, for the first time in his life, he refuses. "The only thing I want after six days on that train is to sleep in my old bed," he yawns.

The next morning Charles wakes up to the smell of one of the hearty breakfasts for which his mother is known across the county. He smiles as he thinks of the fresh bread, strong coffee, eggs, bacon, hotcakes, fried potatoes, his mother's award-winning butter, and other pastries all waiting for him at the massive table that fills most of the kitchen. At that table all of the major decisions for the family have been discussed and made. Charles thinks, "There is no better place to tell the family about the horror I lived."

He pulls himself out of bed and carefully navigates the steep staircase to the first floor. He enters a kitchen buzzing with organized chaos. His mother is barking orders to his sisters in German. The teenage girls' snarky answers to their mother are in English. His father, who has just returned from the barn, snaps at his disrespectful daughters to mind their mother. His two younger brothers agree with their father, which provokes a bitter retort from their mother. Charles takes his usual chair amid the pandemonium, feeling at peace for the first time in more than a year.

After his first serving of breakfast is gone, Charles looks up from his plate and says, "I know you are all curious. Do you have time for me to tell you about the war?" His mind returns to the place it had been yesterday when the train whistle brought him back to the present.

"We were in the Philippines less than two weeks when we prepared for our first battle. At that time, Spain, the enemy I signed up to fight, was all but defeated, but it still held the overcrowded central city of Manila. The Spanish commanders were under orders not to surrender to the Filipinos, who were seeking revenge against the Spanish. Unknown to us, the American and Spanish commanders had agreed to a mock battle where the Spanish would surrender central Manila to the Americans, leaving the Filipino insurgents outside the city walls. With nineteen of our fellow soldiers dead by the time the American flag was hoisted over Manila, the battle did not feel fake to me." August gave his son a disapproving look. He was sure the boy was not telling the truth. The United States, of which he is now a proud citizen, would never risk his son's life with such a deal.

Charles ignores his father and continues. "It was only four days after the 'mock battle' that the reality of war hit us with the crack of a gun. James Buckley, who two weeks before was one of the soldiers I laughed at swatting mosquitos on the dock, was hit and became our first casualty.

"After James's death, we were spared from battle for months. Besides boredom, our greatest enemy was malaria and dysentery. That is why I am so thin. We all became sick at some point. We lost our second member, Frank Upham, in March—not to a bullet but to disease. After nine months in the country with only two deaths, we were becoming confident that we would all go home soon."

His family was silent as they listened, but they could barely hear Charles when he began talking again. He whispered, with his head down, "Then a new war began. The Filipinos were not appreciative that we had liberated them from the Spanish. They insisted that they had not fought Spain to trade being ruled by King Alfonso and his mother for President McKinley. Bitterness turned to open warfare in February. Our new mission was to capture the ungrateful leaders of the insurgency. In late March, we marched through the jungles along the Laguna de Bay, capturing Santa Cruz and Pagsanghan. We had one day's rest after the battle of Pagsanghan before we began marching north to capture Paete.

"When we arrived in the Philippines, we were all issued an old Springfield single-shot rifle that used black powder. With the dampness, it was slow to fire and so inaccurate I couldn't have hit a deer if it was standing on the porch. Even worse, it emitted such a cloud of black smoke that if we fired, the enemy would know exactly where we were. It was so bad that our commander ordered us not to fire on the enemy unless we were under fire."

August exclaimed, "What the hell do I pay taxes for?"

Charles rolled his eyes at his father's outburst and continued. "On the last day of March, each company was given twelve Krag-Jorgensens. That was enough for our scouts and designated sharpshooters. The late afternoon sun was beginning its descent when we arrived at a narrow pass between the lakeshore and the cliffs that had to be three hundred feet tall. Unsure what was ahead, our commander sent Isadore, Peter, Alfred, William, and Tom and three others with their new weapons to scout our position. They walked into a trap. As they passed through a clearing, as many as fifty Filipino insurgents opened fire at close range. They killed Isadore, Alfred, and William immediately. Peter was severely wounded, but he was pulled to safety by Tom Sletteland, who fired from behind a pile of rocks to protect him and the bodies of our friends until we arrived to rout the bastards.

"When we arrived at the clearing, my three friends were lying face down with their blood soaking the ground below them. As teenagers, we lay on similar open fields watching the white clouds pass through the blue sky, dreaming about the girls in town. Seeing them dead on that open field was the worst moment of my life."

Minnie's stomach suddenly contracts into a painful knot. "If Charles had been a better shot, would he also have been lying dead on that jungle grass?" she wonders. To loosen the knot, she says a quick prayer of thanksgiving as Charles continues.

"We had to wait for our long trip home to grieve. The enemy was on the run, and we did not stop our pursuit. For the next two months, we liberated a different village almost every day. The heat was unbearable. Many of our mules dropped dead pulling our wagons. It rained often. At night we were so tired that sleeping on the muddy ground felt as comfortable as my old bed did last night.

"We were overjoyed when after two months of heavy fighting, there were no more deaths. With our year nearly over, we looked forward to leaving the tropics. But before we left, we all gathered at the graves of our friends to assure them they will never be forgotten."

Charles shocked his normally stoic family with his words. A year of war had been neatly packed away in his mind. As he feared yesterday, telling his story to his family released his emotions, and tears ran down his cheeks. For the first time in almost twenty years, Minnie reached out to comfort the pain of her third child.

There was no need for more words. What had happened that afternoon in Paete had been well reported in the community. Flags had flown at half-staff across the town. Casseroles, pies and other baked goods had been delivered to the grieving families. The families were assured that the bodies of their sons would be returned for a proper burial. That would be in the future; however, this morning what was important to the Hein family was that their son was at the family table enjoying a second stack of his mother's pancakes.

One year and two weeks later, Charles exits a westbound train at the depot. The transition to civil life has not been easy. Within days of coming home, he decided farming was not his future. Six months ago, after serving in the honor guard for the burial of his friends in their hometown, he moved to St. Paul.

Working as a day laborer is not easy, but he is supporting himself. Living in a boardinghouse on University Avenue is not much different from sleeping in the old farmhouse with his brothers and sisters. He thinks his possibilities are unlimited, and he is sure he will soon own a business.

First, though, he has important business to finish at home. A statue to honor Company C's sacrifices, and his six fallen friends in particular, will be unveiled outside the Walsh County Courthouse.

When the cloth is pulled from the tribute, he stands at full attention. With the warm October sun heating his neck, he raises his hand for a final salute to his six friends who once also had unlimited possibilities and opportunities.

He stands a little straighter and pulls his shoulders further back after reading the words of General Lawton that were engraved into the marble: You can't stampede the First North Dakota!

Charles yells, "Damn right!"

Evangelical Church of Peace on the corner of North Broadway and West Winona Avenue, now 7th Street NW, Rochester, Minnesota. Photo courtesy of the Olmsted County Historical Society

Part IX
The Evangelical Church of Peace

October 6, 1904 – Viola Township, Minnesota

A cloud of dust, kicked up by the horses and buggies carrying guests to the wedding of Albert Heyn Jr. and Lydia Neumann at St. Paul's Evangelical Church, is visible for miles across southern Viola Township. When the buggy transporting the senior Albert Heyn crosses the Chicago Northwestern railroad tracks at the Doty station, the occupants can see above the dust clouds the pointed roof of the tower that protects the church's bell. A mile and a half farther down the road, a solitary pine tree, limestone grave markers, and the wooden clapboard church painted white with green trim become visible. With its tall bell tower and stained-glass windows, the structure looks bigger and grander than other houses of worship that have been built by the German pioneer farmers in Olmsted County. Behind the church and cemetery, the grove of trees that protect the worshipers from the harsh winter winds is starting to change into its fall colors of red and orange. Arriving at the church, Albert can see to the east a house built for the pastor's family last year that is painted the same colors as the church and a simple white building where the congregation educates their children. The parsonage and school are surrounded by a fence, which protects the pastor's garden and animals. Walking through the door of the church, Albert thinks that the congregants of this church are very industrious and prosperous farmers.

Following the custom of the church, the men sit on the west side of the sanctuary, and the women and children sit on the east side. After taking his seat in the front row next to Albert Neumann, the bride's father, Albert looks around the room and is amazed that there are no empty seats. Precisely at three o'clock, the organist begins playing the wedding march, and the guests stand and face the back of the church to witness the bridal couple enter. Albert Sr. is impressed by how handsome and happy his second oldest son, twenty-four-year-old Albert Jr., looks today in his new black suit and white tie, with a rose pinned to his lapel as he holds the hand of his twenty-one-year-old bride. The groom gives his bride, dressed in a dark linen dress embroidered with bright flowers to match the colors of the real ones in her hair, a quick look of love and lust. Lydia blushes and returns his look with a proper shy, innocent smile.

When the music ends, the young couple stands at the altar facing Karl Buck, a thirty-year-old pastor with a quickly receding hairline, pince-nez wire-rim glasses, and a neatly trimmed goatee. He immediately begins reciting the marriage vows in his native German language. The words Albert hears resemble those spoken at his oldest son Edward's wedding three years before, but they are not exactly the same. To follow along, he opens a church hymnal and begins reading the order of the wedding ceremony. He is curious that this book is not his familiar Lutheran and Reformed Hymnal but rather the hymnal of the Evangelical Synod of America. Farther back in the church, Albert's brother-in-law Paul Priebe has similar thoughts.

Following the ceremony, more than one hundred guests climb back in their buggies to form a wedding parade led by the newlyweds in a buggy driven by Walter, the best man and brother of the groom. The parade ends six miles later at the Neumann farm, a typical set of buildings owned by a prosperous German immigrant who has spent thirty years winning the battles against weather, disease and fickle prices. There is a large red barn; other red buildings that protect crops, machinery and animals; and a two-story white house that contrasts with the red buildings. The house, built in a style popular in the late 1800s, looks like two houses with a common wall. One two-story structure facing the road contains the parlor and bedrooms, and the second structure, which attaches perpendicular to the first, is the kitchen, dining rooms and more bedrooms.

Standing on the long porch that runs the length of the second structure, the newlyweds accept the congratulations of the guests as they enter the house to enjoy a delicious wedding lunch of fresh meats and breads, plus a lovely wedding cake.

Albert spends the first hour of the party at the dining room table, accepting compliments from family, friends and new acquaintances for raising such a fine son. When he is given a piece of wedding cake by the maid of honor, Lydia's oldest sister Anna, he observes that in the corner of the parlor his brother-in-law Paul is engaged in a serious conversation with Pastor Buck. Paul, who left his father's farm as a young man, is a natural salesman who has worked at and owned various retail businesses in Rochester. Albert knows that he is always working on another deal, and he wonders what he is selling today. Albert excuses himself from the table and takes his piece of wedding cake across the room to join the conversation. He quickly becomes interested in the topic.

In this parlor on a farm far from their homeland, Albert discovers that Paul and the pastor are discussing an issue that has divided German Protestants for almost a century. Which Germans in Rochester are eligible to receive the sacraments?

The king of Prussia, Friedrich Wilhelm III, who attempted to consolidate his power by ordering the merger of the competing Lutheran and Calvin Reformed churches into the Evangelical Church in the Royal Prussian Lands, created a theological division among his Protestant subjects. Many who left the country seeking freedom from his decree created Old Lutheran churches across the midwestern United States. When new neighbors who were faithful followers of the new church arrived, also seeking economic opportunities, the disagreements of the old world were brought to the new one.

Paul explained, "The only German Lutheran Church in Rochester adheres to the strict conservative rules of the Missouri Synod. To partake in communion, German-speaking residents of Rochester are required to be members in good standing of the church. Even sadder, Pastor Nichols will not conduct funerals for everyone—families who are not members of Trinity Lutheran Church must find ministers who do not speak German for their funerals."

Pastor Buck asked, "Why are these families not joining the church?"

Paul responded, "One reason is that members of the church cannot also be members of a fraternal organization. Broadway in Rochester is lined with prosperous businesses owned by German immigrants and their children. Those fraternal organizations are a great source of business contacts. Why should I have to choose between my family's spiritual or financial well-being?"

Pastor Buck told the two men, "My church is a member of the Evangelical Synod. We practice open communion and do not have such strict rules concerning fraternal organizations."

Albert says that his concern for the church situation in Rochester is more emotional than doctrinal. "Ten years ago, I was a charter member of St. John's Evangelical Lutheran Church of Haverhill. I worked with my neighbors, just like we had many times before when we needed a new larger barn, to build a place of worship. Every time when I sat on the iron seat of one of my implements and looked up the knoll of the hill at that small white church, my tired ass hurt a little less."

As often happens when the rules are strict, and the believers are rigid, disagreements result, and reconciliation is challenging. Albert and the pastor of his church had one of those disagreements, and it created a permanent rift between Albert and the church he had helped build. "My family continues to attend the church on the hill, but the wound from that quarrel has not healed. After Auguste and I retired to Rochester last year, I did not feel welcome at Trinity Lutheran Church. My wife and I have been faithful members of a church since we were confirmed together on a blustery April Sunday forty-three years ago. Not being members in good standing of a church causes us great pain."

After listening to the brothers-in-law, Reverend Buck's missionary zeal is stirred. "If the situation in Rochester is as you have described, I am confident that my synod will be interested in establishing a new church in Rochester."

Albert and Paul promise that they will organize other families in town if Reverend Buck promises to conduct the first service. Standing in the now nearly empty room, the trio shake hands. A fork in the road of the history of the German community in Rochester has been reached.

November 6, 1906 – Rochester, Minnesota

Albert places his elbows on the table, intertwines his fingers, rests his forehead on his two thumbs and closes his eyes. To the other men around the table, he looks like he is deep in prayer. He is not. As he listens to two visiting pastors discuss the fate of his church, his mind replays the events of the past two years.

He thinks about how bright the fall sun shone through Albert Neumann's parlor window two years ago. That afternoon he was excited when his handshake with Paul Priebe and Pastor Buck set in motion the founding of the Evangelical Lutheran Church of Peace. Today no fall sunlight beaming through the stained-glass windows of Bethel Lutheran Church illuminated the men of the new congregation. Albert, the president of the small congregation, thinks that is fitting: he is concerned that he has just presided over the meeting that will end his dream.

After Albert and Lydia's wedding, Albert Sr. and Paul returned to Rochester and eagerly asked other German families about their interest in starting a new church. Several weeks later, the two men reported to Pastor Buck that they had found nearly a dozen families. Now, recalling those conversations, Albert understands that in his eagerness to find a new home for worship, he failed to listen to the words of a majority of the families. Many families wanted a new church in order to break away from Trinity Lutheran Church and its long-serving minister, Charles Nickels—not to leave the teachings and literature of the Missouri Synod.

Pastor Buck reported to the board of his Evangelical Synod of America, headquartered in St. Paul, that there was an opportunity for the synod to expand into the rapidly growing city of Rochester. Several days later Reverend Buck received a telegram authorizing him to travel to Rochester to lead the first service.

On the first day of Rauhnachte, Pastor Buck kissed his wife and children goodbye, put on his big black buffalo coat, and climbed into the sleigh driven by Peter Hanenberger. They traveled twelve miles across the cold, wind-swept prairie of rural Olmsted County to the corner of Grove and Fourth, where he delivered the first sermon to the new Rochester congregation. If his mother were still alive, she would scold Albert for attempting to start a church on the first day of this evil time. After today he would have agreed with her.

The small congregation of Salem Evangelical Church, which is not affiliated with Pastor Buck's synod, graciously offered their church to the group for the afternoon. Frostbite was numbing his fingers and toes as Pastor Buck walked into a church warmed not only by the stove burning in the corner but also by the bodies of those waiting for him. The size of the crowd invigorated the frozen pastor to deliver for more than an hour one of the most inspirational sermons of his career. After the service, before he climbed back into the sleigh, a group of men asked if he would return every other Sunday to conduct more services. Later that afternoon, when he returned to his little house by the frozen Zumbro River, Albert felt confident that 1905 would bring a new option for German worship in Rochester.

During January and February, Pastor Buck bravely continued to defy the cold northwest winds that blew the snow into drifts taller than Peter Hanenberger's sleigh to make the biweekly trek from his home to Rochester. One journey was so treacherous that it required four days for Peter and him to complete.

On March 12, 1905, Pastor Buck delivered another inspiring sermon, which was followed by a vote to organize a new church. Pastor Buck leaned back in his chair with a satisfied smile after the vote, thinking, "My sacrifices of the past several months were worth it."

The next day three immigrant farmers and six immigrant businessmen met at the German Library Hall to sign the constitution and charter of their new church, which they named *Evangelisch Lutherische Friedesgemeinde*—Evangelical Lutheran Church of Peace. After the signing, the founders left the hall where Dr. Mayo and the Sisters of St. Francis had treated tornado victims to enjoy a celebratory beer at Herman Kruse's saloon.

Albert thinks, "It was the last time the words *community* and *peace* accurately described us or our church."

Last year as the spring and summer progressed, the small congregation grew. Everyone agreed that a full-time minister was necessary for their effort to be successful. Pastor Karl Koch, chairman of the Home Mission Board of the Minnesota District of the Evangelical Synod of North America, promised the newly elected officers that his synod would immediately begin a search for a permanent pastor.

Pastor Buck ended his exhausting shuttle between his home church and the new one in Rochester. In the interim, Pastor Franz Oppermann, a traveling missionary for the synod in Minnesota and the Dakotas, came to Rochester to continue his work. Pastor Oppermann had the privilege a year ago to baptize little Clarence Mueller at their host church's baptismal font. Albert, the congregation's new president, proudly witnessed the event from his seat in the front row, hoping it was the first of many baptisms in the church.

The officers had been told that finding a minister with the missionary zeal to establish a church with a nearly empty collection plate would be difficult. When the desired qualifications for the position were discussed at the officers' meeting, pastors Koch and Oppermann witnessed a small disagreement among the members. One group said, "We are unfamiliar with the teachings of the Evangelical Synod. Our interest is to break away not from the Missouri Synod but just the local church." The other members, including Paul and Albert, were equally emphatic, "We have issues with our old synod. We are looking forward to joining a new one whose rules are less strict." Later at dinner, the two pastors agreed that for the new synod to be successful in Rochester, they would have to find a leader capable of bridging the differences.

At the end of this year's Easter service, Pastor Oppermann added to the joy of the day by announcing to the congregation after the final blessing, "The synod board has found you a minister. Pastor Heinrich Albrecht will begin standing at this pulpit after the first of the month."

Albert had been impressed when the call letter was presented to the officers. The new pastor was a thirty-five-year-old father of five. He had more than fifteen years of experience with the Minnesota Lutheran Synod headquartered in New Ulm. Previously he led a congregation near Litchfield, Minnesota, but he had been without a church for nearly a year.

Albert did ask, "If his uncle is the president of the Minnesota Lutheran Synod, why has Pastor Albrecht been without a congregation for a year?" He received no satisfactory answer. Albert had a second concern, "Does the Minnesota Synod follow the same teachings as the Missouri Synod? Will our new minister continue to lead us in the same direction as you and Pastor Buck?"

Albert was assured that the theological differences between the two synods had been explained to the new minister. Now, six months later, with his church torn apart, Albert thinks, "Both signers of the one-year contract were so desperate to fill the vacancy that the differences in beliefs of the two synods were settled with empty words and a handshake."

One detail of the mutual agreement between the new pastor and the synod was not disclosed to the congregation. Both men agreed that the annual salary of five hundred dollars offered by the congregation, without a parsonage for the family to live in, was not feasible for a man with five children and a father-in-law to support. To finalize the contract, Pastor Koch agreed that Pastor Albrecht could supplement his income by selling insurance for the Germania Life Insurance Company of St. Paul.

Members of the congregation gave a May Day basket filled with yellow and purple spring flowers to Pastor Albrecht's wife as his family stepped off the train to begin his pastoral duties. The officers helped the new minister rent a home from Peter Dansingburg, a successful Rochester businessman, on the southeast corner of the intersection of North Broadway and Winona Avenue. This section of town, alternately called the bloody third ward or lower town, had been devastated by the tornado twenty years before. Later that first afternoon, Paul sat on the front porch with the new pastor, reliving the destruction he had witnessed on the day after the disaster. The old rocker that he had given to the family creaked from the stress of his large body as he commented, "This is a mighty fine house that was built to replace the one I saw splintered apart that day."

Red and yellow tulips were blooming everywhere, and the oak trees were almost ready to pop their leaves on the first Sunday of May when Albert entered the church to hear Pastor Albrecht preach his first sermon. After the motivating message, the congregation strolled to the public square for a picnic of sausage, sauerkraut, dark rye bread, and ice cream made fresh that afternoon to celebrate. When the new pastor finished his second dish of ice cream, he told his new congregants, "My family and I are overwhelmed by the welcome we have received this week. We are looking forward to being in Rochester for a long time." The men all agreed: now that the Church of Peace had a permanent pastor, it was time to build a church for worship.

One month after assuming the pulpit, the new pastor traveled to St. Paul to attend the annual Evangelical Synod district conference. He enthusiastically reported on the progress of the young church and the congregation's desire to build. When he returned to Rochester, he reported to the officers, "At the end of the meeting, the congregations at the conference voted to contribute to a building fund for our new church."

With that good news, there was minimal debate before the officers voted to create a building committee made up of Emil Oestreich, Paul and Albert. The new committee immediately commissioned a local architect, John Gotthard Jonson, to create plans for a worthy house of worship. Several days after the fireworks of July 4 quieted, Mr. Jonson presented his preliminary designs to the church directors and the building committee. Jonson's plan had peaks facing four directions, with a large window suitable for the finest stained glass under the front three peaks, balanced in the corner by a large steeple with a door and stairs below. When asked about the building materials, Mr. Jonson replied that he expected that the church would be built of a wood frame and white brick.

Looking at the designs, Albert thought of the postcard he had just received from Pauline's August. On the front was a picture of their new brick church with a steep roof and a large place framed for a future stained-glass window over the door. Albert was excited for the day he could send a similar postcard to his brother-in-law.

While Mr. Jonson was designing the structure, a search for a suitable location was underway. A survey of the members overwhelmingly expressed the preference to locate the new church on Zumbro Avenue near most of Rochester's other churches. The architect had estimated that building a church that would comfortably seat two hundred people, with a balcony and a basement, as the committee requested, would cost as much as four thousand dollars. Even with the backing of the synod, funds for building the church were going to be very limited, and a less expensive location had to be found. Pastor Albrecht reported to the committee that lots were available on the northwest corner of the intersection from his home, and he strongly felt that locating the church near his home would be helpful for the growth of the congregation. On July 9, at a meeting of the directors, building committee and other interested members, it was agreed that the church would pay Mr. Sanderson, a resident of Minneapolis, $250 for his lot on the northwest corner of the intersection.

With a building design and a location secured, the third stage of the project could begin. Emil Oestreich, a member of the building committee and a local contractor, was awarded the contract to build the structure. With funds raised by the synod and local donations, he purchased materials and, within a month, dug the foundation and basement.

Six weeks ago, on the last Sunday of September, a gray cloud started forming far to the west of the hole Oestreich had dug. The families of the congregation and numerous residents of the county gathered at the building site to worship and celebrate the placement of the cornerstone in the new church's foundation. Albert and Paul stood at the edge of the hole, boasting to the other members how much they had accomplished in the two years since they shook hands with Pastor Buck. Their friends teased the brothers-in-law, "The seed you planted that day has grown into a hole in the ground." All the men shared a hearty laugh as the rumble of thunder could be heard in the west. While the families scattered to avoid the physical storm, a spiritual storm was building between Pastor Albrecht and the synod. That storm threatened the building intended to fill the hole in the ground.

In June, after attending the Evangelical Synod conference, Pastor Albrecht began to introduce Lutheran books and literature into the church. Several members reported to Pastor Koch in St. Paul their fear that he was working to have the new church join a Lutheran synod. Two weeks before the cornerstone ceremony Pastor Koch caught the morning Chicago Great Western train from St. Paul to inspect the situation.

The city hall clock tower was ringing twelve times when he stepped on the depot platform and began walking the three blocks north to Pastor

Albrecht's home to state his concerns. After that meeting, Pastor Koch went to the homes and businesses of the members to ask their opinion of their new pastor and the direction he was taking the church. He found that Pastor Albrecht enjoyed strong support within the congregation. Some of those he interviewed expressed resentment that the Evangelical Synod board was attempting to interfere in the new church. Pastor Koch thought to himself, "They are conveniently forgetting that the synod is paying their pastor's salary and financing the building of their church."

Albert joined Pastor Koch at the train station before he boarded the five-o'clock train to return home. Watching it chug down the tracks, Albert was confident that the synod and the new pastor had settled their differences.

Ten days after the laying of the cornerstone, there was a knock on Albert's front door. Standing on his green ivy-laced porch was a spectacled young man wearing a fine suit. The young man stretched out his hand to introduce himself. "I am Pastor Walter Bunge, your new minister," he said.

For a moment, which felt to the recent graduate of the University of Minnesota to be an hour, Albert stared at his visitor in stunned silence. When he regained his composure, he invited the young man into the house. The pastor was offered a seat at the table, given a proper cup of coffee and a piece of cake, and asked to explain why he was in Rochester.

Pastor Bunge said, "A week ago, I was called into Pastor Koch's office. At that meeting, I was told that as of Saturday, October 6, I will be the new minister for the Evangelical Church of Peace."

Albert told the young man, "When Pastor Koch left Rochester, he implied that the differences between Pastor Albrecht and the synod had been settled."

Pastor Bunge responded, "I was told by him that after two weeks of no communication from Pastor Albrecht, he decided to terminate his contract. When I left the office, I was given a sealed envelope that I was told to give to the pastor when I arrived in Rochester." His hands were trembling when he continued, "Unknown to me, the letter inside the envelope was the first and only notice that the unsuspecting pastor would receive from the synod to inform him that he was immediately terminated from his position."

Albert raised his head from his coffee, giving his guest a bewildered look.

The young pastor continued, "As soon as I arrived this morning, I walked directly from the train station to Pastor Albrecht's home. I was greeted at the door with the same hospitality that you have been showing me. That quickly ended when I pulled the envelope out of my suit pocket. There was an astonished silence around the table for several minutes as the adults of the family passed the letter between themselves. Then there was a violent eruption of anger. The window behind my chair vibrated as words normally heard at the local beerhall were used in a church parsonage. I was told in a loud and threatening manner to leave immediately.

"I stood in the street for several minutes as strong words were still screamed at me from the porch. I did not know what to do. Pastor Koch gave me your address. I need the advice of a respected elder."

Albert exhaled loudly after hearing the story. He then offered the visitor a room for the evening. For the rest of the day, Albert and the new pastor went to the homes of the other board members to explain the situation. Universally, they all advised that there should not be a scene at the service tomorrow. One church member, however, became so angry that for the second time that day, the young man was nearly physically thrown out of a house.

It was a sleepless night as Albert processed the day's unsettling events. All night he tossed and turned, anticipating the afternoon's service. "What should my response be? Everyone advised us not to make a scene. What should I do if Albrecht does not follow the same advice?"

The next morning, at the old ceramic washbasin by the back door, Albert washed his face and combed his beard. He then changed into his best black suit. When he finished dressing, he motioned to his houseguest that it was time to leave for the service. As he walked out the door, he stopped at the hall mirror to place his bowler hat on his head and to practice his scariest stern and fearless expression.

With Pastor Bunge in tow, the Heyn family arrived at the church thirty minutes before the service, never saying a word during the trip. Walking across the transom, Albert could see that the rumors of the impending conflict in the church had spread across the city. Bethel Lutheran Church was packed with not only the regular attendees but also Lutherans of various nationalities, Methodists, Congregationalists, and a couple of atheists. All were expecting to be entertained by the imminent events.

Albert looked down the aisle at the large wooden pulpit that dominated the altar. Pastor Albrecht had arrived at the church earlier. Behind the ornate podium, he stood erect, firmly grasping the polished wood. If Pastor Bunge were to attempt to lead the service, there would be a physical confrontation.

Albert straightened his short, thin body to its maximum height, threw his chest out, and removed his black bowler from his head. Pastor Albrecht's grip on the pulpit became so tight that even those in the back of the church could see his knuckles turn white. The room filled with electricity, generated by the audience looking first at Pastor Albrecht, then to Albert, and then back and forth over and over. A squeak of a mouse could be heard in the corner of the deathly quiet room as everyone silently anticipated the excess energy soon to be explosively released. The bodies of the men of the congregation were tense as they prepared to join the brawl they were sure was coming.

Albert's penetrating eyes stared directly into the eyes of the trespassing pastor as he began walking down the aisle with Pastor Bunge following two steps behind. The silence of the church was broken by Albert and Bunge's footsteps on the wooden floor and the ugly comments hurled at them. Albert stopped two feet from the pulpit. For a second, Pastor Albrecht shook with fear, but he quickly regained his composure and locked eyes with the president of his congregation.

Behind him, Albert could hear the shuffles of men preparing to join the impending melee and the gasps of the worried women. The tension was suddenly peacefully released by Albert, who solemnly bowed his head either to the cross on the altar or to the pastor in front of it. Then he took his usual seat in the first row with Pastor Bunge. Listening to Pastor Albrecht's sermon from Matthew 12, Albert thought the text was appropriate for the day, "Whosoever shall exalt himself shall be abased and whosoever shall humble himself shall be exalted."

Two days later, a strong beam of fall sun was warming the back of Albert's neck as he read the latest issue of the *Olmsted County Democrat.* Auguste, peacefully sewing a new quilt for the winter, was suddenly startled when Albert swore and ripped the paper in two. He held the two pieces of newspaper back together enough for her to read the headline: "Church Has Two Pastors; Peculiar Situation Is Forced on Members of the Church of Peace."

After being married to the stubborn man for nearly thirty-five years, Auguste quietly resumed sewing as her husband ranted. "The paper interviewed Pastor Albrecht and his supporters but not me or Pastor Bunge. Now the readers will believe that this is a fight between the members of our church and a big city synod. Albrecht says the synod knew his beliefs when we offered him the contract, and the members interviewed say they were happy with the direction he was taking our church. I am not happy. If I wanted to remain a member of the Missouri Synod, I would have joined Trinity Lutheran Church."

One paragraph caught Albert's attention when he reread the article in the crumpled newspaper. It said that Pastor Albrecht admitted to working as a representative of the Germania Life Insurance Company because the small church could not provide him an adequate salary. Albert had wondered how the pastor was managing to support his family with his small salary from the church. This was the first time he learned that the pastor had outside employment.

After the dramatic Sunday service and the article in the newspaper, a special church officers' meeting was called. The meeting was tense. Pastor Bunge asked to speak while reaching into his breast pocket to remove an envelope. When he was recognized, he said, "This week, I received this sealed envelope from Pastor Koch."

He opened the envelope. Then in a voice reserved for a congregant straying from the Ten Commandments, he described the contents, "This envelope contains a copy of a letter from Pastor Albrecht to the Germania Life Insurance Company. In the letter, the pastor explains his work for the company. I also have two of the company's canceled checks that the pastor has endorsed."

Pastor Bunge then passed the offending documents around the table to be read. Albert and the other church officers shook their heads in sad disbelief. After all the documents had circulated, Pastor Bunge picked them up, placed them back in the envelope, and slid the envelope into the breast pocket of his coat, as he had been instructed by Pastor Koch.

The stunned officers quickly made a motion to declare the pulpit vacant. This was followed by a second motion to appoint Pastor Bunge as the new pastor of the church. Both motions passed easily.

The next Sunday afternoon, Albert returned to his seat in the front of the church to hear Pastor Bunge's first sermon. The worshipers were far fewer and much less enthusiastic than the previous Sunday.

When the motions to declare the pulpit vacant and then filled by Pastor Bunge passed, Albert and the other officers around the table hoped that the controversy would end. Yet anger and misunderstanding cannot be settled by a simple motion affirmed by the pounding of the presiding officer's gavel. Several more weeks of conflict continued to tear the church apart. If the differences were going to be resolved, a special meeting of the twenty-four members of the congregation, the three representatives of the synod, and the two pastors had to be called. This afternoon Albert made another dramatic entry into Bethel Lutheran Church, took his place at the head of the table, and pounded the gavel sharply to call the meeting to order.

The chair next to Albert, reserved for Julius Karau, the church secretary, was empty. Albert made the simple request that one of the other twenty-two members volunteer to record the meeting, but the only response he received was arms folded across chests and bowed heads. In the uncomfortable silence, Albert asked, "How are we going to resolve our differences if deciding who should record the meeting is a problem?"

To break the stalemate, Pastor Koch whispered to Albert, "Pastor William Meyer, president of the Minnesota District of the synod, is the highest-ranking person in attendance. He has the power to appoint a secretary for the meeting." Albert allowed no time for objections after Pastor Meyer appointed Pastor Bunge to be the secretary.

During the afternoon, all of Albert's leadership abilities were required to prevent the meeting from dissolving into a fistfight as tempers flared, voices roared and accusations were thrown. Deep and hard divisions within the congregation were revealed. Good Christian men were treating each other with the same level of anger usually reserved for the enemy on the battlefield.

After two hours of bitter debate, Pastor Koch asked to speak. He slowly and firmly summarized the synod's position and then closed his remarks with a simple question, "Does the Church of Peace want to continue to be a member and receive the financial assistance of the Evangelical Synod? If the congregation votes to leave the synod, we are prepared to send Reverend Bunge to another church."

An exhausted quiet, a contrast to the chaos of the past two hours, fell over the room as the men processed Pastor Koch's speech. The blissful silence was suddenly broken by Paul's booming voice, "I move that we stay with the Evangelical Synod." In a quieter voice, William Lenz said, "I second the motion."

Silence returned to the room when Albert asked, "Is there further discussion? Hearing none, all in favor of the motion vote *yes.*"

Only two affirmative votes were heard. Albert's heart sank, just as it did while the tornado was blowing apart his farm. He said, "All those opposed vote *no.*" Instead of the expected chorus of *no* votes, there was another long silence followed by the sound of a chair scraping across the floor.

The members who voted *yes* and the visitors from the synod turned in the direction of the offending noise to see Pastor Albrecht stand and gather his papers. Suddenly the room erupted with the sound of scraping chairs and rustling papers. The other twenty church members and the pastor's father-in-law were following his lead. Then in unison, the twenty-two men turned their backs to Albert and the synod and marched two by two down the aisle of the church, the last pair slamming the church door as they exited.

One more loud noise was heard in the church this afternoon after the door slammed. Albert pounded his gavel as he announced, "The motion to stay in the synod has passed 2 to 0."

After the reverberations of the slamming door and pounding gavel, the three visiting pastors sat speechless. Pastor Meyer exhaled loudly to break the stillness and said, "I think the situation at this church is too serious to be successfully resolved. The synod should send Pastor Bunge to Sanborn, Minnesota, and abandon this church."

The familiar pain in Albert's stomach returned as he waited for the responses of Pastors Koch and Buck, both of whom had as much of their lives invested in this church as he did. With a measure of respect that had been missing earlier today, Pastor Koch replied to his superior, "The congregation has voted to stay in the synod. We should support their decision. I believe Pastor Bunge should stay in Rochester to complete our mission."

Silence returned to the room after Pastor Koch spoke. Albert, with his head bowed, hears the pastor's words through the fog of thoughts and memories passing through his head. Suddenly, he snaps his mind back to the present, opens his eyes, lifts his head from his hands and sits up straight. With the confidence of a sixty-year-old man who has faced and overcome dislocation, destruction and death, he announces, "Our Church of Peace is going to be built both physically and spiritually on the foundation at Winona and Broadway."

May 12, 1907 – Rochester, Minnesota

Mother's Day. Albert has witnessed the pain of birth many times. His first memory of birth is the terrifying cries of his mother when his sister Ottilie was born. Five times he heard his wife holler the same screams as she gave birth to their sons. He lost count many years ago of how many cows, horses and pigs he had helped deliver their offspring.

After every birth, even though he had not experienced the pain of the mother, Albert was exhausted. Tonight, after the fourth dedication service for the new home of the Church of Peace, he sits in one of the new pews and is suddenly overcome with that same exhaustion. The women cleaning up the church will vehemently argue that Albert's pain in starting this new church is nothing like the pain they experienced in childbirth. To Albert, the male observer, his relief now is exactly the same feeling he always had after a successful birth.

Since November, when Pastor Albrecht and his supporters stormed out of Bethel Lutheran Church, until this morning when the congregation marched out of the same building on their way to their new house of worship, the physical world changed from crisp fall winds to biting cold winter gusts, and then to refreshing spring breezes. In the spiritual world of the remaining members of the church, winter with dangerous subzero cold, strong squalls, and endless blizzards started immediately that afternoon in November. Only during the past several weeks had the hope and renewal of spring warmed their souls.

The first spiritual blizzard struck shortly after the tempers cooled last November. Emil Oestreich, a supporter of Pastor Albrecht, had been awarded the contract to build the new church. He completed the foundation and basement before the controversy erupted, but then construction stopped. Albert and Paul, the remaining members of the building committee, met with the contractor after several weeks of no activity and asked when the construction would resume. Before turning his back to his two old friends, Emil replied, "My contract stated the completion date of the construction, not the start date."

The outraged brothers-in-law consulted with George Granger, a local attorney, about their options to force or break the contract. They were advised to send a notice that if work did not resume in two weeks, the contract would be null and void.

The committee immediately started a search for a new contractor. There were many qualified builders in Rochester, but the reputation of the divided congregation resulted in most of them refusing to bid in order not to appear to take sides. The only exception was Henry Schellin, a carpenter who was eager to establish himself in Rochester after moving there from Winona. The congregation and Mr. Schellin quickly came to an agreement; after two more weeks of no activity, a new contract was signed.

A second blizzard struck the congregation in two waves when the new contractor began his construction. Schellin warned the officers that he thought that the congregation had a problem with not just the human foibles of competing visions but also the blueprints for the building. He told the stunned men, "Mr. Jonson, the architect, designed the building with no trusses to hold up the roof. I am certain that after reviewing the design that calls for only two-by-fours nailed to the cross beams of the ceiling and the roof rafters, the ceiling will sag, and the walls will bulge. Potentially the building could collapse."

Mr. Jonson had moved to Seattle, and the tired church officers were unable to clarify the plans. They dismissed Schellin's concerns, telling him to proceed with construction. When the contractor attempted to argue with the officers, Paul became angry. His loud booming voice bellowed, "Just build the church to the specifications we paid for!" Today, between two of the services, Albert looks at the ceiling and thinks, "I wonder who will be proven correct."

The second, more serious wave of the storm followed later on that night's agenda. In the summer, money was raised from the congregations of the Evangelical Synod to buy the lot and start construction. Individual church members also pledged contributions. Relying on these pledges, the lot was purchased, the basement dug, the foundation laid and the necessary building materials ordered. But now, the controversy within the congregation had become so well known in the city that the lumbermen refused to deliver the building materials without payment in full.

Treasurer John Acker had been authorized to apply at a local bank for a construction loan. At the meeting, he reported, "The bank will not authorize the loan without a church member's personal guarantee."

Each member at the table responded that he was just a small businessman without the assets to guarantee a note of that size. Slowly heads and bodies turned to Albert, the only member with enough net worth to satisfy the bank.

Albert told the others, "I have to talk to Auguste." He then pounded the gavel to adjourn the meeting.

When he arrived home, his wife's reaction was not what he expected. She was a devoted Christian woman, who because of her weakening heart sometimes did not have the strength to attend church. On those Sundays, she required her family to recite the sermon to her word for word. This day she put her hands on her ample hips and scolded her husband. "How many times have you borrowed money to expand the farm without asking me? Why, when it was time to grow the House of God, do you need my approval?"

The next day, the chastised Albert was at the bank, preparing to sign the note. As he dipped his pen in the inkwell, the banker told Albert,

"If you have as much faith in your church as you do in your farms, I am sure that this note will be repaid." Albert signed the documents, and the funds were available to buy the materials. The bright blue, post-storm sky improved the spirits of the congregation.

As usual, during Minnesota winters, the third spiritual blizzard followed quickly behind the second by only a few days. Pastor Albrecht continued to live in the house across the street from the construction. He conducted informal services at the home of William Beise, several blocks away, for the families who had broken away from the organized church. Albert had heard, from the few participants who still spoke to him, that after the service, the worshipers would roll out a barrel of beer, empty it and then, as they staggered away, throw money on top of the barrel to pay not only for the beer but also the pastor's salary. The members of this unorganized congregation told him, "We are planning to build a competing church next to Pastor Albrecht's rented house."

Other rumors spread around town that some members of the group were boasting that they were waiting for the new Church of Peace to be built—and fail. Then they would take over that building. Albert wanted to confront his former friends, but Pastor Bunge consulted patience.

Pastor Albrecht, living with a clear view of the activities at the construction site, quickly tested Pastor Bunge's own patience. On two occasions while helping Schellin close up the building before winter, the pastor was standing on the scaffold furiously pounding nails when a group of curious passersby stopped to inquire about the building and the beliefs of the church. From his vantage point, Pastor Albrecht would see the people gather and then, braving the cold wind, walk across the street to join the conversation.

The first time, after the visitors left, Pastor Albrecht told Pastor Bunge, "You are not allowed to talk to my people."

After the offending pastor returned to his house, Schellin, who had witnessed the conversation, told Pastor Bunge, "I have never seen an interaction that peculiar between two ministers."

Later, when a second group asked the same questions at the construction site, Pastor Albrecht was more forceful. He yelled at the visitors, "Leave and never talk to Pastor Bunge again!" The group on the street was shocked by the forcefulness of the pastor but did not confront him. Instead, they shook their heads and, embarrassed, walked away.

When he heard about these interactions, Albert thought that the time for patience was over. Telling a fellow man of the cloth that he was not allowed to speak to citizens in a public roadway was unacceptable, and the harassment had to stop.

The first full moon of December filled the sky over Rochester, illuminating Albert and the officers of the congregation on the porch of Pastor Albrecht's landlord, Peter Dansingburg. They were welcomed out of the cold into the house's warm library. Peter Dansingburg sat in an expensive highback chair on one side of the fireplace while his wife, Eliza, sat in a matching chair on the opposite side. The directors each took a sip from a fine china coffee cup before offering the couple $1,200 to purchase the house Pastor Albrecht was renting and the lots where the opposing group planned to build a new church.

Knowing his weak position, Treasurer Acker had a quiver in his voice when he told the couple, "We do not have the finances to pay the money up front. Instead, we are offering you one dollar down, with a contract for deed for the balance, payable someday in the future when we have the ability to refinance."

Quiet filled the room, interrupted only by the crackle of the fire. The men anxiously waited for their host to laugh them out of the house. Instead, Albert observed a brief serious discussion between Mr. and Mrs. Dansingburg, followed by their surprising response, "We accept the offer."

Albert was unaware of the importance of Eliza Dansingburg, a dedicated Methodist, to the transaction. Shortly after the headline in the *Olmsted County Democrat* announced in bold print that the Church of Peace had two ministers, Pastor Albrecht visited the Dansingburgs. He assured his landlord that he had a one-year contract with the synod that would continue to pay the rent.

Later the church's second pastor visited the Dansingburg home to inform them that the rent for the house on North Broadway was not the responsibility of the Evangelical Synod. Eliza Dansingburg argued with Pastor Bunge. "Pastor Albrecht said that the synod would still be responsible for the rent."

The young pastor explained, "Pastor Albrecht has a call to the congregation, not a contract, and that call was rescinded."

After this initial tense conversation, the young man developed a rapport with the elderly businesswoman, and they enjoyed a peaceful cup of coffee and a piece of cake together. After Pastor Bunge left the home, Eliza Dansingburg told her husband, "I do not approve of being told a half-truth by a Lutheran minister."

The next evening Peter Dansingburg sat in the same chair to receive an offer from Pastor Albrecht and the leaders of the competing congregation for the same properties. Mr. Dansingburg, who was tired of being in the middle of the conflict, leaned back in his chair and told his visitors, "The properties were sold to the Church of Peace last night."

With a satisfied smile, Eliza Dansingburg turned to the shocked Pastor Albrecht and said, "You, your pregnant wife, and your small children have to move out of our house before the blue moon on New Year's Eve."

During the physical winter, the winds that blow the snow into huge drifts between the storms can be more dangerous than the storm. The rumors and falsehoods that blew through the community between the spiritual storms were equally hazardous to the congregation. Passionate winds blew against the Church of Peace when the news that it was sending a pastor and his family out into the cold at Christmastime blustered through the community.

One large drift that continually needed to be cleared was Pastor Albrecht's employment with the Germania Life Insurance Company. One day Pastor Bunge entered the lobby of the Minnesota House hotel to meet with John Acker, the owner. In the center of the room, Pastor Albrecht was speaking to a large group of men. When he saw his replacement, he broke away from his conversation. He turned to Pastor Bunge and loudly accused him of spreading false rumors about his work for the insurance company. For several minutes in front of everyone in the packed lobby, he hurled insults at Pastor Bunge.

John Acker told the other church directors, "When Pastor Albrecht finished his insults, Pastor Bunge dramatically and in full view of all of us, pulled from his suit pocket the envelope that he had placed there on the afternoon the pulpit had been declared vacant. Slowly he opened the envelope, removed the letter and canceled checks, and then waved the contents in Albrecht's face. In the same calm, clear voice he uses every Sunday in the pulpit, he asked if Pastor Albrecht recognized his penmanship on the letter and his signature on the canceled checks. For several minutes there was no response. During the extended silence, my customers lowered their heads and shuffled their feet until Pastor Bunge returned the envelope to his pocket with the same dramatic flourishes as when he removed it."

This dangerous drift was cleared for the last time when the young pastor turned his back to his aggressor and walked out of the lobby.

Some of the winds that blew had the potential to be dangerous. One afternoon when Albert was shopping on Broadway, a worried clerk whispered to him, "I overheard a drunken Emil Oestreich boast that he was going to beat Pastor Bunge and then throw his body into the Zumbro River." Albert, who had known Emil and his family for many years, thought it was just the beer talking, but passions were so high he decided not to take a chance. As solemn and serious as he was the day the young man first knocked on his door, he told the pastor to hide for a few days until tempers cooled.

As the cold of January and February passed, the warm, stronger sun of March began to melt the remnants of the storms. The building at the corner of Broadway and Winona was closed in, membership was growing and the rumors were fewer. The church began to look forward to both a physical and a spiritual spring. But before spring arrives in the physical world, there is always one last blizzard that can be the most overwhelming of the season. This year it was the same for the congregation in the spiritual world.

On a warmer-than-average day that gives hope for the coming spring, Albert climbed the steps of the red brick courthouse to retrieve the church's incorporation documents. Because the bank notes Albert had guaranteed were not enough to finish the building, the congregation applied for a loan of two thousand dollars from the Church Extension Fund, an agency of the Evangelical Synod of North America that loaned money to congregations to build churches. Proof of incorporation was one of the requirements for the application. Behind the dark wood counter of the registrar's office stood a very familiar clerk who had helped Albert many times when he bought and sold his various properties. After their initial greetings, the clerk went to the shelves to get the documents. Albert stood at the counter for what seemed an extraordinary amount of time before the clerk returned with an embarrassed look on his face. "Your incorporation papers have never been filed," he told Albert.

The frustrated president of the congregation shook his head in disbelief when he understood that the church did not legally own the partially built church, the parsonage or the surrounding lots. Fortunately, that storm was quickly overcome, and the necessary paperwork was registered that afternoon.

The second wave of this spiritual storm was not as easily calmed. A second requirement for the application was a strict accounting of the funds that the district and its congregations had provided for the establishment of the church. No such records existed, and the small congregation was astonished to learn that their loan application would be denied unless the documentation was provided. They were told that the agency had several times financed the building of a new church only to have the congregation leave the Evangelical Synod for a Lutheran one after the construction was complete. After several defaults, the agency had instituted this strict policy from which there would be no concessions.

This was the point in a storm when a freezing person thinks about lying in the snow to die. Before the discouraged members of the Church of Peace lay down in their spiritual snowbank, a cry for rescue was made to Pastor Koch in St. Paul. Pastor Koch wrote a letter attempting to save his mission in Rochester. In his letter to the agency, he explained the torrid history of the church and vouched for the character of the church officers and the pastor he has placed at the church. His appeal to the agency moved the unmovable, and an exception to the no-exception rule was made. The loan was approved, and the congregation survived another storm.

When Albert was an adolescent, celebrating the renewal of spring by dancing around the maypole on the first day of May was one of his favorite activities. Two days after his sixtieth birthday, he knew that his days of dancing around the maypole were over, but the spirit of renewal that the day symbolized still stirred him as if he were sixteen. On May Day 1906, he welcomed Pastor Albrecht as the church's first permanent minister. One year later, he celebrated by touring the nearly completed house of worship. After the continuous blizzards that had assaulted the congregation, the renewal and hope of spring would be recognized on the second Sunday of May with dedication ceremonies at the new church.

Albert woke up this morning with a combination of anticipation and fear, the same feelings he had forty years ago when he crawled out of the bed he shared with his brothers on the day he left for America. The ornate clock on the wall was chiming the half-hour as he left the house for his last six-block walk to attend a Church of Peace worship service at Bethel Lutheran Church.

Seven months before, when he took the same trip with Pastor Bunge, his mood and the weather were cold and dark. Today, his arthritic knees moved almost as fast as the Zumbro River as it pushed the remnants of the winter snows to the Gulf of Mexico. His ears were filled with the song of the busy robins building their nests. His eyes saw the full buds on the lilacs waiting for enough heat to follow the pink crabapple flowers into a colorful bloom. His lungs were filled with the sweet smell of freshly turned soil. Albert thought this was the day farmers dream about during the cold depths of winter.

Entering the church, Albert saw that just like the first Sunday in October, the church was again filled with Lutherans of various nationalities, Methodists, Congregationalists and a couple of atheists. Today they were there to witness a celebration, not a conflict.

Suddenly the hum of the expectant congregation fell silent as the bell of the host church began pealing. The church's organ played a quiet prelude as the attendees turned to watch, for the last time, Pastor Bunge walking down the aisle to an occupied pulpit. This time it was occupied not by a competing pastor but by Reverend Osmund Oftedal, the Norwegian pastor of the host congregation. He greeted the German-speaking pastor in English before quietly stepping away from his pulpit. Pastor Bunge led the assembly in prayer and then delivered a short sermon thanking the Bethel Lutheran congregation for their generosity in providing his small congregation a place to worship.

Following the congregation's last "Amen" in this building, Pastor Bunge invited the host congregation to join the members of the Church of Peace at the first worship service in their new church. The pastor stepped around the pulpit and down the two steps in front of it and walked back up the aisle followed by his visiting colleagues, the officers and members of the congregation, leaving the clapboard church for the final time without any angry comments, ugly looks or slammed doors.

Back in the bright sun, Albert saw a large cheering crowd that had not found room in the church. Quickly a parade two blocks long was organized for the one-mile walk to the new church. It was led by seven Evangelical Synod pastors followed by the officers, members of the congregation, the Sunday school, other congregations and finally, the Sunny Side Club of Rochester.

When the procession walked the half-block to the corner of Prospect Avenue and Zumbro Avenue, the pastors turned right, but Pastor Buck's head turned left to look at Salem Evangelical Church, where he had preached the first sermon the day after Christmas two years ago.

Three blocks down Zumbro Avenue before their left turn at Broadway, Albert looked at the bank that held his guaranteed notes for the construction. As he turned his head to look at the building, his good ear could hear the banker, who was marching with the Sunny Side Club, talking to the other prominent businessmen and doctors who were members of the civic improvement organization.

Less than one hundred yards after turning the corner, Albert, Paul and the other remaining charter members stared in unison to their left at the German Library Hall, remembering the happy day they signed the constitution and charter. Three blocks later, the procession was slowed by a passing train. While waiting for the train, Albert looked at the back of Pastor Koch's head and thought about the afternoon last fall when Koch had reassured him that the differences between the synod and Pastor Albrecht had been settled.

After the train passed, Albert could see the steeple of the new church three blocks ahead. Prior to arriving at this destination, Albert glanced to his right at the home they had purchased from Peter and Eliza Dansingburg. At the sight of the house, he turned and nodded at the

Dansingburgs, who were also marching with the Sunny Side Club. His attention was immediately drawn back to his left, where he could see Henry Schellin standing on the top step of the church.

Albert and Pastor Bunge waited at the base of the steps for the entire procession to arrive. Then they walked up the ten new brick steps shoulder to shoulder, greeting Henry at the top. The assembly fell silent as the pastor turned to offer a brief prayer of thanks for the building, the congregation and the assembled visitors. When the prayer was finished, the pastor and Albert, with a dramatic flair, accepted the keys to the church from Schellin. Then they continued their thespian performance by dramatically unlocking the doors, throwing them wide open and leading the worshipers into the new church.

Even though they had built the church large enough to support a growing congregation, not everyone standing outside the building this morning was able to come in. Those lucky enough to find a seat admired the room painted in lightly tinted colors of cream and rose, giving a bright, festive impression. One day the congregation will replace the clear glass in the building's three large windows with stained glass, but today the rays of morning sun moving from the back of the building to the matching window on the worshipers' left added brightness to the room. The older members of the congregation appreciated that the natural wood pews were large and comfortable.

In the distance, the city hall bell rang ten times. Pastor Bunge, his dark black vestments contrasting sharply with the heavenly blue altar alcove behind him, began the first of the day's three services. Speaking in German, he led the congregation in the building's first hymn, invocation, prayer and dedication.

Following the dedication Amelia Buck, the woman who packed food and warm clothes for her husband and then prayed for his safe return from the frozen prairie when he first organized this congregation, sang a solo. As she sang, Albert thought an angel from heaven had entered their new sanctuary. A huge lump formed in his throat.

Pastor William Meyer, the man who was ready to quit after the disastrous meeting last October, walked to the pulpit to deliver the dedication sermon. He read the words of Paul to the Corinthians, "We have spoken freely to you, Corinthians, and opened wide our hearts to you. As a fair exchange—I speak as to my children—open wide your hearts also."

More music by the congregation and the children of the Sunday school filled the cavernous room before Pastor Karl Buck stood to deliver his sermon. For a brief moment, he said nothing as he looked down from his perch at the young couple he had married two and a half years ago, now attempting to quiet their two young sons. When the disruption ended, he began to deliver a sermon as eloquent as the one he delivered at the first service on the second day of Christmas 1904. He reminded the congregation of the complaints that began this adventure and admonished those in attendance to continue their open-door policy of not restricting God's sacraments based on membership either in this church or a fraternal organization.

Pastor Bunge completed the first service with the benediction, followed by the congregation singing a final hymn and then marching out of the church to the sounds of Pastor Haussler's postlude. When Albert returned to the bright sunny day, he was greeted with loud cheers and hearty slaps on the back for good work well done.

After the service, long tables were set up to serve the gathering a delicious Sunday dinner, which was completed just in time for a 2:30 English-language service led by Pastor Paul Bierbaum and Pastor Jahn. Older members, including Albert, were distressed about the congregation worshipping in English, but the progressive younger members argued that they had to offer English services if the church was to grow. Albert had begrudgingly accepted that the young people saw themselves as Americans, not Germans. In his own family, his two older grandchildren could understand German but primarily spoke English. Albert and Auguste's nieces and nephews were marrying into English, Scandinavian and Czech families.

The final service tonight at 7:30 was a bridge between the past and the future delivered in a combination of German and English. The last sermon was delivered by Pastor Koch, whose stubborn determination to keep this congregation in the Evangelical Synod had made this successful day possible. Just like any doctor or midwife who oversees a difficult, painful birth and then is the honored guest at the baby's baptism, he delivered the final message of the day with fervent joy.

When the sounds of the final postlude by Pastor Bierbaum ended, the congregation that filled the church, even at this late service, filed out of the building—except for Albert, who is too tired to move. He sits alone in the nearly empty church looking at the new altar. His joyful thoughts of birth and a successful new church are suddenly pushed from his mind when he feels a presence next to him. Turning to his left, he sees his father, mother, sisters and son. Startled, he looks behind him to see his grandparents, aunts, uncles and neighbors from the farm in Gembitz Hauland. Turning his head to the front of the church, he sees Pastor Wenig behind the new pulpit, looking as stern as he did the day he confirmed Albert. Slowly the spirits form a long receiving line to offer congratulations. When his father shakes his hand, a cold shiver runs through his body, startling him awake.

Albert emits a deep sigh. Disturbed by his dream, he decides it is time to go home. His work, for this chapter of his life, is over.

Aunt Mary Erdmann hosting her nephew Albert at her son Charlie's farm Willow City, North Dakota. Family photo

Part X
Final Legacies

February 19, 1916 – Minneapolis, Minnesota

The western sky of Minneapolis is painted with colorful streaks of orange against a fading blue background as the sun begins to set. The passengers of a passing train see the silhouette of a solitary man standing by a flower-laden mound of dirt in Layman's Cemetery. For a brief moment, the passengers forget their impending arrival in the city and share the obvious grief of the stranger.

It has been an unseasonably warm day, but now as the sun falls, so does the temperature. After the train passes with the gawking passengers, the man stands alone in Section S of the cemetery and pulls a flask from his worn coat. He takes a stiff drink of whiskey to cut the chill and dull the pain.

Julius wipes the spilled remnants of whiskey from his beard with a shaky hand. He looks down at the mound of dirt covered with floral bouquets and sadly recognizes that no amount of whiskey will dull today's pain. The quiet of this final resting place for the workers who built the city is pierced by the lonesome whistle of the train, announcing its forthcoming arrival downtown. His senses feel that they are all being attacked at the same time.

The sounds of the melancholy whistle and the squawking ravens in the trees create a gloom in his mind as dark as the moment before a summer thunderstorm strikes. His cheap whiskey tastes bitter on his tongue. A cold wind causes his large red nose to tingle while it smells the unusual scent of fresh flowers in February. His vision torments him the most: one eye sees a fresh mound of frozen dirt covering his only daughter, and the other sees the footprints in the packed snow of the mourners who, an hour earlier, had unknowingly stood on his wife. When the two visions combine in his brain, they create a sad picture reflecting what Julius has known for many years: he is alone in the world.

The last time he felt this alone was more than forty years ago as he walked down the gangway of a ship in New York harbor. That afternoon he shrugged off his loneliness as he walked from the docks at Battery Park to the train station in central Manhattan. With his small inheritance in his pocket, he marveled at the crowded streets that separated the multistoried brick buildings. Every store window exhibited a treasure that the inexperienced farm boy could never have imagined. He absorbed the sights and sounds of the new world with a nineteen-year-old's immature optimism of the unlimited opportunities before him.

He remembers his amazement as he rode the train north along the Hudson River and observed the variety of humanity that, eight weeks earlier, he had not known existed. Sitting next to him on the hard wooden seats were immigrants from across Europe, Yankees and former slaves. Most passengers were seeking their fortune farther west, but many like him were hoping to fill one of the many jobs available at the rapidly expanding factories in the cities where the Hudson and the Mohawk rivers converged.

At the train station in Troy, New York, he was welcomed by his widowed brother-in-law, who helped the disoriented boy find work at one of the city's many ironworks, rent a room from the Malz family and join the new Trinity German Lutheran Church. By the next spring, the young man had accumulated money and property worth the unbelievable sum of one hundred dollars. Not yet legally eligible to manage his own affairs, Julius asked his sister's former brother-in-law, Ernest Bethmann, to be his guardian to conduct his business. On May 4, 1874, as Julius watched Ernest sign a $200 bond to administer his finances, the drudgery of the farms scattered among the forests of Gembitz Hauland was banished from his life forever.

Free from his mother's vigilant eye, the temptations of the many saloons near the ironworks became a magnet. After a week of working twelve-hour days as a molder, Julius and his landlord's son Herman would join their coworkers at one of the taverns. Julius smiles as he remembers the pair of twenty-year-olds on those fun nights, bucking and frolicking like one of his mother's prized heifers loose in the pasture for the first time in spring. The beer flowed freely, and the occasional siren song of one of the barroom maids was answered. The next morning, sitting in a pew of his church at the corner of River Street and Hutton Avenue, Julius convinced himself that he was just a young man sowing wild oats. As he listened to Reverend Goessling's sermon drone on, he dreamed of finding a wife, starting a family and pursuing a career where he did not get dirty every day.

The work in the foundries was hard, dangerous and too often inconsistent. Six days a week, Julius would pour melted iron into forms that, when cooled, became machine parts, household goods and horseshoes that were consumed by the rapidly expanding economy of the country. Inside the cavernous buildings along the river, he worked alongside Irish, Germans, Poles, Yankees and Black men from the south. The men, who spoke many different languages, were mixed together randomly to prevent union organizing, and they had to rely on hand signals and trust as they poured the dangerous melted iron into the forms. Exhausted at the end of the long week, Julius needed the saloons to push from his mind his defeatist thoughts that maybe America was not the land of opportunity he saw on the docks of New York.

Near the iron factories that primarily employed men were many textile factories that employed young women. There were many opportunities for the workers of the two industries to meet. One day Julius saw a girl with shiny brown hair and a playful smile pass him on the street. He brazenly stopped her to introduce himself. Julius remembers being smitten from her very first words that introduced herself as Gertrude. Three years after he arrived in Troy, they were married. Taking another look at the trampled snow in the cemetery, he is still proud that, unlike his four brothers, he found a girl born in America who had no family ties to home. As always, he set his own independent course in life.

Marriage started easy for the newlyweds. Houses owned by the various companies were numerous in the city, and they rented one on the hill above the Marshall Textile factory. On warm Sunday afternoons, they crossed Congress Street to enjoy leisurely picnics along the banks of the Poesten Kill River. After eating all of the food in the basket, they would lie back in the long grass, look up at the blue sky and dream of their future. Gertrude would name each of the white feathery clouds with a name she planned for their future children. Julius dreamed out loud that tomorrow he would not return to the hot dirty factory floor but rather would sit behind a desk at the brownstone Burden Iron Works headquarters. Together they designed a fine stone mansion on a hill, paid for by the profits of Julius's business.

After nearly a year of nights in the iron bed Julius had purchased when they married, Gertrude became pregnant. During that time, his adolescent dreams of nonphysical work and elegant houses were being destroyed by adult reality. Every train that departed the Troy depot left behind immigrants without a trade seeking unskilled work in the factories. The owners of those factories, living in the mansions he and Gertrude dreamed of building, took advantage of the excess supply of labor. It was unnecessary to improve working conditions and pay if a new refugee was always willing to work at any cost. Rather than moving west to improve his growing family's fate, the impending responsibilities of fatherhood froze Julius in place, and he surrendered to his reality by drowning his disappointments at the saloon.

Another lonesome train whistle cuts the silence of the cemetery. Alcohol-induced tears cloud his vision as he remembers another Saturday night when the quiet of the houses on narrow Prospect Avenue was disturbed. The thin windows of his small, flat-roofed house had been incapable of containing the first squeals of his newborn daughter.

Earlier today, looking for the last time at his little girl lying in her casket, he thought of that night. She was perfect. Her face was bright pink, and her eyes were closed tight as she protested her entry into the world—unlike today when her face was white, and her eyes were barely closed as she appeared to calmly accept her departure from this world. His memories and the cold cause a shiver to run up Julius's back. He wonders if he would be standing here now if he had kept his promise to Gertrude that night to do better.

His promise was short-lived. As their first child took her first wobbly steps, they dreamed of giving Julia a brother or sister, but as time passed, their hopes of adding to their family were like more and more bricks that constructed a sturdy wall of disappointment. There had been a few failed pregnancies and then just infertility. The continued drudgery of Julius's low-paid work, the succession of company houses, and the unsuccessful efforts to have more children resulted in Julius and Gertrude standing on opposite sides of their brick wall, which grew so tall they could not see each other anymore.

Julia was nearly three when her uncle Adolph moved into their house. Immediately on that September afternoon, the young man could feel the uncomfortable tension inside the house.

Julius found his brother a job as a molder at his factory. One evening as they walked home from work, Julius shocked Adolph. He pointed to one of his favorite saloons and told his innocent little brother, "If you need a sexual release, you can find it there." The young man was blushing bright red as his brother warned him to be careful. In a conspiratorial whisper, he confessed, "I have been unfaithful to Gertrude. Several weeks after one of my adventures, I developed an uncomfortable sore. Sure that I had syphilis, I secretly visited the company doctor and was given a mercury treatment." Julius swore his brother to secrecy. "I have not told Gertrude that I had been infected."

Adolph then understood the terrible tension in the house. He carefully avoided adding to the discomfort while he saved for his escape. Two years after arriving in Troy and determined to avoid the mistakes of his brother, he boarded the train for Minneapolis, praying that his brother would somehow find his way.

At the memory of the caboose of that train slowly disappearing down the tracks, Julius turns his head to the south to look at the house at 3009 Cedar Avenue. It is the house Adolph and Louise shared with his family when they arrived in Minneapolis from Troy. As darkness settles over the city, the house does not look to him as he remembers it on that spring day. That day it reflected how he felt: it was new and cheerful, standing on the edge of a city with an unlimited future. Now it looks tired and unmaintained, as he does.

Just as he had done at every crossroads in their marriage, Julius promised his wife he would improve in Minnesota. The day he stepped out of the house on Cedar Avenue dressed in a new black suit and a white shirt with a collar starched so stiff he was afraid it would cut his throat was one of the proudest of his life. Finally, he had a job commensurate with his intellect and ambition. When he returned home at the end of the day from his work as an agent for the Metropolitan Life Assurance Company, his muscles would not be sore from lifting molten iron. His new suit would not be black from soot, and his ears would not ring from the clanging of the hammers shaping iron.

That night Gertrude told him how proud she was watching him walk to the corner that morning. She said that she still thought he drank too much, but she was sure that life would be better here. If she had looked carefully at her husband's face that night, she would have seen a quick look of guilt when she added that maybe now they would have another baby.

Gertrude's stumble on her way to the witness stand at the Barrett trial was the beginning of the end of any hopes for a brighter future. Over time her gait worsened, and she had shooting pains in her body. The strong independent woman had repeated episodes of weakness. Both Julius and Gertrude were concerned, but not until Julia asked, in a voice combining childish innocence and adult directness, "Is my mama dying?" did Gertrude agree to see a doctor.

The family was never whole again after she received her diagnosis. The doctor's words sounded like a cannon firing next to Julius's ears when he said that Gertrude was suffering from tabes dorsalis caused by untreated syphilis. As though that first cannonball had not done enough damage, the doctor then almost gleefully announced that among the symptoms of the disease were miscarriages and infertility. Julius's secret activities at the saloons of Troy were finally exposed.

Those words began a long, downward spiral that led to his standing here alone today. He recalled that the times were not all bad, however; after the initial shock of the diagnosis, an uneasy truce came over his marriage in the last decade of the nineteenth century.

Selling life insurance during a financial panic was not lucrative. But Minneapolis was a hub for the rapidly expanding railroads, and Julius found a new job as a travel agent. He enjoyed the freedom of traveling across the Midwest, working at the various depots. When those jobs slowed, he would occasionally refresh his old skills and return to work as a molder for short periods.

Forced to care for her ill mother while her father was away, Julia grew mature and independent at a much younger age than her cousins. When she turned eighteen, she found a job as a clerk for the Plymouth Lumber Company. For six years, she shuttled the six blocks between the yard on Lyndale Avenue and their home. During the day, she served Mr. Messer by recording the company's orders for lumber and coal. At night, she cooked and cleaned for the family with the same impressive organizational skills.

With the dawning of the new century, the disease Julius gave his wife progressed to a fatal end. Dementia clouded Gertrude's thinking, she could not walk without great pain, and her heart slowly failed. Shortly after her forty-ninth birthday in 1902, her heart that had thumped in Julius's ear on those lazy Sundays as they lay along the banks of the river took its last beat.

The weather during the three days between her death and burial reflected the turmoil of their marriage. As she lay in their iron bed taking her last breaths, spring was descending on the city. The temperature was nearly sixty degrees that Friday afternoon. Julia opened the windows to the unseasonable warmth, vanquishing the stale air heavy with the sour smell of death.

On Monday afternoon, as the few mourners gathered in the parlor for the funeral, the windows were closed to protect them from the subzero cold that had blown in from the north. Julius remembers that icicles had formed in his beard as his wife was lowered into the ground. More than the wind hurt that afternoon, so did the cold disapproving stare of his brother Albert who arrived on the train that morning. Ashamed by his brother's disapproval of his life, Julius turned away, thinking that the bite of frigid air on his face was an appropriate end to a marriage that began warm and ended cold.

The years since Gertrude's death have been unstable for Julius. Without the anchor of a wife, he wandered from city to city across the Midwest. Ten years ago, he returned to live with Julia in Minneapolis when he found work as a broker, but that lasted only a year before he wandered away again. That was the last time he lived with his daughter. His relationship with Julia was sometimes strained, but he was proud of the life she built here.

Several years after her mother's death, she found a new clerk job working for John Martin at the Itasca Lumber Company. Her efficiency was well rewarded. She established the stable home that had eluded her as a child. When her father left Minneapolis for the last time, she moved into the house where she would live for the rest of her life.

Most customers who entered the office of rough and tumble fuel yards were shocked to see a woman behind the counter at Itasca Lumber. Over time, though, the tough men who loaded their wagons at the fuel yards to provide heat for the residents of Minneapolis came to respect the serious young woman. She was comfortable at her job. When the men offered invitations to picnics or concerts, she turned them down. After witnessing her parents' struggles, she had no interest in making the same mistakes. She was happy organizing her work. Had the company not gone out of business, she would have stayed there forever.

The loss of her job (and also her comfortable routine and social life) was distressing, but it did not last long. The fuel men of the city, many of whom were at her funeral today, told John Ekstrum, the president of Flour City Fuel and Transfer, about the exceptional woman they had worked with at his competitor. Flour City was expanding and needed an office manager at the Northside office. Ekstrum thought the men had begun drinking early that day when they suggested he put a woman in charge of his office, but he agreed to meet with her. That afternoon, as he leaned back in his chair looking across his desk at the young lady with the sad eyes, he decided he had not become successful by playing it safe. Against his better judgment, his company became the first in Minneapolis with a woman managing a fuel yard.

Ekstrum, a Swedish immigrant, was the successful man Julius had dreamed of becoming. Maybe that is why Julia worked so hard for him.

This man, who offered his condolences to Julius today in an expensive three-piece suit, with black hair cut perfectly to the latest style and a neat mustache, came to this country with his parents as a young boy. Only a few years older than Julia, he had everything Julius had wanted—many children, a fine house and a successful business. As a young man, he had joined the Minneapolis police force, rising to the rank of sergeant for three years while he and a friend sold cords of wood door to door. Seeing a business opportunity, he invested one hundred dollars to start a company that sold coal in the winter, wood in the summer, and moving and storage services for people in transition. He turned his one hundred dollars into an incorporated company with four locations now thought to be worth three hundred thousand dollars. Julius bitterly thought that every time Julia met with Ekstrum, she saw the successful man that her father always said he would be but never was.

The core business values of Flour City are to "shoot straight" and "deliver on time." Julia's organizational skills and natural efficiency reflected those values. When Ekstrum spoke with Julius at the funeral home, he confided, "I had some doubts about placing a woman in charge of the office, but she astonished me and all who knew her with her remarkable efficiency. I couldn't have found one man in a thousand who would do the work as well as she did."

Julia's independence extended from the dirty coal and lumber yard to her personal life. She was able to save money to buy fine clothes and furniture for her apartment. One morning as the burly men were receiving their orders for the day, they were surprised when she asked, "Which of you is going to teach me how to drive a car?"

Most responded, "A woman is not capable of operating a motor vehicle." Those unwise men received the same angry glare as when they delivered a load late. One enlightened young driver concerned that the quality of his future loads might be in danger if he didn't offer to help, agreed to teach her. But first, he said, "You need a car to drive." Outside the office, one of the older drivers told him, "If you think you have cleverly ended Julia's fantasy, you do not know her very well."

That weekend she rode the University Avenue streetcar toward St. Paul. Just after the city line, she got off and walked to her cousin Charles's house on Curfew Avenue. After the war in the Philippines, Charles moved to St. Paul, lost a leg that had been seriously wounded during his military service, married a Catholic woman with Czech heritage, had a daughter, and became a successful real estate salesman.

Determination and willingness to defy tradition were traits these two cousins had received from their grandmother. Even still, Charles was shocked that afternoon when his cousin Julia asked him for a loan to buy a new Model T Ford. As he took a long slow sip of his coffee, feigning that it was too hot, he thought of the first time his grandmother came to Grafton. Through the steam of his coffee, he saw the same commitment on his cousin's face that he saw when his grandmother announced she was going to own land in North Dakota. As he lowered his cup to the saucer, Charles knew it was useless to argue.

Within weeks the young fuel man who had thought he was so smart when he joked about Julia owning a car was sitting, terrified, in the front seat of a new Model T, teaching his boss to drive.

Today Charles volunteered to serve as administrator for Julia's estate. He promised to quickly liquidate her assets for the best price, settle her debts and transfer the balance to Julius. While he appreciated his nephew's offer, Julius also felt envious. There will be no assets to disperse when he dies—and if there were, there would be no one to disperse them to.

The final end of Julius's dreams began three weeks ago. A letter had arrived in Kansas City from Julia, loaded with comments about the weather, gossip about the men at the fuel yard and a mention that she had a bad cold. A few days later, he received a telegram stating that she had been admitted to Fairview Hospital, and he needed to buy the first ticket to Minneapolis. When he arrived at the hospital, he could hear her coughing and gasping for breath as he neared her room. He had never felt more hopeless than when he was sitting next to the hospital bed as his only child was slowly strangled to death by her own fluids.

Earlier this afternoon, Julius was proud to see that his daughter was held in high esteem in the city. Every chair in Heinrich's Funeral Home was filled by her uncles, cousins, a large group of the city's fuel men, and even a reporter from the *Minneapolis Morning Tribune.* Julia's life had been important enough that her funeral would be reported in tomorrow's paper. The recognition eased his grief but could not replace his daughter.

Julius takes one last mouthful of whiskey and looks down at the two graves. It all started with so much hope. He was sure he would be the richest man in his family, with a fine house and several children. Rather than resting here in unmarked graves among the city's forgotten working men, women and their children, he had thought they would spend eternity on the other side of the city at Lakewood Cemetery, among the famous politicians and businessmen. Julius says to himself, "Gertrude and Julia should have one of the large marble monuments like Maria and Albert bought for August and Auguste." He takes one more look at the mound of dirt before him and thinks that now that Julia has taken his place next to her mother, he will spend eternity separated from his family.

The sun has set, and physical darkness has descended around Julius. He places the empty flask into his pocket and walks toward the gate at Cedar Avenue. Passengers on a downtown-bound streetcar see the sad man walking alone. They are curious when he strangely tips his hat in the direction of a single tree, which, unknown to them, marks the grave of the man who drove their route long ago with mules. With that gesture, the man is saying goodbye to his past with little hope for his future. Slowly he fades away into the dark night.

June 27, 1920 – Elgin, Minnesota

The Sunday morning air is hot and steamy. Sleep last night for the residents of this little village nestled between two branches of the Whitewater River was nearly impossible. Before leaving for church, Gustav stops to read his thermometer. Already the red mercury has pushed past the 70-degree mark.

The air is so humid that Gustav and Bertha are laboring to breathe when they arrive at the church steps. They greet their fellow congregants, most of whom were born within a ten-mile radius of each other in what was then Prussia but is now Poland; they share seven decades of comfortable familiarity. Discussions about the weather are interrupted by the tolling of the church bell announcing that the service is about to begin.

Before seventy-five-year-old Gustav climbs the steps, eighty-year-old August Polikowsky waves his cane at him. He loudly greets his old friend, "*Schönen polnischen Tag*!" Gustav returns the greeting with an epitaph not normally heard on the steps of a church. The wives of both men give their husbands their usual disapproving glare. Gustav whispers to his wife a justification for his retort, "I never before have been told to have a 'Happy Polish Day' as I enter a Lutheran church."

The two couples take their preferred seats facing the ornate white altar that was purchased when the church was built fifteen years ago. In the center, the statue of Jesus stands on a gray base with arms extended as if to urge the two men to quietly reconcile. The service prelude can be heard from the organ in the balcony when Gustav makes eye contact with his old friend. He nods his head and gives him an amused wink. When the gesture is returned, Gustav's white mustache pushes up on his face as he smiles in satisfaction that his fiery response has not disappointed his longtime antagonist.

Earlier this week, August was returning from the post office when he saw Gustav reading his newspaper on his front porch. The slightly built man took the second porch chair to escape from the heat and enjoy a lively discussion about the world's problems in his native language. He found Gustav angry, with a bright red face and hands trembling so hard that the newspaper sounded like a flag whipping in the wind. August asked his friend, "What has gotten you so worked up this morning?"

Gustav responded, "Governor Burnquist has issued a proclamation that all the citizens of the state should, on the twenty-seventh, properly observe 'Polish Day' to celebrate the first anniversary of the creation of the independent country of Poland."

August laughed, which led to a bitter response. Gustav told his visitor with the Slavic name, "If you and your father had not had the good sense to marry German girls, you would still be one of the Wedel family's many serfs in Tütz." That comment resulted in an equally inflammatory outburst from August.

Hearing the loud voices on the porch, Bertha stopped her sewing to investigate. She was relieved when she saw it was just two old men continuing the perpetual argument that had been fought since the first German colonist was invited by the Polish nobles to develop their lands. Shaking her head, she went to the kitchen to make lemonade, leaving the two men to the only stimulating activity they could still do.

Squeezing the lemons into the pitcher of cool water, Bertha thought, "When a bull is turned loose in the pasture, it does not discriminate by the breed of the cow. Why did those two old fools think that our grandfathers were different? Besides, everyone knows that a crossbred hog always produces the best bacon." Bertha ended their argument by delivering the pitcher of lemonade. Today she hopes the word of God will cool the men's passions.

Reverend Christian Affeldt and Jesus look down from the altar at a sea of white hair, wrinkled skin and bent bodies. These old congregants were very clear when he accepted their call last year that he must deliver every Sunday's first service in German. The old men told him that they left where they were born to escape poverty—but not their language or the traditions of their church. For them, this service is a thick rope that tethers them to the happy days of their youth.

When Reverend Affeldt begins his sermon, he grabs the far edges of the pulpit to gain some relief from the sweat that is sticking his shirt to his armpits. The heat and the sound of the paper fans the women use to cool themselves lull Gustav nearly to sleep. In his near unconscious state, his anger at Governor Burnquist and at the suffering the Minnesota Commission for Public Safety had inflicted on the German-Americans pushes all other thoughts from his mind.

The commission was created by the legislature three years ago to mobilize the state's resources to support the war. Members of the commission soon used their broad powers to prosecute what they determined to be disloyalty to the war effort. Unfortunately, they defined disloyalty broadly, especially if you spoke German.

The governor, born to immigrants from Sweden, simply had no compassion for the pain the largest immigrant group in Minnesota had experienced during the three years before the United States entered the war. After the war began in 1914, every letter from home announced the death or maiming of a nephew, niece's husband or son of an old schoolmate. Rather than receiving sympathy from the governor and their fellow Minnesota neighbors, the German immigrants were told that there were now only two parties in Minnesota, "loyal" and "disloyal."

Prior to the war, the barber shop was a neutral place to exchange the latest gossip and freely express opinions. Under the new definition of who was a loyal Minnesotan, customers who previously enjoyed the political freedom to express their opinions in their native language were now in danger of being branded traitors. They now worried that the neighbor waiting for his turn for a haircut could be seeking an opportunity for revenge for past personal conflicts. Opinions that previously could be freely expressed were being reported to the authorities. Suddenly the simple act of getting your hair cut became a perilous activity.

The day after he attended Albert's funeral, Gustav read a story in the *Rochester Daily Post and Record* that after a haircut, an unnamed man from Elgin was being investigated for telling the barber, "I will not donate to the Red Cross or buy Liberty Bonds. The President is no better than a damned red hog." After the article was published (including a sentence stating that the unnamed man was worth eight thousand dollars), every successful German farmer in town was under suspicion of being disloyal.

Gustav looks through his partially closed eyes at the recently widowed Charles Uecker. The man's oldest son had been a partial owner of a bank in South Dakota. He got into trouble during the height of the hysteria for exhibiting Christian charity. One of his customers, also getting a haircut, had expressed pro-German sympathies. The farmer was promptly arrested and held in jail on a $5,000 bond. The younger Uecker, a savvy businessman, knew that if his customer was not freed, he could not plant that year's crops and would be unable to repay his loans. Uecker and a fellow businessman posted the bond to free the man. When the news spread of what this banker with a suspicious name had done, the town turned on him. On a Sunday night, a group of men pasted large sheets of paper painted yellow on the windows of the bank. The next morning a run on the bank was organized in an attempt to bankrupt the business. To save his bank, the young Uecker sold his share of the business and had the farmer's bond revoked.

Incendiary articles written by the War Savings Stamp Committee were common in the weekly newspaper. In those articles, even naturalized Germans were suspected of being traitors. One article advocated repealing any naturalized German's citizenship. Another called for the wealth of those citizens to be confiscated by the government. Finally, one article advocated shooting treasonous German-speaking citizens who would not denounce their homeland. Nowhere in those newspapers had Gustav read where the governor had condemned such fearmongering.

Burnquist's public safety commission also received 175 complaints about German being the language of instruction in the state's schools. An order was issued that starting with the school year in 1918, all primary instruction in Minnesota would be in English. To his left, through the yellow and green stained glass, Gustav can see the small building that served as the first church and was now the congregation's parochial school. The congregation buckled to the pressure, and primary instruction changed to English.

Gustav was sad and angry when many of the congregation's young families welcomed the change. While he, and the others sitting around him, aggressively held on to their past, the first generation born in this country saw themselves as Americans. They wanted to worship and educate their children in the language they spoke daily. The old immigrants were shocked that their grandchildren could barely speak German.

The generational transformation from German-American to American with German ancestry occurred not only in schools and churches but also in the war effort. When war was declared, many sons and grandsons of the first generation enthusiastically joined the adventure to fight their evil Hun cousins.

After Albert's funeral, Gustav returned to the church his brother had founded to enjoy fellowship, a ham sandwich and a cup of black coffee. In the far corner of the basement, Adolph's second son Frederick, named after the grandfather he never knew, was confidently entertaining his cousins and siblings with stories of the adventures he was expecting the next day when he enlisted. Gustav remembered talking with similar bravado at that age when he left home to fight the Austrians. He also remembered having less enthusiasm for war four years later when he fought the French. Gustav asked his baby brother, "Can you believe that one generation of the family fought on French soil to create Germany, and the second will now fight in the same place to destroy it?"

Adolph, not wanting to argue politics with his stubborn brother at his other stubborn brother's funeral, just shrugged. That did not stop Gustav from continuing. "Long ago, the late afternoon sun would blind me when I defended myself against the enemy. Now forty years later, your son will have the same problem defending himself in the early morning."

When Frederick took a seat with his father and uncle, Gustav commanded him to be safe. Then he waved his arthritic hand at the boy. Exerting his authority as the patriarch of the family, he ordered, "Don't kill one of your Aunt Pauline's children."

Frederick's blue eyes diverted from his uncle, and his face turned red. He had not considered that he and one of his Westphal cousins may be shooting at each other. More embarrassing was the thought that he would not recognize him before pulling the trigger.

Shortly after their church's school began teaching the children in English, the next horror of the depressing year of 1918 struck. By mid-October, the Spanish Flu pandemic was sweeping through the area, closing schools, businesses and churches. The Plainview city hall was turned into a Red Cross hospital to treat the sick and dying. For three weeks, the weekly newspapers devoted nearly a page to obituaries of those who succumbed to the virus. Soldiers returning home from the war and those patients who had recovered were required to quarantine for at least a week. People were urged not to leave their homes and, when they did, to wear masks. Cruelly, the disease did not take the old like Gustav, who had already lived a good life, but rather young mothers and fathers and their small children.

Quarantined in their house, Gustav and Bertha reminisced about the dark winter nights during typhus epidemics when they were children. Just like now, they had spent their days isolated and afraid. The families of the dead stood alone over graves without the community support they deserved and needed. The couple sighed in unison as they thought, "If you live long enough, new experiences are limited, and you are forced to live through the re-runs."

As the dark year ended, letters arrived from the village's soldiers in France. The young men regaled their families with stories of wartime adventures, which were then proudly shared with everyone in town.

Other letters were also quietly received from relatives back home who described their own experiences. Rather than printing these letters in newspapers, the recipients read them to each other through muslin face masks in small, quarantine-defying gatherings. Although the letter writers tried to be positive when relating the events that had occurred since the war began, all letters closed with a sentence hinting at despair. After vividly describing the produce she harvested from her large garden, Bertha's stepsister Ernestine concluded her letter by writing, "Our family is lucky to have the produce. Many of our neighbors are starving. Horses are now worth more as food than for pulling a plow."

Two letters were in Gustav's mailbox on a cold December morning. One was from Adolph, saying that Frederick had written that he was safe; he was going to enjoy the French countryside before his expected return home in the spring. The second letter was a Christmas greeting from Gustav's niece Bertha in Gembitz Hauland. It was long and cheery, full of news about her large combined Westphal family. Her letter closed not with optimism about the future but gratitude for the past. Her last sentence simply stated: "I am relieved that my stepbrothers Adolph and Walther, who were wounded in France, have recovered from their injuries."

By Christmas, once the initial horror of the pandemic had passed, the united citizenry had divided into petty disagreements about how many could worship together, whether to hold public funerals, and if the government had the right to force people to wear masks. News from Europe was still sporadic and worrying. At the end of the church service the Sunday after Christmas, the old men of the congregation defied the gathering restrictions and navigated the treacherous narrow steps to the basement for coffee and leftover Christmas cakes.

At the long wooden tables, the formerly strong young men who had fought wars, crossed oceans, broke prairie sod and pounded together the rafters of many impressive buildings complained about the weather, their families, the politicians and their latest physical ailment. Earlier, these men with worn-out knees and hips had struggled to kneel and pray in the small space between their seats after receiving communion. Now as they shared the limited news they received from the newspapers and home, they thought that their lingering pain was a small price to pay to be able to ask God to protect the family they had left behind on the other side of the ocean.

When the Armistice was declared in November 1918, the Allies agreed that the nation of Poland should be re-created but made no final decision on the new country's borders. The initial truce simply stated that until the peace treaty was negotiated, the border should honor the German borders of August 1, 1914. That decision left the Duchy of Posen, where most of the coffee drinkers had been born, in Germany.

For the first three days of Rauhnachte, the front pages of the newspapers reported on increasing chaos and suffering in Europe. Bolshevism was expanding beyond the borders of the former Czarist Russia, gaining adherents among rebelling Poles and many of the starving people of defeated Germany. Fear that the rising tide of these dangerous beliefs would swamp the victorious Allies, including the United States, was replacing anti-German hysteria. The defeated German army was now being ordered to defend both Berlin and the plains of Pomerania and East Prussia against the advancing Bolsheviks. Tensions were high for the Minnesota congregants as they worried if their family in Europe would ever find peace.

The next morning the newspaper only intensified the fear in Gustav's house on Park Street. On the second day of Rauhnachte, there was a riot in Posen between the German authorities and the Polish residents. Ignace Jan Paderewski, a famous pianist and political leader, had been welcomed to the city by its Polish residents with patriotic parades. In a speech, he announced that Poland was once again independent and in charge of its own fate. The German authorities asked him to leave the city, but instead, the Polish residents of the city they called Poznan took down the German flag at the Bazar Hotel and replaced it with the flags of Poland and the Allies. When the German soldiers tried to remove the offending flags, a riot broke out.

Another story at the bottom of the page was even more distressing. As Gustav heard a horse whinny as it passed the house, he read confirmation of his sister-in-law's previous letter. The people of Germany were quitting their vegetarian diets to once again eat horses. Gustav looked at his grandchildren playing on the floor and silently thanked God he had made the distressing decision to leave and come to America. "What would the future of those children be if I had not?"

Former President Theodore Roosevelt's sudden death and the increasing anarchy in Berlin pushed the news of the fighting in Posen Province out of the newspaper. Each day that winter, after hearing the soulful whistle of the train announcing the mail's delivery, the old men would rush to the post office, hoping for news from home. Finally, on a warm muddy spring day, Gustav received another letter from his niece Bertha.

The next Sunday, Gustav returned to the battered tables in the church basement to share the distressing news in his letter. For once, the men did not share opinions, and the women did not interrupt to pour another cup of coffee. Instead, everyone quietly listened to Gustav read a harrowing tale of an underreported war that was fought this winter on the land where most of the people there at the church had gasped their first breaths, caught their first fish and stole their first kiss.

Liebe Tante Bertha und Onkel Gustav

The time since my last letter at Christmas has been some of the most distressing and fearful of my life. Shortly after the riot in Posen, the Poles created militias to free the cities and villages south of the city from rule by our government. Then they turned their attention north toward us. Their armies created a battlefront from Wagrowiec to Obornik. Then they easily marched north through our farms all the way to the Netze River. Along the way, their troops took shelter in the homes, businesses and churches that you helped build, Uncle.

I remember Oma always fretting that the ten days between Christmas and Epiphany

> *was a time of darkness and evil. This year as we celebrated the three Wise Men bringing their gifts to the baby Jesus, we had hope that they were also bringing us a gift. That day our demoralized army recaptured Czarnikau and Kolmar. But the joy was short. The Poles headquartered themselves in Podanin to direct the recapture of Kolmar. Two days after Epiphany, they were successful.*

Mike Wandrey gasped, “That is where I was born.”

August Polikowsky swore. The village where he began married life had been at the front of a war. A tear followed the creases in his wife Christina’s wrinkled face as she thought of bullets blasting holes in the walls of the room where she had given birth to her oldest children.

The brief interruption gave the women time to refill the coffee cups before Gustav began reading again.

> *The battlefront between the Poles and the German armies moved back and forth across our farms and villages until mid-February. As we begin our spring planting, a fitful peace has returned after the Allies and the Germans renewed the truce. There is still an occasional skirmish, but I assume that once the peace treaty is signed, we will become Polish citizens. In gatherings after church, everyone in the community is deciding if we accept the injustice and keep our farms or follow our cousins west to Berlin and other dirty cities.*
>
> *God willing, I won’t follow them. My son Arthur is determined to maintain the farm. When the church burnt, I said in*

a letter to Oma that the family's memory surrounded me in the fields, meadows and forests. If we leave, I will be walking away not only from a farm but also from Oma, Papa, Mama and you.

Beste Grüße deine liebe Nichte Bertha

When Gustav finished, the room remained silent, except for a few sniffles from the ladies as they washed the communion dishes.

The Christmas letters this winter described the Polandization of their former villages. In rare moments of reflection, the German immigrants accepted that the Poles were only exacting revenge for their treatment by the Germans. After the Franco-Prussian War in 1871, Chancellor Bismarck imposed the Germanization of the region. Polish parents were required to teach their children in German and record their births, marriages, deaths and business transactions in that same language. The ancient names of the villages of the region were given new German names. Those changes were confusing not only for the Poles but also for the Germans. One day Gustav left a farm in Niewiemko where he was building a house, and the next morning, he returned to finish his work in Neuhutte.

The Poles did not forget the humiliation they had suffered. Gustav and Bertha's nieces and nephews no longer lived in Gembitz Hauland but rather in Gebiczyn. To record a land sale, they traveled to the administration office in Czarnkow, not Czarnikau. To enter the city, they no longer crossed the Netze River but the Notec. They were not sure their births, marriages, and deaths were recorded correctly because everything was now written in Polish.

Many German families did sell their farms and homes and moved west to cities economically devastated by the war. Before rumbling over the dirt roads with their remaining possessions loaded on wagons and trucks, they promised those left behind that, unlike their siblings and cousins who left earlier, they would return to reclaim their land. Others (like Bertha's stepsister) said, "We accept our fate but pray every Sunday that the new Polish government will be short-lived. Just like it was one hundred years ago during the time of Napoleon."

Gustav snaps back to the present as the young pastor mercifully cuts his sermon short. The temperature inside the building is now practically unbearable. Gustav greets the pastor at the door. The thick outside air is a welcome relief as he shakes the pastor's hand with a tremor that has become more prevalent. Pastor Affeldt smiles when Gustav tells him that he enjoyed the sermon. He wonders how his audience does not know that he can see who is sleeping from his perch in the pulpit.

As Gustav descends the church steps, the bells are ringing loudly. He is still bitter that the bright sunny Sunday has been designated by the state to celebrate the Poles, but he takes satisfaction that the loud bell is now likely disturbing the Americans with German ancestry and the Yankees of the village. They all know that their neighbors born in the evil German Empire have had their sins washed away.

Three weeks after Polish Day, Gustav is riding in a car driven by his youngest son Ted on a 150-mile trip to Pine City for the funeral of his brother Adolph. The conversation in the car is confusing and disjointed. As an older man often does, Gustav frequently changes the subject. One minute he is delighted that soon Burnquist will no longer be governor. Then he comments on the poor quality of the wheat. Midsentence, he starts talking about a dining room table his father had purchased at Adolph's father-in-law's auction.

Gustav tells Ted, "The last Christmas before Papa died, ten of us were sitting shoulder to shoulder around that table. When Adolph left the table early, he had to crawl under it to escape. Now August, Maria and I could comfortably eat at any table shoved into a corner."

Ted reminds his father that during the holidays, his house now bursts with his ten children, their spouses, grandchildren and one great-granddaughter. Gustav agrees but responds, "Today, I feel alone."

Traveling north, the scenery changes to pine trees and swamps with farm fields cut into them. Gustav marvels that his brother found a farm near Pine City that reminds him so much of where they had been born. In the distance, he sees a herd of cows seeking shelter from the heat under a grove of trees. He is shocked when one of the cows turns her head to observe the passing car—and has a white hourglass marking on her face, like the cows his mother had been so proud of. Ted is subjected to another long story about the cow his grandfather had received from his new father-in-law as a dowry.

Gustav leans back in the seat and closes his eyes, appearing to rest before the funeral. Instead, he is deep in thought. The seventy-five revolutions the Earth has made around the sun since he was born replay in his mind. As a young man, he had accepted progress. Now he believes that the world is discarding what it considers unnecessary baggage too quickly. For him, too much of that unnecessary baggage is now reduced to random memories that can be shared only with a rapidly shrinking group of family and friends. Soon new sections will need to be added to the cemeteries to bury the baggage of the past.

February 6, 1931 – Grafton, North Dakota

A large crowd endures the near-zero cold outside the imposing St. John's Catholic Church on Kittelson Avenue. A dreary undertaker, exhausted from overwork, paces the sidewalk and directs the final preparations for six of his clients to be carried into the church. To separate the growing crowd, the drivers of two black Model A hearses blow their horns, disturbing the solemnity of the moment. When they stop at the church steps, eighty-two-year-old August nimbly jumps out of his son Emil's car. His son quickly runs to help his father, but he is too late. Leaning heavily on his cane, the elderly man has found his own footing on the icy street. His five daughters encircle him, urging him to return to the car or go into the church. The stubborn old man swings his cane at the pesky girls, telling them to leave him alone.

Through the frosted glass on the side of the hearse, he watches the casket of twenty-five-year-old Joseph Leach being slid out of the vehicle. The pallbearers then carry Joseph up the steps. Leach's wife has a little daughter next to each hip, tightly holding her dress, and a one-month-old son in her arms as she follows the casket up the steps and into the church.

As soon as the Leach family has climbed the first set of steps, six more strong neighbors remove the casket of August's sixteen-year-old granddaughter Genevieve from the second hearse. When the wooden casket reaches the first step, the grandfather extends his shaky free hand to gently touch the polished wood. While his granddaughter begins her last climb up the steps, the two hearses pull away to get the next set of caskets.

When they return, six members of the Grafton Municipal Band pick up the casket holding the body of their friend and bandmate Edward, August's nineteen-year-old grandson. Again the little grandpa with his usual cigar hanging from his mouth and signature black bowler hat on his head, touches Edward's coffin as it passes by. He repeats the gesture when the casket of his twenty-year-old granddaughter Elizabeth follows her brother and sister.

The strain of standing and the tolling of the bells causes pain in the old man's back and ears, but he fights through, waiting for the two hearses to return again with the caskets of his daughter-in-law, Delphine, and son Edward. His view clouded by age and tears, August regains his strength and stands straight as the casket of his youngest son passes him.

Now the undertaker motions for the Hein and LaFromboise families to follow the procession into the church. August stubbornly ignores the offer of help from his son and daughter-in-law as he begins to slowly climb the steep steps. After his arthritic knees and hips successfully navigate a step, he pauses for a breath before he attempts the next. At each rest, he looks ahead to the next step, where his now orphaned grandsons, fourteen-year-old Richard, twelve-year-old Wilfred, and four-year-old Marvin, are following their parents and siblings into the family's church for the last time.

With each step, memories flood the old man's mind. On step four, forty years peel away, and he is again looking for the first time at his newborn son cradled in Minnie's arms. Reaching step eight, time advances a quarter century, and he remembers the three times he sat on his old porch drinking a celebratory beer with his son after Delphine gave birth in the same room where Edward was born. At step twelve, he relives the day seven years ago this week when he stood in the new veterans' section of Roselawn Cemetery on the edge of St. Paul at the grave of his son Charles. By the time he reaches the church door, he is sitting next to Minnie's deathbed. As he crosses the threshold, he thanks God she is not here today. When they were young, they lost a baby, but no parent, he thinks, should live long enough to attend two funerals of adult children.

August's eyes need a few minutes to adjust to the darker room. When he is able to focus, he sees the undertaker in front of the altar, directing the final placement of the six caskets on the biers among the flowers. The fragrance from those huge baskets of flowers, which fill every corner of the cavernous church, overwhelms his large nose. Arriving at his place of honor in the front, August leans for support on the back of the front-row pew, waiting for the mourners behind him to fill every available seat.

When Father Corry begins speaking in Latin, August knows he will not be able to understand the service. His active mind instead recalls the events of this incredible week.

The tragedy that now stretches across the width of the church began a week ago last night when his son and daughter-in-law hosted their traditional winter party. The couple, who had always been very socially active in the community, invited fifty of their friends, but only twelve, between the ages of sixteen to forty, braved the winter weather that night. Fortunately, August thought, more members of the family had not been invited.

Before midnight Delphine sent her three youngest children to bed. As the boys fell asleep, they enviously listened to their parents, siblings and guests talking and laughing while playing games. Little did they know that when they woke in the morning, their lives would have changed forever.

At midnight the hostess offered a lunch of wieners, buns, two kinds of cake, olives, coffee and a homemade salad made of shredded cheese, mayonnaise, a lettuce leaf and peas. The peas were canned on a hot, humid June afternoon the previous summer. When Delphine opened the jar, she noticed a white liquid floating on top of the tiny khaki green vegetables. North Dakota farmers like her husband had been fighting the farm depression since the end of the war, and their wives did not waste food. Delphine simply poured the liquid off and mixed the peas into the salad.

After an enjoyable evening, the guests were hungry. Most ate healthy portions of all the food before they left at one o'clock. The next morning when the small boys woke up, they ate the leftover wieners for breakfast.

A week ago today, the partygoers were doing farm chores, cooking for their families and attending school. As the morning after the party progressed, however, many of the guests were slowed from their usual activities by indigestion and queasiness. Little thought was given to the ailments, as they all were familiar with the side effects of having too much fun the night before.

Arthur Jorandby spent the day after the party working on the farm with his father and complained about not feeling well. At the end of the day, he felt dizzy and had terrible stomach pains. Harry Chapiewski played his practice basketball game at the armory before he developed similar symptoms. His mother Bebe and her friend Angelina Stokke met that afternoon to prepare a joint family dinner. Like the others, the two women did not feel well, which they blamed on indigestion caused by overwork. Elsewhere in town, Arthur Lessard, Angelina's nephew, and Marguerite McWilliams, a telephone operator, were also ill.

That evening while August ate his supper, he was unaware of what was happening in the other homes of Grafton. At the table, it was casually mentioned that some family members were sick at Edward's farm. August dismissed it as a bad case of stomach flu. The retired farmer was more concerned about who was feeding the inhabitants of the barn than he was about the health of those in the house. August went to bed that Friday night without any idea that this weekend would be the saddest of the more than 4,200 he had lived.

Saturday afternoon, the grim reaper, his scythe sharpened, arrived ready to cut a clean slice through Grafton. Late that afternoon, August was awakened from his nap by voices on the porch. All day he had noticed unusual activity in and around the house. Every time he asked what was happening, he was always given a vague answer. Now, as he heard a church bell in the distance, he demanded to know the truth. His ashen son-in-law, Charles, finally relented and told him that the thirty-year-old naval veteran of the Great War, Arthur Jorandby, had just died from a sudden mysterious disease.

August was curious why one death caused such a strong reaction from his burly son-in-law. Both men had experienced many sudden deaths of apparently healthy young people before; it was a fact of life everyone had learned long ago to accept.

Then he was told the gravity of the situation. At the Chapiewski home, sixteen-year-old Harry was only hours from dying of the same disease. Harry's mother and her friend Angelina were lying in beds in adjoining rooms, their throats nearly paralyzed. August was surprised but still did not comprehend the full tragedy.

His son-in-law told him that all of the sick people had attended Edward's party two nights ago. His daughter Hulda then interrupted her hesitant husband, telling her father that five members of his son's family had the same symptoms. The old man shocked everyone in the room by forcefully pounding his cane on the floor and loudly ordering, "Bring mich auf die Farm."

Hulda had seen that no-nonsense glare in her father's eyes many times. She knew that arguing was useless and simply turned to her son and asked him to start the car.

The western horizon was a bright combination of red and orange as the light of the day faded away. At the farm, August's walk from the car to the house was illuminated by the first weak light of the nearly full moon. Family, doctors and law enforcement crowded the porch and the yard as the old man struggled to climb the two icy wooden steps. When they saw the family patriarch, people in the crowd respectfully moved, parting to let him pass.

Inside the house, August climbed the narrow, steep stairs to the second-floor bedrooms. His daughter Mary poked her husband to follow closely to catch him if he lost his balance, but there was no need for her concern. The determined man quickly reached the upper landing and went directly to the bed of his grandson. He had seen many gruesome deaths, but none like this. Lying in bed, his fully conscious grandson, with fear visible in his eyes, struggled for each breath as he slowly drowned in his own fluids. The grandfather spent only a minute saying goodbye before he continued his journey across the hall to his granddaughters' room.

August leaned his head against the slanted ceiling after he entered the small bedroom. On one side of the narrow room lay the oldest girl, Elizabeth, nearly as sick as her brother, and on the other side was Genevieve, who was not as sick as the others. The room was filled with the few town doctors discussing whether Genevieve should go to Deaconess Hospital. August spent a few minutes saying goodbye before he left the crowded room.

He next entered the bedroom of his son and daughter-in-law. Immediately he saw that Delphine's throat was almost totally paralyzed. She was only hours behind her son on the journey to heaven. Next to her, Eddie could still talk and eat but was too dizzy to stand. The man, who still had half his life to live, had accepted his fate. After his father sat in the chair by his bed, the dying son asked if there was anything he should tell his mother when he saw her.

His stoic father quietly replied, "Tell her that I am looking forward to seeing her soon."

In the living room downstairs, August found a chair in the corner and was quickly surrounded by worried daughters. When the wall clock announced that it was seven-thirty, there was frantic activity in the room above him. Within minutes he was told what he already knew: his grandson, who two nights before had a bright future continuing the family's long farming legacy, had just died.

Within four hours, the church bells announced to the residents of Grafton that the community had lost three young men. The bells could be heard faintly across the prairie when August, who at opportune moments claimed to be deaf, clearly heard a doctor whisper to the sheriff that the county would lose three mothers by sunrise.

August's overprotective daughters tried to convince their father to return to Hulda's house for some rest, and the tired old man reluctantly gave in. As he fitfully dozed off, the bells at St. John's Church began tolling forty-four times. In the middle of the night, August was awakened by thirty-six tolls of the same bell. When silence returned to the clear night sky, the only sound in the dark room was the pendulum of the clock in the living room—but soon, the church bell began tolling again thirty-seven more times. The doctor's prediction that before morning three mothers would die was correct. His daughter-in-law, Bebe Chapiewski, and Angelina Stokke were gone.

The first cold rays of sun on Sunday morning were shining in the east windows of the Hein farmhouse when Elizabeth gasped her last breath. In twelve hours, the rambunctious family of eight lost three members.

Usually, August would not have hesitated to walk fifteen minutes to church, but that morning he was too tired and distraught to argue against riding in his grandson's car. Climbing the church steps, his fellow congregants diverted their eyes and quickly took their seats to avoid speaking to the grieving old man.

Fear and rumors about what killed the seven townspeople were spreading as fast as a prairie grass fire. The overwhelmed doctors and law enforcement assured the worried public that others were not in danger. They were sure that the mysterious killer illness was botulism caused by food served at the Heins' party. They knew of other outbreaks of the disease in nearby states during the past ten years that had resulted in similar tragedies.

Other doctors and investigators from across North Dakota had been called to treat the sick and find the source of the bacteria. When they arrived in town, each was asked if there was a cure. They sadly reported that there was a serum, but it was not available in North Dakota or Minnesota. Vials were coming to Grafton from Chicago, but the serum needed to be administered at the first sign of symptoms and would arrive too late. The town would have to wait for the plague to take its course over the next couple of days.

The family pretended to eat their Sunday dinner, pushing their neighbors' sympathy food around their plates, when the bells of St. John's again began tolling. They counted twenty-seven hits of the bell's clapper against its sound bow for each year of the life of Angelina Stokke's nephew Arthur Lessard.

That afternoon as the exhausted August slept in his chair, the town continued filling with reporters, law enforcement and the curious. He was awakened from his nap by the familiar sound of the Federated Church's bell ringing, softer than the larger and higher bell at the Catholic church. Marguerite McWilliams was the ninth party guest to die in just twenty-four hours and five minutes.

That night the few residents of the town who could sleep were awakened by the bell of St. John's Church. The tired patriarch placed his chin on his chest as forty-one sorrowful tolls announced to the town that his son was gone. To push the pain from his consciousness, August imagined that he was instead hearing the joyful rings of the three bells in Gembitz Hauland day he married Minnie. He found himself envious of his son. Unlike the forty-nine years he had shared with Minnie, his boy's marriage lasted only twenty-one, but Eddie was separated from Delphine for a mere twenty-three hours, not nine years.

At the White House on Monday morning, President Hoover ate his breakfast while he skimmed the newspaper headlines from across the country. Waiting for his second cup of coffee to cool, the President read that nine residents of a small farming community in the Red River Valley had died on Saturday and Sunday from suspected botulism. Every paper he read had a bold print headline and a story about the horrific weekend in North Dakota. The Associated Press article written before Edward's death said that three more deaths were expected by the end of the day. The stern President who led the effort to feed the starving people in Europe after the war finished his breakfast, closed the newspapers and began his busy day.

On Monday, the groundhog came out of his den, saw his shadow and returned to hibernation for another six weeks. In Grafton, August thought he was reliving the previous day. At 7:45, one of his daughters told him that another granddaughter had died. With Genevieve's death, the family of eight was now reduced to three terrified young boys.

At noon August was again pushing a serving of one of the mountains of casseroles delivered by neighbors around his plate. Just like the day before, as he was ready to leave the table, the tired bell in the spire of St. John's Church tolled thirty-five times for Joseph Leach. When the bell stopped, everyone prayed that this announcement of the death of Delphine's nephew would be the last.

Never in the nearly fifty years since August first stepped off the train at the new Great Northern depot had he seen the town as busy as it was this week. Mourners, medical professionals, investigators, journalists and the morbidly curious blocked the roads to the farm, stood vigil outside the hospital and booked every hotel room.

On Monday, a hastily called coroner inquest was held. Since the first person fell ill, it was assumed that the salad with peas was responsible for the mayhem, but there was now a search for absolute proof. Inspectors combed the farm looking for the source of the bacteria. They removed all of Delphine's canning from the cellar and discovered many jars with broken seals, popped lids and a milky white liquid floating on top of the canned produce. The authorities even dug up her frozen garden to test for bacteria in the soil.

The five survivors from the party, along with the three spared sons, were interviewed as to what they did and did not eat. Elmer Stokke said that he had received a disapproving eye roll from his now-deceased wife when he, as he always did, refused the salad. William Ware said that he did not like peas and had shoved them to the side of his plate. The final three survivors said that their sensitive stomachs rejected the salad after the first bite. Unknown to their hosts, they had become nauseated and vomited on their way home.

The final piece of evidence the coroner wanted to analyze was the contents of the victims' stomachs. After giving the man the necessary information for his family's death certificates, August became very upset when he was told that their bodies would have to be cut open.

By Tuesday morning, that news and all the activities of the past four days overwhelmed not only August but also his three orphaned grandsons. Every time another stranger entered the home, the confused four-year-old Marvin became frightened and hid behind the nearest skirt. As plans were made for the family funerals, Richard and Wilfred made one simple request, "Please save our mother's wedding ring so we have something to remember her by."

One night, family and friends were crowded around the dining room table, which had been extended to its full length. Suddenly, Richard announced over the loud din, "I wish one of our sisters had survived so Wilfred and I could save the farm." The room fell silent, and the grandfather's mind returned to a night when he was the boy's age. That night he was also sitting next to his eighty-two-year-old grandfather at a crowded table, mourning the death of his father. Suddenly, his mother silenced the room by announcing that she would save the farm. August, today the grandfather, stared at the boy and thought, "It is not just the physical resemblance to my father and mother that has survived but also their determination and courage."

When the young men of the county left to fight a war, the streets around the armory were always packed, and the businesses were closed to honor the young heroes. On Tuesday, those same streets, around the same building, were once again packed to honor the first victim of the illness, Arthur Jorandby. When the one thousand mourners entered the only building in town large enough to hold the gigantic crowd, they saw a flag-draped casket with two veterans of Walsh County Company C standing guard at each end. Flowers surrounded the speaker's podium, and a life-size eagle replica stared down at the casket from the stage curtain. The irony that this man, who as a teenager, survived attacks by German U-boats had been felled by a simple jar of peas did not escape anyone in the audience.

On Wednesday and Thursday, the businesses again locked their doors to pay respects to the victims and their families. On Wednesday morning, St. John's filled to capacity in every pew, niche and corner for the joint funeral Mass for the Chapiewskis and Angelina Stokke. Later that afternoon at the Federated Church, mourners gathered for the funeral of Marguerite McWilliams. Yesterday, mourners returned to St. John's for the funeral of Arthur Lessard.

This morning for the third day in a row St. John's is filled to capacity, with some mourners forced to stand outside in the cold. The unfortunate ones outside warmed themselves gossiping about William Ware, who had eaten only a mouthful of salad with no peas. The news that he was in the hospital with early symptoms was wrong, but he still looked weak as he slowly struggled up the steps. They heard that he had been given the serum that was rushed to town, but they worried that it was too late to stop the sad progress of the poison. The consensus of the crowd outside the funeral was that the grim reaper may yet leave town with a baker's dozen of souls.

Sweat dampens August's shirt from the heat given off by the crowd of cramped mourners, and he feels uncomfortable. His mind snaps back to the present as Father Corry delivers the Gospel from Chapter 19 of

Luke. August finds little comfort as the priest reads verse 44: "They will dash you to the ground, you and the children within your walls . . . because you did not recognize the time of God's coming to you." Delphine's mother breaks into uncontrollable sobs.

As the service ends, Father Corry walks among the six caskets swinging a thurible of incense on a long chain, irritating the lungs of the old man and adding to his discomfort. When the priests complete their ritual, the church's choir sings for the third time in as many days, "Beautiful Isle of Somewhere." Two by two, the coffins are carried out of the church to the lyrics, "Somewhere the sun is shining. Somewhere the songbirds dwell."

With only two hearses available, August remains in his seat as the first two caskets are transported to the cemetery a mile and a half away. After twenty minutes, the hearses return to take two more of his family to their final resting place. He waits another twenty minutes before following his son and daughter-in-law out of the church. He leans heavily on his cane as the soloist sings, "Somewhere the clouds are rifted. Somewhere the angels wait. Somewhere, somewhere, beautiful isle of somewhere."

At the top of the steps, he does not feel as steady as he did earlier. This time when Emil offers his arm, the proud old man willingly accepts help. At the car, Emil opens the passenger door for his father, who stiffly sits, then swings his legs into the car. While following one of the hearses to Fifth Street, August watches block after block of his fellow citizens standing at attention, hats and hands on their hearts, paying their respects. The quiet, simple gestures give the tired man comfort.

That comfort does not last long. When the procession passes the edge of town, August can see in the distance a wind bank of pine trees planted around the flat cemetery. Between the trees, he sees many cars and a large mound of dirt. As the procession approaches the cemetery, August sees the Leach family standing around Joseph's casket as Father Corry commits the young family man to the earth. In the western section of the cemetery are the coffins of his grandchildren, their funeral bouquets blown apart by the strong Red River Valley winds as they wait for the arrival of their parents.

To protect August from the harsh wind, Emil drives his car, to the shock of his father and wife, across the graves so that the old man will not need to leave the car. But as he has done throughout this horribly dreadful week, August has his own idea. As soon as the car stops, he opens the door, takes a puff of his cigar, and walks to his rightful place among the mourners in the middle of the long line of caskets.

The wind howls in August's ears, and he can barely hear the priest utter the final words that will send five members of this branch of the family tree to the other world. August has often stood at a grave staring at a solitary casket while the preacher promises that all who are gathered will see the deceased again. Even when he was young during horrific pandemics, August never before saw a hole large enough for five caskets. Father Corry walks down the row of caskets and makes crosses of ashes on the top of each while saying, "Ashes to ashes, dust to dust" five times.

The repetition causes August's mind to drift again. He turns to look across the prairie at the city cemetery where Minnie lies. The frostbitten man is relieved that Minnie is comfortable as she greets her son, daughter-in-law and three grandchildren on the other side of the grave. Almost numb from the cold, August looks at the mourners surrounding him. "How many will be standing at my grave when the circle of my life meets its beginning?" he wonders.

Lost in sorrow, August suddenly feels an arm around his waist. He looks to his side to acknowledge the person and is stunned to see his mother. Startled back to reality, he sees that it is not Anna but rather Maria, his last sibling.

For a brief moment, the short woman, her gray hair fixed into a neat bun, says nothing. She does not need to. Maria is the last member of his family who has stood with him at the graves of their father and stepfather on afternoons almost as cold and much gloomier than today. In a near whisper, she reminds her older brother, "We have stood so many times at other cold, wind-blown cemeteries saying goodbye to our family, friends and neighbors. After we walked away, we always survived and prospered through blizzards, droughts, wars and difficult economic times. You are too strong and too stubborn not to endure this tragedy."

Together the brother and sister share their first joint prayer in many years, staring at the coffins lined up like soldiers marching into battle. Then just like the day their mother buried their stepfather, the elderly siblings turn their stiff, sore backs to the past. The strong wind is blowing into their faces as arm in arm, they take their first step forward into the future. Returning to Emil's car, August knows his baby sister is correct. He is strong enough to survive this tragedy.

October 15, 1941 – Glenburn, North Dakota

Lying in an ornate iron bed big enough for two, Maria is alone, impatiently waiting to die. From the time the sun rose this morning until it set this evening, she had one foot on each side of the precipice that divides this world from the next.

Every quarter hour, a member of her family takes a turn holding her wrinkled hand. Each finds it unimaginable that the woman who had relished her power as the matriarch of their large family will soon be gone. Maria tries unsuccessfully to tell her grieving family that she is excited to join their father in heaven, but they can see only angry frustration on her paralyzed face.

Earlier, when the warm October sun had streamed on Maria, sweat drenched her body as her brain slowly shut down one small section at a time. Ottilie, in whose home she had been visiting, thought that the warm sun was making her mother uncomfortable and pulled the curtains closed. The act produced a fierce reaction from the mostly unresponsive woman: Maria grabbed her daughter's dress with her still functioning hand, the only way she could still communicate that she wanted her final vision of this Earth to be the endless North Dakota horizon she had grown to love. Her shocked daughter did not understand, and she wrested her mother's fingers from her dress and quickly left the darkened room with tears streaming down her face.

Had Maria and her seven siblings created a tontine with the inheritance they received from their father, she would have won. Last year, on the fifty-seventh anniversary of standing at the grave of her oldest sister, Maria stood for the last time at a grave of a member of her generation who began spiritual life at the altar of the dilapidated Gramsdorf church. After the service for her sister-in-law Louise, Maria took a prominent chair in the church basement. One by one, her nieces and nephews paid homage. Each was desperately clinging to this last link they still had to their parents. Maria found it a very lonely place to sit.

Resilience had filled every cell of the short grandma until earlier this week when her blood was suddenly blocked from flowing to her brain. Whether it was losing her father when she was eight or her husband forty-five years later, she always held her head high and bounced back. While other widows retreated to one of their children's back bedrooms, Maria oversaw the expansion of the Erdmann farms on both sides of Willow Creek. Rather than existing as a kindly, useless grandmother, she drew from the experiences of her own mother to persist.

The last quarter century had tested that resilience. Her grandchildren will remember her standing on the porch, hands firmly planted on her hips, staring straight ahead at the North Dakota horizon. She looked to them to be as strong and immovable as the Turtle Mountains in the distance. What their young eyes did not see was a woman slowly worn away by the winds of change blowing across the flat prairie.

First, Maria endured the anti-German hysteria during the Great War. Then there was the collapse of the commodity prices when that war ended. Many families with whom she had worked side by side to create the neighborhood lost everything. In her family, Amandus loaded his family and possessions into a truck and joined the convoy heading west to Washington for a better life.

Many North Dakota farmers tried banding together to form the Non-Partisan League to fight the grain companies, the banks and the railroads. While this gave the farmers some control over their lives, they could not reform the weather. Black clouds of economic distress darkened the world's stability—but on the Great Plains of the United States, there were very few black storm clouds to water the family's crops. Wheat that normally reached Maria's waist before harvest would barely touch her knee. Families who could barely survive the low commodity prices were now driven into abject poverty. On trips to Bottineau, Maria could count not only the ribs of horses standing in the dried-up pastures but also the ribs of many children through the rags they called clothes.

As old age advanced, Maria would forget things, but she never forgot to remind her children of the need for frugality. They were told that they always needed to prepare for a crop failure. In the good years, she regularly descended into her children's cellars to inventory the shelves to make sure they were loaded with canned vegetables and meat. When she returned to the main floor of the house, she would scold everyone within earshot if she thought that not enough food was saved for the expected bad years.

Eight years ago, the new president declared that "all they had to fear was fear itself," and hope for a return to prosperity filled the new four-square houses her children had built for their growing families. Then the winds began blowing. Clouds of dirt as black as the most dangerous thunderstorm formed in the western sky and descended on the farms. Even in the new houses, families were forced to stuff towels and rags into every crack. It did little good. Every morning, the fine grit invaded the house. In the usually clean, orderly kitchens, small drifts of dirt would pile up on the way to the stove. Every cup of coffee Maria drank had a little extra flavor from the ever-present dust in the air. For a brief time, the doubts she had when August first brought her to this endless prairie resurfaced. When others felt discouraged, however, she defiantly told her children, "I was here when the prairie sod was first broken. I am staying until it regrows over me."

She is now happy that day will be soon. While the new president of her adopted country promises that happy days will come again, the new chancellor of her birth country promises that glory will return to Germany.

Two years ago, the German armies navigated around the destroyed bridge on the Notec River in Czarnkow, freeing her nieces and nephews from Polish rule. Maria found no joy in that news. How, she wondered, did tanks rolling across her relatives' farms alleviate their suffering? Peace was more important for her sister's descendants than which country governed them.

Maria has lived through three wars fought to bring permanent peace to Europe. Each time she prayed for the safety of a brother, son, friend or nephew. With the continent again destroying itself, she does not think that her old body has the energy to pray and worry anymore. If the United States joins the conflict, she knows that her grandsons and grandnephews will go to Europe. The family survived the Great War with no casualties: they may not be so lucky this time. If that tragedy happens, she wants to be the greeter at the Pearly Gates, not the one being greeted by a member of a younger generation.

In the two years since the Nazis roared across the Polish plains, she has worried about the safety of grandnephews she has never met. Five years have passed since her goddaughter Bertha wrote to tell her of the death of her brother Arnold. Since then, Maria has received no letters from Pauline's children. The newspapers reported in detail about the German army's expansion of the war into Russia. Over and over, Maria told her children, "I am sure some of the young men dying at the city limits of Moscow are your cousins." With no way to refute her fears, all they could do was shrug their shoulders and shake their heads.

For the last time, Maria briefly returns to consciousness. Through one blurry eye, she sees all of her children standing around the bed, prematurely grieving her death. On her forehead, she feels Pastor Tyler gently tracing the sign of the cross. With that gesture, a deep feeling of peace overcomes her, and her labored breaths become further apart.

As Maria's eye closes, the cloudy images of the Rothgarn bedroom and her children fade away. Suddenly all of her senses are working again. She is sitting on her mother's bench outside the stone house that her father built looking at the old tree near the barn loaded with this year's apples. Behind the tree, she can hear the family's cows mooing gently. She rubs her hand across the bench, worn smooth after decades of her mother holding court there. The fall air is fresh and crisp. She is filled with happy contentment.

In the distance, she hears the rumble of a wagon pulled by two roan horses. On the wagon seat are her father and stepfather, with her mother wedged tight between them. Instead of being loaded with wheat or bricks, the wagon box is packed with her seven laughing and teasing brothers and sisters. Her father pulls the reins as he orders the horses to stop. Then he yells to Maria in a forgotten booming voice, "It is time to leave! Jump in the back with your brothers and sisters."

Maria finds that her old legs can move again. She runs to the back of the wagon and climbs in as her father turns the team. Pauline whispers that they are going to a party at the beerhall across from the church.

When they arrive at the familiar crossroads, there is a large festive party. Old friends and family, whose bones lie in cemeteries around the world, play music, drink beer and eat food from tables loaded so heavy that they bow to the ground. Children who never had the opportunity to grow into adults run between the tables. Those fortunate enough to have achieved very old age sit under the large tree by the church and observe the chaos. Between the horns blaring, children's screams, horses' whinnies and dogs barking, the sounds of King Friedrich Wilhelm's gifts to the parish can be heard ringing loudly. Overhead the sky is a cloudless blue, which contrasts with the green pines and yellow poplars swaying gently in the breeze. Total peace and joy overcome Maria as she is welcomed to the grand reunion.

When the second barrel of beer is tapped, the happy party is abruptly interrupted. Rumbling past the cemetery are tanks. In every direction, gray man-made bugs scurry across fields, destroying farmers' labors. Overhead the sky suddenly turns black when the sun is blocked by thousands of airplanes. The whistle of their engines can be heard over the tops of the trees as they prepare to drop bombs. Young men who a few minutes ago could not see the party now rise from the battlefield to enjoy a ghostly stein of beer.

The trapped spirits push forward to seek safety in the old church that nearly half a century ago had turned to ash. Pastor Wenig swings the doors open wide. Maria stands in the front of the throng, at the threshold her mother carried her across to be baptized. She looks into the building but does not see the familiar old altar where she stood to be married. Instead, there is a blinding bright light. Peace overwhelms her as she steps over the transom to the light. The last North Dakota air expels from her lungs when Pastor Wenig slams the doors to the church shut. Maria has won her race against the horrors of the next war.

Albert (1847 - 1918) and Auguste (1874 - 1914) Heyn's fortieth wedding anniversary. Gustav Hein (1845 - 1924) to the far right. Family photo

August (1849 – 1937) and Minnie (1853- 1922) Hein. Family photo

August (1846 - 1909) and Maria (1856 - 1941) Erdmann with children. Family photo

Julia Heyn (1878 - 1916) daughter of Julius (1854 - unkown). Family photo

One of the three iron bells given in 1835 to the community of Gembitz Hauland by King Friedrich Wilhelm IV. Gebiczyn churchyard Fall 2019. Personal photo

Part XI
Epilogue

October 30, 2019 – Gebiczyn, Poland

Two sisters and their husbands leave the western town limits of Gebice in a rented Volkswagen. In the nineteenth century, they would have been leaving Gembitz in a "people's wagon" powered by two horses on our way to the train station in Budsin for a journey to America. Today, they are American tourists on a one-day break from a two-week tour of the largest cities of Poland to visit some of its smallest villages.

A half-mile after the sign marking their exit from Gebice is the next sign, pointing to a small road veering to the right and saying they are three kilometers away from our destination, Gebiczyn.

At that intersection one hundred and fifty years ago, my great-great-grandfather Albert Heyn was two miles into a five-thousand-mile journey to become the first of his family to emigrate to America. He turned east. I turn south. When the blinker clicks off, the family's circuit from Gembitz Hauland to Minnesota and back to Gebiczyn has closed.

Tall pines with thin trunks have been planted almost to the edge of the narrow road. There is a narrow light at the end of the tunnel of trees. Like characters in a sci-fi novel, we are sucked into another time dimension when we reach the end of that tunnel.

After we emerge from the pine tunnel, a green sign announces that we have entered the boundary of Gebiczyn. To the right, past the wheat stubble, a herd of Polish Red-White cows rests in a late-season pasture on the banks of the Ryga River. From a distance, I can see their high and wide udders, open deep chests, and feminine faces. I think of the Dairy Herd Improvement Association awards that once hung in the milk house of Grandpa and Grandma's old barn. Did my family's ability to breed an outstanding cow begin generations ago in one of these pastures?

We rumble over a bridge with white iron guardrails that protect us from driving into the meandering river. The pastures and fields abruptly end. Trees have overtaken the land. In between the trees are houses in various states of repair. One house has a large vine covering its south wall. Slowly, year by year, the vine grows across the slate roof, returning the structure and the surrounding land to its natural state. The next house is new. Land that once provided a meager income is now purchased by city dwellers to build weekend homes among the tall pines.

Looking between the low-hanging branches that cast a dark shadow over the road, we see an orange brick building ahead. We arrive at a crossroads with three buildings and a row of bright blue mailboxes and park in front of the community's one new building. I retrieve a print copy of a 1908 postcard I found online. That old postcard shows three separate photographs of buildings in Gembitz Hauland. I compare the images on that card to the three buildings in Gebiczyn.

The first picture is of the new Lutheran church. The precise brick masonry with numerous peaks and arching windows reflects the commitment of the congregation to stay in this place. Looking to the southwest, I can see that except for a green chain-linked fence that has replaced a wooden one, the sturdy building has not changed.

The postcard's second photograph is of the school. After completing the church, the bricklayers moved across the road to build a place for their children to learn to read, write and worship in the faith of Martin Luther. A cement marker in the brick commemorated the completion of their work in 1907. Today the building has an addition, a new entrance and new windows, but the cement sign is still there. Without that marker, the only hint of the building's age would be the green moss growing across its roof.

The postcard's final picture is of Gasthaus Hecht. It appears to be a series of connected buildings that served as both home and business.

Standing in the doorway of their inn are Herr and Frau Hecht, ready to greet thirsty customers. The buildings, where once farmers bragged about their crops, complained about their wives and exchanged gossip about the opportunities in the new world, are gone. Now the third structure of the community is an unremarkable white building that is the village hall.

The old schoolhouse is now a home. Its resident, wearing gray sweatpants and four layers of mismatched shirts, stumbles out of the door. He holds the leash of his little brown dog as protection from the community's rare visitors. Through a combination of hand gestures and translating apps, we explain we are not a threat to him or his home. Assured that we are not dangerous, he walks us to the church.

The small church built by German Lutherans is now home to a small community of Polish Catholics. The residents of the cemetery down the road must have rolled over in their graves in unison on the day their church was renamed for Saint John of Dukla, a patron saint of Poland and Lithuania.

Above the padlocked drab brown doors is a portrait of Pope John Paul II dressed in bright white clothes and surrounded by pink flowers. Two of his fingers touch his temple, giving him the appearance of being deep in thought. His eyes look out from his position above the door to a carved statue of a woodsman. It was created by a local artisan associated with Gebiczyn Fundacja, a community service foundation that has been established on Minnie Redel's old farm. Is it on purpose that the Polish pope's head is turned away from the bell given to the Lutheran community by their Prussian king to solidify his Protestant rule here?

Between the top of the door and the portrait is a half-moon space where there should be a window. Instead, it is filled with white cement. Above the pope's picture are three larger spaces framed by brick where large stained-glass windows should also be. Those spaces are also filled with cement. A casual observer would assume that once there had been stained glass in those openings, bathing the congregation in colorful light. Throughout our trip, we have seen pictures of beautiful buildings that were unnecessarily destroyed during World War II. When I look at the old postcard, however, I see that the ugly cement between the brick window frames was there when the church was finished. Stained glass was not broken into thousands of shards by a senseless shell of a tank: the windows never had stained glass. These windows that were never windows are a reminder of the many unfulfilled dreams of the residents of Gembitz Hauland.

No steeple was built on this church. Perhaps the congregation was afraid they would lose another church to lightning, or perhaps after almost ten years, they did not have the money to build a proper belfry. Instead, the old bell hangs to the right of the church in a small iron tower protected by a rusting tin roof. Anton hands us the bell's rope. How many times, I wonder, has this bell pealed with joy for our family's baptisms and marriages and tolled with sorrow for our emigrations and deaths? Today the sound is a combination of the two as it once again celebrates a milestone for the family.

With the last peal of the bell, we say goodbye to Anton. We take the same road that Anna and her eight children walked as they followed Friedrich's coffin from the church to the cemetery. Before we arrive at the cemetery, the forest again engulfs us. A narrow dirt road veers to the left. I carefully navigate the two ruts that serve as a road for a quarter of a mile until I see a blue sign that tells us we have arrived at Gebiczyn 66, the place where Friedrich and Anna created the family. I take another left turn and can see a brick house between the trees. How different is this view, I wonder, from the one Friedrich and Anna saw 175 years ago?

We are greeted by the current Polish owner, a short woman in her seventies with a large nose, sun-weathered skin and an engaging smile. Enjoying a break from her chores, she chatters freely. Pointing to the house, she explains that it was partially completed when her family arrived from Ukraine after World War II. She points to a plaque near the peak that says that Adolph Westphal, the oldest son of Pauline's August by his second marriage, was building this house the year Hitler's army rushed across Poland. At the end of the war, rather than finishing the home, he was forced to flee to the west.

I stand in the middle of the farmyard and imagine past lives here. To the east is a large field. Did Friedrich teach his sons to plow a straight furrow in that field? To the left are several small buildings with a pen of chickens. Was that where Anna kept her chickens and milked her cows? A large garden surrounds the house, and I can see cabbages the size of basketballs. Did Anna grow her cabbage for her sauerkraut there? Apple trees with large apples are to the west of the house. Did the family also have their orchard there?

I look back down the driveway. Is that the same view Anna saw when Friedrich's horse returned without him? Did she stand in this place six times to wave goodbye to her children leaving for America? Laundry hangs on the line behind the house. Is that where the lightning bolt ended Pauline's life?

A family's land has an eternal hold on them that emigration, war and time cannot break. Even though I have never been to this place, the magnetic pull of this land that must be stored somewhere in my DNA is strong even after 130 years. An old Siberian saying states, "It is not where you know the trees but where the trees know you that is your home." The trees surrounding me do not know me. This place is now someone else's home. It is time to turn my back on this little farm and disappear just as the rest of the family had through the tall pines. Before we do, I stop at the edge of the woods to take one final picture. Did each member of the family also stop here for one last look at their old home before they left to create a new one?

Before we begin our journey to Poznan, we stop at the cemetery. The trees are so thick that the cemetery is nearly lost among them. We find two brick posts that have been partially leached white by rain and snow at the edge of the road to welcome us to the burial ground. Originally each pillar had an iron cross pointing straight up. One pillar's cross is still there, but rather than directing us to heaven, it points at a ninety-degree angle to lead us into this overgrown place with sapling trees, bushes and moss-covered by a blanket of brown oak leaves. From each pillar, a rusting cable is strung between cement posts to mark the perimeter of the cemetery. Green moss grows on the few remaining markers, making them unreadable. Numerous concrete borders outline the forgotten graves. Once flowers would have been planted within those borders. How beautiful and peaceful this place must have been.

Vandals tipped many markers face down to hide the German

names. The only words legible on those stones now are "Rest Peacefully." I stand before one of those stones and imagine that it is Pauline's grave. Who stood where I am the day she was buried? What were they thinking as Pastor Ludowig droned the familiar final words of commitment? On that July day, was the heat unbearable, or did the shade trees provide a welcome relief? Today, no warm rays of sun can get through the trees to take the chill out of the air.

Did a cool breeze comfort the newly widowed August as he stared at his wife's coffin? Did his four oldest children cling to him for comfort and security, or were they accepting their mother's death with German stoicism? Did he bounce three-month-old Emma in his arms to quiet her as she howled, missing the comfort of being fed from her mother's breast?

How did Anna grieve? Had she experienced so many deaths that she was numb? Or did she shriek mournful wails as her oldest child was lowered into the ground?

Did Minnie Redel hear the pastor's words? Or was she lost in her grief as she stared at the fresh mound of dirt that seven days ago filled what is now the grave of her third husband?

Was Gustav standing between his mother Anna and his mother-in-law Minnie? Could he hear the pastor's words as his two-month-old daughter Martha cried in harmony with her cousin Emma? Did he glance at his mother and wonder if he should cancel his eight tickets to sail to America?

Was Maria leaning against a tree to relieve her discomfort as she entered the ninth month of her fourth pregnancy? Is this where she decided that it was time to join her brothers in America?

When standing at a new grave, you feel a strong desire for time to stop. Yet time never does, and eventually, you turn your back to the grave and move forward. Now was that time for me. Before I drive away, as all mourners do when they leave the cemetery, I take one last look to sear the sight in my memory.

Before returning to Poznan, we make one last stop. On the edge of Budzyn is the 1879 train station, where Anna boarded the train that began her journey to America. We park by the old loading dock and walk around the building to the door that Anna walked through to board her train.

While standing in that doorway, I see two deer lope across a freshly plowed field. In North Dakota the previous summer, I saw two deer standing in a soybean field on Anna's former land. Logic says that this is coincidental, but those two whitetails bounding across the black field and those two wide-eyed heads that popped out of that bean field feel like symbols of the family's dash from the old to the new world.

I think of the crypts of Polish kings and queens from almost one thousand years ago that we had seen five days ago at Wawel Cathedral in Krakow. Chiseled in marble and granite, their images are preserved as a tribute to their real and mythical successes. Where, I wonder, are the similar monuments and tributes to the people buried among the overgrown trees, tangled weeds, and weathered markers we had just left? The people who fought the wars, made farms out of swamp and sand, and sent their children across the ocean seeking a better life deserve to have their stories told. Their lives were just as important. With the images of this day fresh, I think that I cannot tell everyone's stories, but I could tell the story of one family. Walking back to the car, I begin my stroll through time with Anna and her children.

About the Author

Gary Heyn was raised on a family farm near Rochester Minnesota. As a boy he was fascinated by the stories of his Great Grandmother Lydia Heyn about the "olden days". Those afternoons on the front porch sparked a life-long interest in history and genealogy.

He is a graduate of the University of Minnesota. In 2019 he retired as the Vice-President of Corporate Governance for Tolomatic a Minneapolis manufacturing company. After retirement, he returned to the University of Minnesota to complete a degree in history. For a class in creative non-fiction writing he wrote several of the family stories he had been collecting as an essay for the class. The class's positive reception to his assignment inspired him to continue. At the same time, while on vacation, he visited the archives in Poznan Poland. He was amazed by the volume of historical documents available for the former German region and frustrated by the minimal amount of history that has been written.

Standing at the Grave is the result of the convergence of retirement, a class of Gen Zs who encouraged an OK Boomer, and the pandemic that has resulted in the resurrection of not only the lives his family but also the other residents of the former Gembitz Hauland as a novel.

Made in the USA
Monee, IL
24 August 2023